12/67

QA
404
F6.8

An
Introduction to
Fourier Methods and
the Laplace Transformation

By Philip Franklin

Professor of Mathematics Massachusetts Institute of Technology

Dover Publications, Inc.,   New York

Library of Congress Catalog Card Number: 58-11275

Manufactured in the United States of America

Dover Publications, Inc.
180 Varick Street
New York 14, N. Y.

PREFACE

This book is an introduction to Fourier series and Laplace transforms. Applications to physical problems involving ordinary and partial differential equations are included. The reader is assumed to have a working knowledge of elementary calculus, but where topics of advanced calculus are needed, they are developed from the beginning. Thus the discussion may help students and technologists to understand works in their field written in terms of harmonic analysis, complex exponentials, Fourier integrals, Fourier transforms, and Laplace transforms. The book is also suitable for use as a class text. Experience indicates that most of the topics can be covered in a one-semester course and that the material appeals particularly to applied mathematicians, engineers, and physicists.

The method of Fourier is interpreted here in a broad sense as referring to any analysis or synthesis of functions by a linear process applied to sines, cosines, or to complex exponentials. The initial chapter deals with complex quantities. It shows how to compute the elementary functions for complex values of the argument and how to read charts for finding such values approximately. It also explains what "complex impedance for a given frequency" means, and how to find it for a simple electrical or mechanical circuit.

The second chapter discusses averages and root mean square values as a preliminary to Fourier series. The series are found for simple functions by integration and for empirical functions numerically from a schedule for harmonic analysis. Fourier series are treated for the general interval, instead of for a period scaled down to 2π, which saves writing but often confuses the reader. After Fourier's theorem for periodic functions, full- and half-range series for functions on an interval are described. The

v

complex form of Fourier series leads to the Fourier integral theorem, Fourier transforms, and their relation to Laplace transforms.

As a preliminary to the solution of specific problems, Chap. 3 treats partial differential equations in a general way. Some simple general solutions as well as some particular solutions of a useful type are found. There is an explanation of the physical significance of the equations governing vibrations, the flow of heat, and the transmission of electricity, as well as Maxwell's equations and their relation to electrostatic fields and electro-magnetic waves.

The following chapter solves boundary value problems for steady and variable heat flow, transmission lines, vibrating strings, and hollow wave guides. In several instances these applications are carried through to the evaluation of numerical results. For each type of application, a specific problem with numerical data is used to introduce the topic and to motivate the discussion, but eventually a general literal solution is derived.

In the final chapter the operational calculus is developed from the Laplace transform point of view and is applied to finding the transients in linear electrical and mechanical systems. The problems involve ordinary and partial differential equations, and in particular the method is used to find transient currents in electric networks and for the lossless transmission line. For easy reference, a table of Laplace transforms is reproduced on the inside of the back cover of the book.

Although there are many comprehensive treatments of some narrower aspect of Fourier methods, it is not easy for a reader with limited time available, or for a teacher giving a brief course, to extract from these the basic information which he needs. By concentrating on essentials, this volume enables the reader to gain a knowledge of Fourier methods in a broad sense, adequate for most applications.

There are thirty-one sets of practice problems, one for each major topic of the book. Answers to all problems are given at the end of the book.

References to alternative and to more extensive discussions are given in the final section of each chapter. A list of these works, with a few additions, is found in the Bibliography.

The author wishes to thank his colleague, Prof. Norman Levinson for valuable help and suggestions on the treatment of the Laplace transform.

PHILIP FRANKLIN

CAMBRIDGE, MASS.
December, 1949

CONTENTS

ix

CONTENTS

CHAPTER 1

COMPLEX QUANTITIES. IMPEDANCE

Expressions of the form $E \sin (\omega t + \phi)$ occur frequently in discussions of mechanical vibrations or of alternating currents in electrical networks. The calculations are simplified if we introduce complex quantities and work with the exponential of $i(\omega t + \phi)$, instead of using real trigonometric functions. In this chapter we shall review the algebra of complex numbers, define the exponential and trigonometric functions of complex quantities, and show how such functions may be used in combination with the notion of impedance to find the steady-state condition in an electrical or mechanical circuit.

1. Complex Quantities

A complex number is an expression of the form $a + bi$, where a and b are real numbers and i is the imaginary unit:

$$i = \sqrt{-1} \qquad \text{and} \qquad i^2 = -1 \tag{1}$$

Most of the rules for manipulating complex numbers are the same as those for real numbers. One useful principle is that, if a, b, a', and b' are all real, then the equation

$$a + bi = a' + b'i \qquad \text{implies that} \qquad a = a' \text{ and } b = b'. \tag{2}$$

Consequently, in any equation simplified to this form, we may equate the real and imaginary parts separately.

The addition of two complex numbers,

$$(a + bi) + (c + di) = (a + c) + (b + d)i, \tag{3}$$

is carried out just as if i were real. Likewise for subtraction,

$$(a + bi) - (c + di) = (a - c) + (b - d)i. \tag{4}$$

1

For multiplication, after multiplying the separate terms, there is one with i^2, which is replaced by -1 in accord with (1).   Thus

$$(a + bi)(c + di) = (ac - bd) + (ad + bc)i. \qquad (5)$$

For division, we may proceed as follows:

$$\frac{a + bi}{c + di} = \frac{(a + bi)(c - di)}{(c + di)(c - di)} = \frac{(ac + bd) + (-ad + bc)i}{c^2 + d^2}$$
$$= \frac{ac + bd}{c^2 + d^2} + \frac{-ad + bc}{c^2 + d^2}\, i. \qquad (6)$$

In place of two real numbers a and b, which remain fixed throughout our discussion, we may use two real variables x and y, each of which takes on any one of some set or succession of values.   This leads us to consider the complex variable

$$z = x + iy.$$

The integral power function $w = z^n$ is defined by repeated multiplication.   From this, for any complex constant A_n, we may form $A_n z^n$, and set up polynomial expressions by adding together a finite number of such terms.

2. Exponential and Trigonometric Functions

To define the exponential, sine, and cosine functions for complex values of the variable, we use the infinite power series

$$e^z = 1 + z + \frac{z^2}{2!} + \frac{z^3}{3!} + \cdots, \qquad (7)$$

$$\sin z = z - \frac{z^3}{3!} + \frac{z^5}{5!} - \frac{z^7}{7!} + \cdots, \qquad (8)$$

$$\cos z = 1 - \frac{z^2}{2!} + \frac{z^4}{4!} - \frac{z^6}{6!} + \cdots. \qquad (9)$$

These series are similar in form to the MacLaurin's series which represent the functions e^x, $\sin x$, and $\cos x$ for all real values of x. This shows that, when $y = 0$, so that $z = x + iy = x$, the values obtained from the new definition will agree with those previously used for real values of the variable.

The series (7), (8) and (9) converge for all complex values of z. Convergent series of this type may be multiplied and added together in the same way that polynomials are combined. It follows that the functions defined by the series satisfy the relation

$$e^{z_1} \cdot e^{z_2} = e^{z_1+z_2}, \tag{10}$$

as well as the addition theorem for the sine

$$\sin (z_1 + z_2) = \sin z_1 \cos z_2 + \cos z_1 \sin z_2 \tag{11}$$

and that for the cosine

$$\cos (z_1 + z_2) = \cos z_1 \cos z_2 - \sin z_1 \sin z_2, \tag{12}$$

and the identity

$$\cos^2 z + \sin^2 z = 1. \tag{13}$$

Similarly, it follows from the series that

$$e^{iz} = \cos z + i \sin z \tag{14}$$

and

$$e^{-iz} = \cos z - i \sin z. \tag{15}$$

We may solve these for $\sin z$ and $\cos z$ and thus obtain

$$\sin z = \frac{e^{iz} - e^{-iz}}{2i}, \tag{16}$$

and

$$\cos z = \frac{e^{iz} + e^{-iz}}{2}. \tag{17}$$

The tangent, cotangent, secant, and cosecant are defined in terms of the sine and cosine by the quotients

$$\tan z = \frac{\sin z}{\cos z}, \qquad \cot z = \frac{\cos z}{\sin z} \tag{18}$$

$$\sec z = \frac{1}{\cos z}, \qquad \csc z = \frac{1}{\sin z}. \tag{19}$$

These are similar in form to relations of elementary trigonometry, which correspond to the special case $y = 0$, $z = x + iy = x$.

We may combine the definitions just given with Eqs. (16) and (17) to obtain expressions for tan z, cot z, sec z, and csc z in terms of exponentials.   For example,

$$\tan z = \frac{1}{i}\frac{e^{iz} - e^{-iz}}{e^{iz} + e^{-iz}} = -i\frac{e^{2iz} - 1}{e^{2iz} + 1}. \tag{20}$$

Such expressions enable us to reduce any combination of trigonometric functions to a form involving exponentials only, and might have been used as the basis of trigonometry.   Specifically, we may take Eq. (7) as the definition of e^z and Eq. (10) as its fundamental property.   Then Eqs. (16), (17), and (20) and those similar to Eq. (20) may be used to define the six trigonometric functions.   The series (8) and (9) then follow from (16) and (17) combined with (7) and (1).   From this point of view Eqs. (11), (12), and (13) and all other trigonometric identities become a consequence of Eqs. (16), (17), and (7).

3. Derivatives

If $f(z)$ is a function of the complex variable $z = x + iy$, and while z is kept fixed,

$$\lim_{\Delta z \to 0}\frac{\Delta f}{\Delta z} = \lim_{h \to 0}\frac{f(z + h) - f(z)}{h} = f'(z), \tag{21}$$

regardless of how $h = \Delta z = \Delta x + i\,\Delta y$ approaches zero through *complex* values, we define $f'(z)$ as the derivative of $f(z)$ with respect to z, df/dz.   This definition is similar in form to that used for functions of a real variable in elementary calculus, but requires more of our function because we now require the limit to be the one value $f'(z)$ while Δy, as well as Δx, assumes any set of real values approaching zero.   However, as we shall illustrate presently, many of the rules of differential calculus carry over to the complex case.

The usual proof for real values, based on the binomial theorem, shows that for any positive integer n, and complex constant a,

$$\frac{d(az^n)}{dz} = anz^{n-1}. \tag{22}$$

Moreover, convergent power series may be differentiated term-wise. Consequently, it follows from the series (7), (8), and (9) that

$$\frac{d(e^z)}{dz} = e^z, \tag{23}$$

$$\frac{d(\sin z)}{dz} = \cos z, \tag{24}$$

$$\frac{d(\cos z)}{dz} = -\sin z. \tag{25}$$

Since the rule for differentiating composite functions

$$\frac{dw}{dz} = \frac{dw}{du} \cdot \frac{du}{dz} \tag{26}$$

also remains valid in the complex case, we may deduce that

$$\frac{d(e^{iz})}{dz} = ie^{iz} \qquad \text{and} \qquad \frac{d(e^{-iz})}{dz} = -ie^{-iz}. \tag{27}$$

We might have used these to derive Eqs. (24) and (25) from Eqs. (16) and (17).

EXERCISE I

Given $z_1 = 2 + 3i$, $z_2 = -3 - 2i$, $z_3 = 3 - 2i$, $z_4 = 26i$, find:

1. $z_1 + z_4$. **2.** $z_1 - z_2$ **3.** $z_2 + z_3$. **4.** $z_3 - z_2$.

5. $z_1 z_2$. **6.** $z_2 z_3$. **7.** $z_2 z_4$. **8.** z_1/z_3.

9. z_4/z_1. **10.** z_4/z_2. **11.** z_3^2. **12.** z_4^2.

Use the power series (7) to check the tabular values

13. $e^{0.02} = 1.0202$. **14.** $e^{0.08} = 1.0833$. **15.** $e^{-0.06} = 0.94176$.

16. Using the values found in Probs. 13, 14, and 15, verify Eq. (10) for $z_1 = 0.08$ and $z_2 = -0.06$.

17. If n is any positive integer, show that

$$\cos nz = \tfrac{1}{2}(\cos z + i \sin z)^n + \tfrac{1}{2}(\cos z - i \sin z)^n.$$

From Prob. 17, with $n = 2, 3, 4, 5$, deduce that

18. $\cos 2z = \cos^2 z - \sin^2 z$.
19. $\cos 3z = \cos^3 z - 3 \cos z \sin^2 z$.
20. $\cos 4z = \cos^4 z - 6 \cos^2 z \sin^2 z + \sin^4 z$.
21. $\cos 5z = \cos^5 z - 10 \cos^3 z \sin^2 z + 5 \cos z \sin^4 z$.

22. If n is any positive integer, show that

$$\sin nz = -\tfrac{1}{2}i(\cos z + i \sin z)^n + \tfrac{1}{2}i(\cos z - i \sin z)^n.$$

From Prob. 22, with $n = 2, 3, 4, 5$, deduce that

23. $\sin 2z = 2 \cos z \sin z$.
24. $\sin 3z = 3 \cos^2 z \sin z - \sin^3 z$.
25. $\sin 4z = 4 \cos^3 z \sin z - 4 \cos z \sin^3 z$.
26. $\sin 5z = 5 \cos^4 z \sin z - 10 \cos^2 z \sin^3 z + \sin^5 z$.

Evaluate each of the following integrals after transforming the integrand to the second form by means of Eqs. (16), (17), (14), and (15):

27. $\int^x 8 \cos^2 x \sin^2 x \, dx = \int^x (1 - \cos 4x)dx$.
28. $\int^x 8 \cos^4 x \, dx = \int^x (\cos 4x + 4 \cos 2x + 3)dx$.
29. $\int^x 8 \sin^4 x \, dx = \int^x (\cos 4x - 4 \cos 2x + 3)dx$.

30. Prove that the indefinite integral $\int^x e^{(a+bi)x} \, dx = \dfrac{e^{(a+bi)x}}{a + bi}$, by using Eqs. (23) and (26) to differentiate the right member.

31. Assuming a, b, and x real, evaluate the two indefinite integrals $\int^x e^{ax} \cos bx \, dx$ and $\int^x e^{ax} \sin bx \, dx$ by equating the real and imaginary parts of the equation of Prob. 30.

4. Computation of the Functions

If $z = x + iy$, we find from Eqs. (10) and (14) that

$$\begin{aligned} e^z = e^{x+iy} &= e^x \cdot e^{iy} = e^x(\cos y + i \sin y) \\ &= e^x \cos y + ie^x \sin y. \end{aligned} \tag{28}$$

This enables us to compute the value of e^z from tables of values of the real functions e^x, $\cos y$, and $\sin y$ with y in radian measure.

If y is not between 0 and $\pi/2 = 1.5708$, we may add or subtract multiples for $\pi/2$ to bring it in the range of the tables. For example, if $z = 2 + 3i$, we need $e^2 = 7.389$, sin 3, and cos 3. Since $3 - \pi = -0.1416$, we have $3 = \pi - (0.1416)$ and

$$\sin 3 = \sin 0.1416 = 0.1411,$$
$$\cos 3 = -\cos 0.1416 = -0.9900. \tag{29}$$

It follows that

$$e^{2+3i} = e^2 \cos 3 + ie^2 \sin 3 = 7.389(-0.9900 + 0.1411i)$$
$$= -7.315 + 1.042i. \tag{30}$$

To compute sin z and cos z, we have, from Eqs. (11) and (12),

$$\sin z = \sin (x + iy) = \sin x \cos iy + \cos x \sin iy, \tag{31}$$
$$\cos z = \cos (x + iy) = \cos x \cos iy - \sin x \sin iy. \tag{32}$$

But from Eqs. (15) and (17), we have

$$\sin iy = \frac{e^{-y} - e^{y}}{2i} = i\left(\frac{e^y - e^{-y}}{2}\right), \tag{33}$$
$$\cos iy = \frac{e^y + e^{-y}}{2}. \tag{34}$$

This suggests that we tabulate the real functions

$$\sinh y = \frac{e^y - e^{-y}}{2} \quad \text{and} \quad \cosh y = \frac{e^y + e^{-y}}{2} \tag{35}$$

read "hyperbolic sine" and "hyperbolic cosine." We may then compute the functions sin z and cos z from

$$\sin z = \sin x \cosh y + i \cos x \sinh y, \tag{36}$$
$$\cos z = \cos x \cosh y - i \sin x \sinh y. \tag{37}$$

5. Hyperbolic Functions

Let us study the hyperbolic functions defined by Eq. (35). Their graphs are shown in Fig. 1. It follows from Eqs. (33), (34), and (35) that

$$\sin iy = i \sinh y \quad \text{and} \quad \cos iy = \cosh y. \tag{38}$$

These relations may be used to deduce formulas for the hyperbolic functions from those for the trigonometric functions. For example, if we replace z_1 by iy_1, and z_1 by iy_2 in Eq. (11), we find

$$\sin i(y_1 + y_2) = \sin iy_1 \cos iy_2 + \cos iy_1 \sin iy_2. \qquad (39)$$

But from this by Eq. (38), we may derive

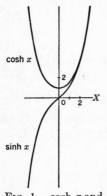

$$i \sinh (y_1 + y_2) = (i \sinh y_1) \cosh y_2 + \cosh y_1 (i \sinh y_2), \qquad (40)$$

so that, if we divide by i,

$$\sinh (y_1 + y_2) = \sinh y_1 \cosh y_2 + \cosh y_1 \sinh y_2. \qquad (41)$$

In this way we show that

$$\cosh (y_1 + y_2) = \cosh y_1 \cosh y_2 + \sinh y_1 \sinh y_2, \qquad (42)$$

and that

$$\cosh^2 y - \sinh^2 y = 1. \qquad (43)$$

FIG. 1.   cosh x and sinh x.

By analogy with the defining relations (18) and (19), we define the hyperbolic tangent, hyperbolic cotangent, hyperbolic secant, and hyperbolic cosecant by the equations

$$\tanh y = \frac{\sinh y}{\cosh y}, \qquad \coth y = \frac{\cosh y}{\sinh y}, \qquad (44)$$

$$\operatorname{sech} y = \frac{1}{\cosh y}, \qquad \operatorname{csch} y = \frac{1}{\sinh y}, \qquad (45)$$

The graph of tanh y is shown in Fig. 2.   Each of the four functions just defined may be expressed in terms of exponential functions by using Eq. (35).   For example,

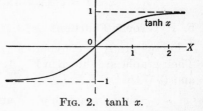

$$\tanh y = \frac{e^y - e^{-y}}{e^y + e^{-y}} = \frac{e^{2y} - 1}{e^{2y} + 1}. \qquad (46)$$

FIG. 2.   tanh x.

For the derivatives of sinh y and cosh y, we may deduce from Eqs. (38), (24), (25), and (26) that

$$\frac{d(\sinh y)}{dy} = \cosh y \quad \text{and} \quad \frac{d(\cosh y)}{dy} = \sinh y. \quad (47)$$

These also follow directly from Eqs. (35) and (23).

The power series for sinh y and cosh y may be obtained by combining Eqs. (38) with (8) and (9), or more directly from Eqs. (35) and (7). The results are

$$\sinh y = y + \frac{y^3}{3!} + \frac{y^5}{5!} + \frac{y^7}{7!} + \cdots, \quad (48)$$

$$\cosh y = 1 + \frac{y^2}{2!} + \frac{y^4}{4!} + \frac{y^6}{6!} + \cdots, \quad (49)$$

All the above formulas involving hyperbolic functions of y hold for y complex, if we use these two series as the definitions of sinh y and cosh y. For complex values, the hyperbolic functions may be computed from

$$\sinh (x + iy) = \sinh x \cos y + i \cosh x \sin y, \quad (50)$$
$$\cosh (x + iy) = \cosh x \cos y + i \sinh x \sin y. \quad (51)$$

If y is a large positive number, e^y is large and e^{-y} is small. By neglecting the e^{-y} terms in Eq. (35), we find that

$$\sinh y = \cosh y = \frac{e^y}{2}, \quad \text{with a fractional error } e^{-2y}. \quad (52)$$

This shows that, with a small error for *large positive y*,

$$\log_{10} \sinh y = \log_{10} \cosh y = 0.434294y - 0.30103, \textit{ nearly}. \quad (53)$$

Since e^{-7} is a little less than 0.001, Eqs. (52) and (53) will give sinh y and cosh y correct to three figures if y exceeds 3.5, and correct to six figures if y exceeds 7. When y is beyond the range of our tables for sinh y and cosh y, it is convenient to use Eq. (52) with a log log slide rule, or with a table for e^y when it is safe to interpolate in the exponential table. Otherwise Eq. (53) is useful. For example, if y in Eqs. (36) and (37) or x in Eqs. (50) and (51) were 12, we would need sinh 12 and cosh 12. They could be found from

$$\log_{10} \sinh 12 = 12(0.434294) - 0.30103 = 4.91050,$$
$$\sinh 12 = \cosh 12 = 81380. \quad (54)$$

To find sinh y and cosh y when y is negative, we use

$$\sinh(-y) = -\sinh y, \qquad \cosh(-y) = \cosh y, \qquad (55)$$

which follow from Eqs. (48) and (49), or from Eq. (35).

EXERCISE II

Evaluate each of the following expressions in the form $a + bi$, with a and b each real numbers:

1. $e^{\pi i/3}$. **2.** $e^{3\pi i}$. **3.** $e^{-\pi i}$. **4.** $e^{6\pi i}$.
5. $\cos 2i$. **6.** $\sin 3i$. **7.** $\cosh i$. **8.** $\sinh 2i$.
9. e^{3-i}. **10.** e^{-2+i}. **11.** e^{4-2i}. **12.** e^{7+10i}.

13. $\sin(1 - i)$. **14.** $\cos(-1 + 2i)$.
15. $\sinh(3 - 2i)$. **16.** $\cosh(-9 + 8i)$.

For hyperbolic functions, prove the following identities:

17. $1 - \tanh^2 x = \operatorname{sech}^2 x$. **18.** $\coth^2 x - 1 = \operatorname{csch}^2 x$.
19. $\sinh 2x = 2 \sinh x \cosh x$. **20.** $\cosh 2x = \cosh^2 x + \sinh^2 x$.
21. $\sinh ix = i \sin x$. **22.** $\cosh ix = \cos x$.
23. $\cosh 3x = \cosh^3 x + 3 \cosh x \sinh^2 x = 4 \cosh^3 x - 3 \cosh x$.
24. $\sinh 3x = 3 \cosh^2 x \sinh x + \sinh^3 x = 4 \sinh^3 x + 3 \sinh x$.

Prove the following rules for differentiation:

25. $\dfrac{d(\tanh x)}{dx} = \operatorname{sech}^2 x$.

26. $\dfrac{d(\coth x)}{dx} = -\operatorname{csch}^2 x$.

27. $\dfrac{d(\operatorname{sech} x)}{dx} = -\tanh x \operatorname{sech} x$.

28. $\dfrac{d(\operatorname{csch} x)}{dx} = -\coth x \operatorname{csch} x$.

29. Check the tabular values $\sinh 0.3 = 0.3045$ and

$$\cosh 0.3 = 1.0453$$

(*a*) by using the power series (48) and (49) and (*b*) by using Eq. (35) and a table of exponential functions.

30. In Fig. 3, with AB an arc of the unit circle $x^2 + y^2 = 1$ and the shaded area equal to $t/2$, show that $OC = \cos t$,

$$CB = \sin t,$$

and $AD = \tan t$. Similarly, in Fig. 4, with AB an arc of the unit rectangular hyperbola $x^2 - y^2 = 1$ and the shaded area equal to $t/2$, show that $OC = \cosh t$, $CB = \sinh t$, and $AD = \tanh t$. This analogy to the circular functions is the reason for the name

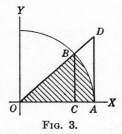

Fig. 3.

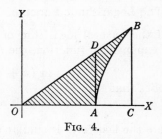

Fig. 4.

hyperbolic functions. HINT: Use polar coordinates r, θ, and call the shaded sector S. For the circle, $r = 1$, $S = \frac{1}{2}\theta$, so that $\theta = t$. For the hyperbola, right branch, if $y = \sinh u$, $x^2 = 1 + y^2$ makes $x = \cosh u$. Then $\theta = \tan^{-1} \dfrac{y}{x}$,

$$d\theta = \frac{x\,dy - y\,dx}{x^2 + y^2} = \frac{du}{r^2}.$$

Hence $dS = \frac{1}{2}r^2\,d\theta = \frac{1}{2}du$, $S = \frac{1}{2}u$, so that $u = t$.

31. If ϕ is in the interval $-\pi/2 < \phi < \pi/2$ and $\sinh x = \tan \phi$, show that $\cosh x = \sec \phi$, $\tanh x = \sin \phi$, $\coth x = \csc \phi$, $\csc h = \cot \phi$, $\operatorname{sech} x = \cos \phi$. Considered as a function of x, $\phi = \operatorname{gd} x$, is called the *Gudermannian* of x. By use of this function, and its inverse $x = \operatorname{gd}^{-1} \phi$, work involving hyperbolic functions can be treated with trigonometric functions and conversely.

32. If $x = 2$, compute ϕ from the defining relation of Prob. 31. Also verify that the values of the functions of x and ϕ taken from the tables satisfy the first two derived equations.

If $\phi = $ gd x and $x = $ gd^{-1} ϕ as in Prob. 31, show that

33. $\phi = 2 \tan^{-1} e^x - \pi/2$.   **34.** $x = \ln \tan \left(\dfrac{\pi}{4} + \dfrac{\phi}{2} \right)$.

35. $\displaystyle\int_0^\phi \sec \phi \, d\phi = x$.   **36.** $\displaystyle\int_0^x \operatorname{sech} x \, dx = \phi$.

37. If angle AOB of Fig. 4 is called θ, from Prob. 30 we have $\tan \theta = \tanh t$. Deduce from this that $\tan 2\theta = \sinh 2t$, so that, with the notation of Prob. 31, $\theta = \frac{1}{2}$gd $2t$.

6. The Logarithmic Function

If the natural logarithm of z, $\ln z$, is the function inverse to the exponential function, the relation

$$\ln (x + iy) = u + iv \tag{56}$$

implies that

$$x + iy = e^{u+iv} = e^u(\cos v + i \sin v), \tag{57}$$

where the last form is similar to Eq. (28). Consequently

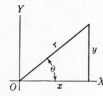

Fig. 5.

$$x = e^u \cos v \quad \text{and} \quad y = e^u \sin v, \tag{58}$$

since x, y, u, and v are all real. It follows that

$$e^u = \sqrt{x^2 + y^2} \quad \text{and} \quad v = \tan^{-1}\frac{y}{x}, \tag{59}$$

so that e^u and v may be used as the polar coordinates of a point in a plane with Cartesian or rectangular coordinates x and y. Let us denote a possible choice of polar coordinates with positive radius vector by r, θ. From Fig. 5,

$$r = \sqrt{x^2 + y^2}; \quad x = r \cos \theta; \quad y = r \sin \theta. \tag{60}$$

The number r is called the *absolute value* of $z = x + iy$, and we write

$$|z| = |x + iy| = r = \sqrt{x^2 + y^2}. \tag{61}$$

We find from Eqs. (58), (59), and (60) that

$$u = \ln r, \quad v = \theta, \tag{62}$$

leads to a value for the logarithm,

$$\ln(x + iy) = \ln r + i\theta. \tag{63}$$

Since θ is determined only to within an integral multiple of 2π, a complex number has an infinite number of possible logarithms. A particular value of θ may be determined from a knowledge of the sign of any two of the functions

$$\tan \theta = \frac{y}{x}, \qquad \cos \theta = \frac{x}{r}, \qquad \sin \theta = \frac{y}{r}, \tag{64}$$

and the numerical value of any one of the functions. Some computers use the tangent relation alone, but refrain from canceling any negative factors. Thus with this convention they would write for $x + iy =$

$2 + 4i, \quad \tan \theta = 2, \qquad \theta = 1.1071,$

$-2 + 4i, \quad \tan \theta = \dfrac{2}{-1}, \quad \theta = \pi - 1.1071 = 2.0345$

$-2 - 4i, \quad \tan \theta = \dfrac{-2}{-1}, \quad \theta = \pi + 1.1071 = 4.2487 \text{ or } -2.0345$

$2 - 4i, \quad \tan \theta = \dfrac{-2}{1}, \quad \theta = 2\pi - 1.1071$

$$= 5.1761 \text{ or } -1.1071 \quad (65)$$

The simplest method of checking a value of θ is to plot the point (x,y). The proper quadrant and a rough estimation of θ may then be read from the diagram. If θ_0 is any one value, all the possible values are given by

$\theta = \theta_0 + 2k\pi, \qquad$ where

$$k = 0, 1, 2, \cdots \text{ or } -1, -2, \cdots \tag{66}$$

Suppose we superimpose on a square grid a series of concentric circles, each marked with a number equal to $\ln r$, where r is the radius, and a series of lines with constant θ, each marked with the value of θ. A few such lines and circles are drawn in Fig. 6, in which the square grid is omitted for clarity. Then by spotting the point x,y on the square grid, and after visual interpolation reading the value of ln r and θ, we obtain the logarithm. For special problems, only a limited range will be of interest, and enlarged charts of this type may be made to give a fair degree of accuracy in the restricted range. Such a chart may be read in a reverse manner, starting with ln r and θ and reading x,y so as to obtain a value for the exponential function.

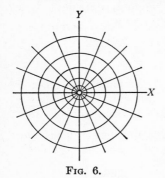

The rule for differentiating inverse functions,

$$\frac{dw}{dz} = \frac{1}{dz/dw} \qquad (67)$$

remains valid in the complex case. But

$$w = \ln z \qquad \text{implies that} \qquad z = e^w. \qquad (68)$$

Fig. 6.

Consequently, by Eq. (23),

$$\frac{dz}{dw} = e^w = z. \qquad (69)$$

It now follows from the last three numbered equations that

$$\frac{d(\ln z)}{dz} = \frac{1}{z}. \qquad (70)$$

We see from Eqs. (63) and (70) that the logarithmic function is defined and has a finite derivative for all finite values of z except $z = 0$. For $z = x + iy = 0$, $r = 0$ so that ln $r = -\infty$ and θ is indeterminate. Hence we do not define ln z for $z = 0$.

The fundamental property of the logarithm

$$\ln (z_1 z_2) = \ln z_1 + \ln z_2 \qquad (71)$$

follows from Eqs. (68) and (10). It is true in the sense that, if any two of the logarithms are given, with particular choices of k in Eq. (66), some possible value of the third logarithm will make the equation true.

7. The Complex Plane

In the last section we were lead to associate the complex number $z = x + iy$ with the point P in a plane where $P = (x,y)$. We may think of the point P, or the vector OP, as representing the complex number. The operations of addition, subtraction, multiplication, and division on complex numbers then correspond to simple geometric operations on the vectors that represent them. We refer to P as the point z. Let

$$z_1 = x_1 + iy_1, \qquad z_2 = x_2 + iy_2. \tag{72}$$

Then, by Eq. (3), for the sum

$$z_1 + z_2 = (x_1 + x_2) + i(y_1 + y_2). \tag{73}$$

Thus OQ, the vector sum of OP_1 and OP_2 according to the parallelogram law, represents the algebraic sum of z_1 and z_2. Similarly

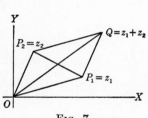 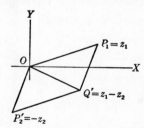

Fig. 7.   Fig. 8.

$z_1 - z_2$ is represented by the vector difference $OP_1 - OP_2$. That is, either OQ' in Fig. 8, obtained by adding OP_2 reversed or $OP_2' = -z_2$ to OP_1 vectorially, or P_2P_1 in Fig. 7.

For products and quotients, we introduce the polar coordinates shown in Fig. 5. Then, by Eqs. (60) and (14), we have

$$z_1 = r_1(\cos \theta_1 + i \sin \theta_1) = r_1 e^{i\theta_1}, \tag{74}$$
$$z_2 = r_2(\cos \theta_2 + i \sin \theta_2) = r_2 e^{i\theta_2}. \tag{75}$$

It follows that for the product

$$z_1 z_2 = r_1 r_2 e^{i(\theta_1 + \theta_2)} = r_1 r_2 [\cos (\theta_1 + \theta_2) + i \sin (\theta_1 + \theta_2)]. \tag{76}$$

Furthermore for the quotient

$$\frac{z_1}{z_2} = \frac{r_1}{r_2}\, e^{i(\theta_1-\theta_2)} = \frac{r_1}{r_2}[\cos\,(\theta_1 - \theta_2) + i\,\sin\,(\theta_1 - \theta_2)]. \quad (77)$$

These results also follow from Eqs. (63) and (71).

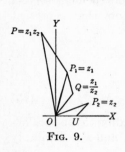

Equation (76) shows that, as in Fig. 9, if OP is the vector for the product and if OU is the vector to the point $1 = 1 + 0i$, then the triangle OP_1P is similar in sense and shape to the triangle OUP_2. Equation (77) shows that if OQ is the vector for the quotient z_1/z_2, then the triangle OP_1Q is similar in sense and shape to the triangle OP_2U. These facts may be used as the basis for a geometric method of multiplying and dividing complex numbers.

Fig. 9.

8. Powers and Roots

The relation

$$(e^w)^a = e^{aw} \quad (78)$$

is a consequence of Eq. (10) when a is an integer or rational number. For other values of a, real or complex, this equation may be used as the definition of the power in the left member. By Eq. (68), it follows that

$$\ln\,(z^a) = a\,\ln z. \quad (79)$$

Let us introduce the polar coordinates of z as in Eq. (74). Then

$$z = r(\cos\theta + i\,\sin\theta) = re^{i\theta}. \quad (80)$$

Also, from Eqs. (63) and (66),

$$\ln z = \ln r + i(\theta_0 + 2k\pi). \quad (81)$$

Hence

$$\ln\,(z^a) = a\,\ln z = a[\ln r + i(\theta_0 + 2k\pi)]. \quad (82)$$

If a is an irrational or complex number, each value of k will lead to a distinct value of z^a, and there will be an infinite number of values of the power.

If n is an integer, positive or negative, kn is an integer and

$$\ln (z^n) = n \ln r + in\theta = n \ln r + i(n\theta_0 + 2kn\pi). \quad (83)$$

Thus only one value of the power is obtained, namely,

$$z^n = r^n e^{in\theta} = r^n(\cos n\theta + i \sin n\theta),$$
$$n = 0, 1, 2, \cdots \text{ or } -1, -2, \cdots . \quad (84)$$

This is known as *De Moivre's theorem* and could have been obtained directly from Eq. (80).

If m is a positive integer, for the mth root or $(1/m)$th power we have

$$\ln(z^{1/m}) = \frac{1}{m} \ln r + i\frac{\theta}{m} = \frac{1}{m} \ln r + i\left(\frac{\theta_0 + 2k\pi}{m}\right). \quad (85)$$

This makes

$$z^{1/m} = r^{1/m}\left(\cos \frac{\theta_0 + 2k\pi}{m} + i \sin \frac{\theta_0 + 2k\pi}{m}\right), \quad (86)$$

m is a positive integer, $k = 0, 1, 2, \cdots, m - 1$.

This choice leads to m distinct values, and every other integral value leads to m distinct values, and every other integral value of k leads to a value of the root equal to one of these. Thus a complex number ($\neq 0$) has m distinct mth roots.

In calculating products, quotients, powers, and roots by Eqs. (76), (77), (84), and (86) it is convenient to have a short expression which can be written on one line to represent

$$e^{i\theta} = \cos \theta + i \sin \theta, \quad (87)$$

such as cis θ, read "sis" θ, or $/\theta$, read "angle" θ. The notation $/\overline{\theta}$, read "lag angle" θ, is sometimes used in place of $/-\theta$. In any of these expressions, we may measure θ, or some part of θ, in degrees. For example, as one factor of a sixty cycle alternating current we might have

$$/377t + 20° = e^{i(377t+20°)}$$
$$= \cos (377t + 20°) + i \sin (377t + 20°). \quad (88)$$

Here the term $377t$ is in radians, which facilitates differentiation, while the phase $20°$ is kept in degrees, more convenient than radians when finding sines and cosines. If bothered by the departure from radian measure, the reader may think of the degree sign as an abbreviation for the factor $\pi/180 = 0.01745$. Using the modified notation just discussed, we may rewrite Eq. (86) as

$$z^{1/m} = r^{1/m} \text{ cis } \frac{\theta_0 + k360°}{m} = r^{1/m} \Big/ \underline{\frac{\theta_0 + k360°}{m}}, \qquad (89)$$

m is a positive integer, $k = 0, 1, 2, \cdots, m-1$.

Let us use this to compute the fourth roots of -16. We have

$$z = -16 = 16\underline{/180°}, \qquad r^{1/m} = 16^{1/4}$$

$$= 2, \qquad \frac{\theta_0}{m} = \frac{180°}{4} = 45° \quad (90)$$

Since $360°/m = 90°$, the four values of θ in Eq. (89) are

$$45°, 135°, 225°, 315°.$$

Thus the four values of the fourth root of -16 are

$$2\underline{/45°} = \sqrt{2} + i\sqrt{2}, \qquad 2\underline{/135°} = -\sqrt{2} + i\sqrt{2},$$
$$2\underline{/225°} = -\sqrt{2} + i\sqrt{2}, \qquad 2\underline{/315°} = \sqrt{2} - i\sqrt{2}. \quad (91)$$

EXERCISE III

Find the absolute value and one possible value of the angle for each of the following complex numbers:

1. $7 = 7 + 0i$.   **2.** $3i = 0 + 3i$.   **3.** $-5i = 0 - 5i$.
4. $-5 + 4i$.   **5.** $2 - 9i$.   **6.** $-4 - 7i$.

7. If a is any *real* number, prove that $|e^{ia}| = 1$.
8. For a and b real, prove that $|e^{a+bi}| = e^a$.

Calculate one value of the logarithm of each of the following complex numbers:

9. $-1 = -1 + 0i$.   **10.** $i = 0 + 1i$.   **11.** $4 - 4i$.
12. $-4 - 3i$.   **13.** $3 + 4i$.   **14.** $2 - 3i$.

Evaluate each of the following algebraically, and check by carrying out a graphical construction:

15. $(5 - 3i) + (-9 + 3i)$.   **16.** $(-7 + 4i) - (3 + 7i)$.

17. $(6 + 2i)(-1 - i)$.   **18.** $(3 - 3i)^2$.

19. $\dfrac{5 - 2i}{-2 - 5i}$.   **20.** $\dfrac{10 + 15i}{2 + 3i}$.

21. $(-2) + (2/60°)$.   **22.** $(3/135°) + (3/45°)$.

23. $(6/115°)(2/-25°)$.   **24.** $(20/5°)(5/20°)$.

25. $\dfrac{6/40°}{3/15°}$.   **26.** $\dfrac{20/-40°}{5/50°}$.

Find all the values of each of the following indicated roots:

27. $\sqrt{-25}$.   **28.** $\sqrt{16i}$.   **29.** $\sqrt{9 + i}$.   **30.** $\sqrt{6 - 2i}$.

31. $\sqrt[3]{-64}$.   **32.** $\sqrt[4]{16}$.   **33.** $\sqrt[5]{32i}$.   **34.** $\sqrt[6]{1}$.

35. Show that $i^i = (0.2079)(535.5)^k$,
$$k = 0, 1, -1, 2, -2, \cdots .$$

36. Show that the vector drawn from the origin which represents the complex number $E/\omega t + \phi$, with t the time and E, ω, ϕ constant, has constant length and rotates with uniform angular velocity.

37. For any complex number z, show that the vectors drawn from the origin representing the mth roots lie at the vertices of a regular polygon of m sides with center of symmety at the origin.

m values of z^{Vm}, for $m=5$

Fig. 10.

9. Inverse Trigonometric Functions

If $\sin^{-1} z$ is the function inverse to the function $\sin z$, then

$$w = \sin^{-1} z \quad \text{implies that} \quad z = \sin w. \tag{92}$$

Hence, by Eq. (16),

$$z = \frac{e^{iw} - e^{-iw}}{2i} \quad \text{and} \quad e^{iw} - 2iz - e^{-iw} = 0. \tag{93}$$

We may write this in the form

$$(e^{iw})^2 - 2iz(e^{iw}) - 1 = 0, \tag{94}$$

a quadratic equation in e^{iw}, whose solution is

$$e^{iw} = iz + \sqrt{1 - z^2}. \tag{95}$$

For z complex there are two values of the square root, as seen from Eq. (86) with $m = 2$. When these are not real, there is no positive root. Hence the plus sign before the radical does not pick out a particular root, as it does for reals. This is why we write $+$ instead $\pm$. It follows from Eqs. (95) and (92) that

$$\sin^{-1} z = -i \ln (iz + \sqrt{1 - z^2}). \tag{96}$$

By a similar procedure we may deduce from Eq. (17) that

$$\cos^{-1} z = -i \ln (z + \sqrt{z^2 - 1}), \tag{97}$$

and from Eq. (20) that

$$\tan^{-1} z = \frac{i}{2} \ln \frac{1 - iz}{1 + iz}. \tag{98}$$

The rules of differentiation for these functions are similar in form to those which hold when the variables are real, namely,

$$\frac{d(\sin^{-1} z)}{dz} = \frac{1}{\sqrt{1 - z^2}}, \quad \text{where } \sqrt{1 - z^2} = \cos (\sin^{-1} z), \tag{99}$$

$$\frac{d(\cos^{-1} z)}{dz} = \frac{-1}{\sqrt{1 - z^2}}, \quad \text{where } \sqrt{1 - z^2} = \sin (\cos^{-1} z), \tag{100}$$

$$\frac{d(\tan^{-1} z)}{dz} = \frac{1}{1 + z^2}. \tag{101}$$

There may be derived either from Eqs. (96), (97), and (98) or by using Eq. (67) and the relations of the type of Eq. (92). The latter method of reasoning shows that in Eq. (99) we must take $\sqrt{1 - z^2} = \cos w$. This is also true of Eq. (96), since putting $z = \sin w$, and the radical equal to $\cos w$ makes the right member $w + 2k\pi$, while using $-\cos w$ for the radical makes the right member $\pi - w + 2k\pi$. Similarly the radical in Eq. (100) should equal sin w, and that in Eq. (97) should equal i sin w. If only one of the functions sin w, or cos w, is known, either value of the radical in Eq. (96), or in Eq. (97), gives a possible value of w. If both sin w and cos w are known, w is determined to within a multiple of 2π and a specific value of the radical is given by the rules just stated which make the expressions in parentheses in both Eq. (96) and (97) reduce to cos $w + i$ sin w.

We shall next prove some further consequences of Eq. (92) by a discussion similar to that of the logarithmic function given in Sec. 6. If $w = u + iv$, it follows from Eqs. (92) and (36) that

$$x + iy = z = \sin w = \sin u \cosh v + i \cos u \sinh v. \quad (102)$$

Consequently, since x, y, u, and v are all real,

$$x = \sin u \cosh v, \qquad y = \cos u \sinh v. \quad (103)$$

Suppose we select a number of evenly spaced values of v, all positive, and of u, all in the range from 0 to $\pi/2$, calculate the corresponding values of x and y, and plot the resulting points. We may then join the points with the same u by a curve, marked with this value of u, and similarly join the points with the same v, marked with this value of v. Taking u in the range $\pi/2$ to π leads to the mirror image of these curves in the x axis, while the ranges $-\pi$ to $-\pi/2$ and $-\pi/2$ to 0 produce the reflections in the y axis of the curves for the corresponding positive values. We could replace the values on the u curves by $\pi - u$, if at the same time we replaced v by $-v$. Also, any value of u could be changed by $2k\pi$, k integral. A few of the curves are shown in Fig. 11. We observe that, similar to Eqs. (13) and (43),

$$\sin^2 u + \cos^2 u = 1 \qquad \text{and} \qquad \cosh^2 v - \sinh^2 v = 1. \quad (104)$$

The result of solving for sin u and cos u from Eq. (103) and substituting in Eq. (104) is

$$\frac{x^2}{\cosh^2 v} + \frac{y^2}{\sinh^2 v} = 1, \qquad \cosh^2 v - \sinh^2 v = 1. \quad (105)$$

This shows that the curves for constant v are ellipses with foci at

−1,0 and 1,0. The result of solving for cosh v and sinh v from Eq. (103) and substituting in Eq. (104) is

$$\frac{x^2}{\sin^2 u} - \frac{y^2}{\cos^2 u} = 1, \qquad \sin^2 u + \cos^2 u = 1. \qquad (106)$$

This shows that the curves for constant u are branches of hyperbolas with foci at −1,0 and 1,0.

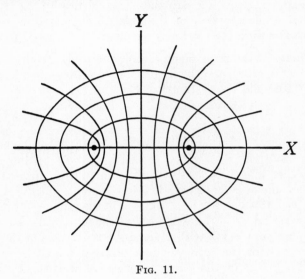

Fig. 11.

The curves just described, together with the x,y coordinate lines, constitute a chart for reading values of the inverse sine or sine. For we may spot the point x,y and read u and v by visual interpolation between the values on the curves, thus obtaining $u + iv = \sin^{-1}(x + iy)$. Or, starting with u,v, we may read x,y, thus obtaining $x + iy = \sin(u + iv)$. A similar chart for the inverse cosine or cosine could be made by replacing each value of u on the sine chart by $\pi/2 - u$.

We may also derive a formula for computing $\sin^{-1} z$ which is sometimes preferable to Eq. (96). The result of solving the second part of Eq. (105) for $\sinh^2 v$, substituting in the first part and clearing of fractions, is

$$(\cosh^2 v)^2 - (1 + x^2 + y^2) \cosh^2 v + x^2 = 0. \qquad (107)$$

This is a quadratic equation in $\cosh^2 v$, whose solution is

$$\cosh^2 v = \tfrac{1}{2}[(1 + x^2 + y^2) + \sqrt{(1 + x^2 + y^2)^2 - 4x^2}], \qquad (108)$$

with the plus sign necessary to make $\cosh^2 v > 1$. This implies

$$\cosh v = \tfrac{1}{2}\sqrt{(1 + x)^2 + y^2} + \tfrac{1}{2}\sqrt{(1 - x)^2 + y^2}, \qquad (109)$$

as the square of the right member of Eq. (109) equals the right member of Eq. (108), and the sign is plus to make $\cosh v$ positive. And Eq. (109) and the first part of Eq. (103) imply that

$$\sin u = \tfrac{1}{2}\sqrt{(1 + x)^2 + y^2} - \tfrac{1}{2}\sqrt{(1 - x)^2 + y^2}, \qquad (110)$$

since the product of the right members of Eqs. (109) and (110) is x, which equals $\sin u \cosh v$, the product of the left members. We may use Eqs. (109) and (110) to calculate $\cosh v$ and $\sin u$, and hence $u + iv = \sin^{-1}(x + iy)$. If only the sine of $u + iv$ is known, we may take v plus or minus, and determine the quadrant of u so that the products in Eq. (102), or

$$\sin (u + iv) = \sin u \cosh v + i \cos u \sinh v \qquad (111)$$

have the proper signs. If the cosine of $u + iv$ is also known,

$$\cos (u + iv) = \cos u \cosh v - i \sin u \sinh v, \qquad (112)$$

by Eq. (37). Consequently, we know $-\sin u \sinh v$, which with $\sin u$ determines the sign of $\sinh v$, and hence the sign of v. The quadrant of u is again found from Eq. (111).

By an entirely parallel discussion based on Eq. (112) we may show that if $u + iy = \cos^{-1}(x + iy)$, then

$$\cosh v = \tfrac{1}{2}\sqrt{(1 + x)^2 + y^2} + \tfrac{1}{2}\sqrt{(1 - x)^2 + y^2}, \qquad (113)$$
$$\cos u = \tfrac{1}{2}\sqrt{(1 + x)^2 + y^2} - \tfrac{1}{2}\sqrt{(1 - x)^2 + y^2}. \qquad (114)$$

If only the cosine of $u + iv$ is known, we may take v plus or minus and determine the quadrant of u so that the products in Eq. (112) have the proper sign. If the sine of $u + iv$ is also known, from Eq. (111) we know $\cos u \sinh v$, which with $\cos u$ determines the sign of $\sinh v$, and hence the sign of v. The quadrant of u is again found from Eq. (112).

To derive formulas for computing $u + iv = \tan^{-1}(x + iy)$, we first note that, by Eq. (98), this makes

$$2u + 2iv = i \ln \frac{1 + y - ix}{1 - y + ix}. \tag{115}$$

By Sec. 6, for the real part of the logarithm, we have

$$\ln|1 + y - ix| - \ln|1 - y + ix| = \frac{1}{2} \ln \frac{1 + x^2 + y^2 + 2y}{1 + x^2 + y^2 - 2y}. \tag{116}$$

This is $2v$, and hence from Eq. (46) we find

$$\tanh 2v = \frac{2y}{1 + x^2 + y^2}. \tag{117}$$

By applying the method of Eq. (6), we have

$$\frac{1 + y - ix}{1 - y + ix} = \frac{1 - x^2 - y^2 - 2ix}{(1 - y)^2 + x^2}. \tag{118}$$

For the polar angle θ of this complex number, we have

$$\tan \theta = \frac{-2x}{1 - x^2 - y^2}, \quad \text{or} \quad \tan(-\theta) = \frac{2x}{1 - x^2 - y^2}. \tag{119}$$

Since the imaginary part of the logarithm in Eq. (115) is $i\theta$, $2u = i(i\theta) = -\theta$, and

$$\tan 2u = \frac{2x}{1 - x^2 - y^2}, \quad \sin 2u \text{ and } x \text{ same sign.} \tag{120}$$

The last remark is equivalent to applying the convention illustrated in Eq. (65) to the fraction in Eq. (120). It fixes the quadrant of $2u$.

In computing $u + iv = \tan^{-1}(x + iy)$ by Eqs. (117) and (120), the first determines $2v$ and hence v in both magnitude and sign.   Equation (120) determines $2u$ to within a multiple of 2π, and hence u to within a multiple of π, if only the tangent of $u + iv$ is known.   If in addition we know either the sine or the cosine of $u + iv$, the quadrant of u may be fixed from any one of the terms in Eq. (111) or Eq. (112).

10. Inverse Hyperbolic Functions

A discussion like that of Sec. 9, based on Eqs. (35) and (46), shows that

$$\sinh^{-1} z = \ln (z + \sqrt{1 + z^2}), \tag{121}$$
$$\cosh^{-1} z = \ln (z + \sqrt{z^2 - 1}), \tag{122}$$
$$\tanh^{-1} z = \frac{1}{2} \ln \frac{1 + z}{1 - z}, \tag{123}$$

and that their derivatives are given by

$$\frac{d(\sinh^{-1} z)}{dz} = \frac{1}{\sqrt{1 + z^2}},$$
$$\text{where } \sqrt{1 + z^2} = \cosh (\sinh^{-1} z), \tag{124}$$

$$\frac{d(\cosh^{-1} z)}{dz} = \frac{1}{\sqrt{z^2 - 1}},$$
$$\text{where } \sqrt{z^2 - 1} = \sinh (\cosh^{-1} z), \tag{125}$$

$$\frac{d(\tanh^{-1} z)}{dz} = \frac{1}{1 - z^2}. \tag{126}$$

As indicated in the supplementary condition of Eq. (124), if $\sinh^{-1} z = w$, we must take $\sqrt{1 + z^2} = \cosh w$.   This is also true of Eq. (121), since putting $z = \sinh w$ and the radical equal to $\cosh w$ makes the right member $w + 2k\pi i$, while using $-\cosh w$ for the radical makes the right member $\pi i - w + 2k\pi i$.   Similarly, as indicated in Eq. (125), if $\cosh^{-1} z = w$, the radical in Eq. (125) and that in Eq. (122) should equal $\sinh w$.   If only one of the functions $\sinh w$, or $\cosh w$, is known, either value of the radical in Eq. (121), or Eq. (122), gives a possible value of w.   If both $\sinh w$ and $\cosh w$ are known, w is determined to within a multiple of $2\pi i$ and a specific value of the radical is given by the rules just stated which make the expressions in parentheses in both Eq. (121) and Eq. (122) reduce to $\cosh w + \sinh w = e^w$.

The problem of finding inverse hyperbolic functions of complex quantities may be reduced to the computation of inverse trigonometric functions by means of the relations

$$\sinh^{-1}(x + iy) = i \sin^{-1}(y - ix), \tag{127}$$
$$\cosh^{-1}(x + iy) = i \cos^{-1}(x + iy), \tag{128}$$
$$\tanh^{-1}(x + iy) = i \tan^{-1}(y - ix), \tag{129}$$

which follow from Eq. (38).

For z and w real, the positive root is always to be taken in Eqs. (121) and (124), since the hyperbolic cosine of a real quantity is always positive. For z real and greater than unity, the principal branch of $\cosh^{-1} z$ is taken as positive, so that for this positive branch the hyperbolic sine is positive and the positive root should be used in Eqs. (122) and (125).

EXERCISE IV

1. If $w = \sin^{-1} 2.6$, and $\cos w$ has a negative imaginary part, show that $\cos w = -2.4i$, and $\tan\left(\dfrac{\pi}{2} - w\right) = -\dfrac{2.4}{2.6} i$.

Compute the value of w in Prob. 1 by using

2. Eq. (96).   **3.** Eq. (97).

4. Eqs. (109) and (110).   **5.** Eqs. (113) and (114).

6. $\tanh i\left(\dfrac{\pi}{2} - w\right) = \dfrac{2.4}{2.6}$.   **7.** $z = \dfrac{2.6}{2.4} i$ in Eq. (98).

8. If $w = \cos^{-1} 5.05$, and $\tan w$ has positive imaginary part, show that $\sin w = 4.95i$, and $\tan w = 0.9802i$.

Compute the value of w in Prob. 8 by using

9. Eq. (96).   **10.** Eq. (97).

11. Eqs. (109) and (110).   **12.** Eqs. (113) and (114).

13. Eq. (98).   **14.** $\tanh(iw) = -0.9802$.

15. If $w = \sin^{-1}(1.2 + 0.4i)$, and $\cos w$ has a positive real part, show that $\cos w = 0.6 - 0.8i$, $\tan w = 0.4 + 1.2i$.

Compute the value of w in Prob. 15 by using

16. Eqs. (109 and (110).   **17.** Eqs. (117) and (120).

18. Prove that $\sinh^{-1} z = i \sin^{-1} (-iz)$, and use this to deduce Eq. (121) from Eq. (96).

19. Prove that $\cosh^{-1} z = i \cosh^{-1} z$, and use this to deduce Eq. (122) from Eq. (97).

20. Prove that $\tanh^{-1} z = -i \tan^{-1} (iz)$, and use this to deduce Eq. (123) from Eq. (98).

21. Check the tabular value $\cosh^{-1} 2 = 1.3170$ by means of Eq. (122).

22. Check the tabular value $\sinh^{-1} 0.5 = 0.4812$ by means of Eq. (121).

23. Check the tabular value $\tanh^{-1} 0.5 = 0.5493$ by means of Eq. (123).

For a and x real, prove the following integrations:

24. $\displaystyle\int^x \frac{dx}{a^2 - x^2} = \frac{1}{2a} \ln \frac{a + x}{a - x} = \frac{1}{a} \tanh^{-1} \frac{x}{a}$

25. $\displaystyle\int^x \frac{dx}{\sqrt{a^2 + x^2}} = \sinh^{-1} \frac{x}{a} = \ln (x + \sqrt{a^2 + x^2}) - \ln a$, where $\ln a$ may be absorbed in the integration constant.

26. $\displaystyle\int^x \frac{dx}{\sqrt{x^2 - a^2}} = \cosh^{-1} \frac{x}{a} = \ln (x + \sqrt{x^2 - a^2}) - \ln a$, where

$\ln a$ may be absorbed in the integration constant.

27. Show that we may compute $u + iv = \sqrt{x + iy}$ from the equations $\quad u^2 = \frac{1}{2}(x + \sqrt{x^2 + y^2})$, $v^2 = \frac{1}{2}(-x + \sqrt{x^2 + y^2})$, using such signs that uvy is positive when y is not zero.

28. Check the computation of cos w from sin w in Prob. 15, by using Prob. 27.

29. Fig. 12 shows the *catenary*, or curve of equilibrium of a chain or heavy flexible cable hanging

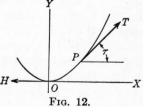

Fig. 12.

under its own weight, w lb. per foot of length s. If the tension is T lb. at $P = x,y$ and $\tan \tau = dy/dx = p$, and the tension is H lb. at $O = 0,0$ where $p = 0$, deduce from the equilibrium of arc OP that $T \cos \tau = H$ and $T \sin \tau = ws$. Hence, if $a = H/w$, $s/a = p$, and

$$a \, dp/dx = \sqrt{1 + p^2}.$$

By solving this for dx, and integrating as in Prob. 25, recalling that $x = 0$ when $p = 0$, deduce $x = a \sinh^{-1} p$ so that $\dfrac{dy}{dx} = \sinh \dfrac{x}{a}$ and hence $y = a \cosh \dfrac{x}{a} - a$.

30. Check the integration of $a \, dp/dx = \sqrt{1 + p^2}$ of Prob. 29 by putting $dp/dx = p \, dp/dy$, solving for y and integrating to obtain $y + a = a\sqrt{1 + p^2}$, so that $ap = \sqrt{(y + a)^2 - a^2}$. Put $p = dy/dx$, solve for dx and integrate as in Prob. 26 to obtain $x = a \cosh^{-1} (y + a)$ and hence $y = a \cosh \dfrac{x}{a} - a$.

31. For the catenary of Prob. 29, show that $s = a \sinh \dfrac{x}{a}$ and that $y = s \tanh \dfrac{x}{2a}$. For supports at the same level, s is the half length and x is the half span. Then $u = x/a$ is determined from $\dfrac{\sinh u}{u} = \dfrac{s}{x}$, using tables of the left member minus 1 for large sags, or for small sags replacing $\sinh u$ by $u + u^3/6$, the first two terms of Eq. (48). Then the sag $y = s \tanh \dfrac{u}{2}$, $a = x/u$, $H = wa$, and $T = H \sec \tau = H \cosh u$.

32. A wire weighing 0.02 lb./ft. is strung between two crossbars at the same level and 100 ft. apart. If the length of the wire is 101 ft., find the sag and the tension at the lowest point and at the ends (see Prob. 31).

33. The main cable of an aerial tramway weighs 8.8 lb./ft. For the first section, the lower end is 900 ft. below a point level with the upper end and at a horizontal distance of 3,000 ft. from it. If the lower end is horizontal when the cable supports no load besides its own weight, find the tension at the two ends of the first section and also the length and weight of this section. HINT: With $u = x/a$, deduce from Prob. 29 that

$$\frac{y}{x} = \frac{\cosh u - 1}{u} = \frac{u}{2} + \frac{u^3}{24},$$

approximately, by Eq. (29). Omit u^3, and $u_1 = \dfrac{2y}{x} = 0.6$. Then $u_2 = \dfrac{2y}{x} - \dfrac{u_1{}^3}{12} = u_1\left(1 - \dfrac{u_1{}^2}{12}\right) = 0.582$. An improved value, 0.5833 is found by computing $\cosh u - 1 - 0.3u$ for u near 0.582 and interpolating to make this zero. Then a, s, H, T may be found from u by Prob. 31.

11. Simple Series Circuits

Suppose that electricity flows through an element containing resistance, inductance, and capacity. We take one direction, that from A to B in Fig. 13, as positive. If after t sec. the quan-

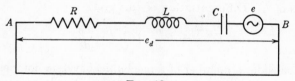

FIG. 13.

tity of electricity which has passed any point of the element in the positive direction is q coulombs, the current intensity i amperes for all points of the element at time t will be $i = dq/dt$. The potential, or electromotive force (emf), at A minus that at B will be the sum of three voltage drops diminished by the e volts applied by the generating source. Thus the total drop

$$e_d = L\frac{di}{dt} + Ri + \frac{q}{C} - e. \tag{130}$$

The first drop is proportional to the rate of change of current $di/dt = d^2q/dt^2$, and the positive constant of proportionality L

henrys is called the *inductance* of the element. The second drop
is proportional to the current $i = dq/dt$, and the positive constant of proportionality R ohms is the *resistance* of the element.
The third drop is proportional to the quantity of electricity
accumulated in the condensers since they were discharged at t_0
or $q = \int_{t_0}^{t} i \, dt$. The positive constant of proportionality is taken
as $1/C$, and C farads is called the *capacity* of the element.

Let us next assume that points A and B are brought into contact, or joined by an ideal conductor, so that they have the same
emf. Then $e_d = 0$, and by combining the relation between q
and i with Eq. (130), we find

$$L \frac{d^2q}{dt^2} + R \frac{dq}{dt} + \frac{1}{C} q = e \qquad (131)$$

as the equation of the simple series circuit for q, and

$$L \frac{di}{dt} + Ri + \frac{1}{C} \int_{t_0}^{t} i \, dt = e \qquad (132)$$

in terms of i. Differentiation of this gives

$$L \frac{d^2i}{dt^2} + R \frac{di}{dt} + \frac{1}{C} i = \frac{de}{dt}. \qquad (133)$$

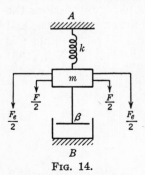

Now consider a member of a mechanical system composed of a
mass attached to fixed members by a
spring and a dashpot.   Let s be the displacement of the mass from equilibrium
taken positive when in the direction
from A to B in Fig. 14.   Then if F is a
force applied to an interior point of the
member, in the direction of AB, the
remaining external force F_e acting on
the member will be

$$F_e = m \frac{d^2s}{dt^2} + \beta \frac{ds}{dt} + ks - F. \quad (134)$$

Fig. 14.

We take the time t in seconds, s in feet, and the forces in pounds.

Then the constant of proportionality for the acceleration is m, the mass in slugs. That for the velocity, β lb.-sec./ft., measures the viscous resistance of the dashpot. And that for the displacement, k lb./ft., is the stiffness of the spring. The mass $m = w/g$, where w lb. is the weight and $g = 32.2$ ft./sec.^{2} is the acceleration of gravity.

If F is the only force, $F_e = 0$, so that

$$m \frac{d^2s}{dt^2} + \beta \frac{ds}{dt} + ks = F \qquad (135)$$

is the equation for the displacement. In terms of the velocity $v = ds/dt$ in feet per second this becomes

$$m \frac{dv}{dt} + \beta v + k \int_{t_0}^{t} v \, dt = F, \qquad (136)$$

where t_0 is the time at which $s = 0$. Differentiation gives

$$m \frac{d^2v}{dt^2} + \beta \frac{dv}{dt} + kv = \frac{dF}{dt}. \qquad (137)$$

A similar set of equations holds for an oscillating shaft,

$$I \frac{d^2\theta}{dt^2} + B \frac{d\theta}{dt} + K\theta = M. \qquad (138)$$

Here I is the moment of inertia in slugs times square feet, or $mr^2 = wr^2/g$, where r is the radius of gyration. B measures the resistance of damping forces, K is the coefficient of torsion, and M ft.-lb. is the applied torque or moment. The variable θ is the angular displacement in radians. Other forms like Eqs. (136) and (137) may be obtained from this by introducing the angular velocity $\Omega = d\theta/dt$ radians per second. Thus

$$I \frac{d^2\Omega}{dt^2} + B \frac{d\Omega}{dt} + K\Omega = \frac{dM}{dt}. \qquad (139)$$

12. Forced Vibrations

For the systems of Sec. 11, it is frequently important to know the response of an applied emf, force, or torque consisting of a single term $E \sin (\omega t + \phi)$. Sometimes the general type of forcing term is a sum of terms like this, or an infinite series like the Fourier series of Chap. 2. In such cases we obtain the response for the sum by adding the responses for the separate terms. And there are times when the response to the sine term gives a sufficient indication of the behavior of the system for any forcing term of the same frequency.

We note that, by Eq. (87),

$$Ee^{i(\omega t+\phi)} = E\underline{/\omega t + \phi}$$
$$= E \cos (\omega t + \phi) + iE \sin (\omega t + \phi). \quad (140)$$

In electrical-engineering literature, the mathematical symbols e and i are replaced by ϵ and j to reserve e for emf and i for current. With this notation

$$E\epsilon^{j(\omega t+\phi)} = E \cos (\omega t + \phi) + jE \sin (\omega t + \phi). \quad (141)$$

This relation is also indicated by writing

$$E \cos (\omega t + \phi) = \text{Re } E\underline{/\omega t + \phi} = \text{Re } E\epsilon^{i(\omega t+\phi)}, \quad (142)$$

$$E \sin (\omega t + \phi) = \text{Im } E\underline{/\omega t + \phi} = \text{Im } E\epsilon^{i(\omega t+\phi)}. \quad (143)$$

The symbol Re, read "real part of," means the component along the real axis, while Im, read "imaginary part of," means the component along the $(i = j = \sqrt{-1})$ imaginary axis. Note that each produces a real value when applied to a complex number.

If we take the expression in Eq. (143) as the applied emf, e in Eqs. (132) and (133), they become

$$L\frac{di}{dt} + Ri + \frac{1}{C}\int_{t_0}^{t} i \, dt = E \sin (\omega t + \phi) = \text{Im } E\epsilon^{j(\omega t+\phi)} \quad (144)$$

$$L\frac{d^2i}{dt^2} + R\frac{di}{dt} + \frac{1}{C} i = \text{Im } j\omega E\epsilon^{j(\omega t+\phi)} \quad (145)$$

To find a *particular integral* of this differential equation, we substitute in the left member

$$i = \text{Im } YE\epsilon^{j(\omega t+\phi)}, \quad (146)$$

where Y is a complex constant to be determined.   We find

$$\text{Im } YE\epsilon^{i(\omega t+\phi)}\left[L(j\omega)^2 + R(j\omega) - \frac{1}{C}\right] = \text{Im } (j\omega)E\epsilon^{i(\omega t+\phi)} \quad (147)$$

By Eq. (2), the imaginary parts will be equal if the complex numbers are equal, or if this equation holds when the symbol Im is omitted.   That is, if

$$Y\left(Lj\omega + R + \frac{1}{Cj\omega}\right) = 1. \quad (148)$$

The expression in parentheses is called the *impedance* of the element for the frequency ω.   It may be recalled by association with Eq. (144), and it may be obtained from the left member of that equation by replacing d/dt by $j\omega$ and replacing integration by $(j\omega)^{-1}$.   We denote it by Z, and write

$$Z = Lj\omega + R + \frac{1}{Cj\omega} = R + j\left(L\omega - \frac{1}{\omega C}\right) = R + jX, \quad (149)$$

where $X = \text{Im } Z$ is the *reactance* of the element for the frequency ω.   We also write, with the convention of Eq. (65),

$$Z = |Z| \underline{/\theta_z}, \text{ where } |Z| = \sqrt{R^2 + X^2}, \tan \theta_z = \frac{X}{R}. \quad (150)$$

Then we may deduce from Eqs. (148), (149), and (150) that

$$YZ = 1, \qquad Y = \frac{1}{Z} = \frac{1}{|Z|} \underline{/-\theta_z}. \quad (151)$$

With this value of Y, the particular integral of Eq. (146) is

$$i = \text{Im } YE \underline{/\omega t + \phi} = \text{Im } \frac{E \underline{/\omega t + \phi}}{Z} = \text{Im } \frac{E}{|Z|} \underline{/\omega t + \phi - \theta_z}$$

$$= \frac{E}{|Z|} \sin (\omega t + \phi - \theta_z). \quad (152)$$

In terms of the original constants, the particular integral is

$$\frac{E}{\sqrt{R^2 + \left(L\omega - \frac{1}{\omega C}\right)^2}} \sin \left[\omega t + \phi - \tan^{-1}\left(\frac{L\omega}{R} - \frac{1}{\omega RC}\right)\right], \quad (153)$$

where the inverse tangent has a positive cosine.

The expression just written remains a solution of Eq. (145) if we add to it the *complementary function* which is the most general solution of the equation with right member zero,

$$L \frac{d^2i}{dt^2} + R \frac{di}{dt} + \frac{1}{C} i = 0. \tag{154}$$

But ϵ^{rt}, or $c\epsilon^{rt}$, will be a solution of this equation if

$$Lr^2 + Rr + \frac{1}{C} = 0, \tag{155}$$

as we see by substituting $i = c\epsilon^{rt}$ in Eq. (154). From this

$$r = -\frac{R}{2L} \pm \sqrt{\frac{R^2}{4L^2} - \frac{1}{LC}} = -\frac{R}{2L} \pm j \sqrt{-\frac{R^2}{4L^2} + \frac{1}{LC}} \tag{156}$$

When R^2C exceeds $4L$, the radicand first written is positive, and its square root is less than $R/2L$. Hence the roots are both real and negative, and we abbreviate them by $-f$, $-g$. If $R^2C = 4L$, the radicand is zero, and the two roots are each equal to $-a$, if $a = R/2L$. In this case the left member of Eq. (155) is $L(r + a)^2$, and the left member of Eq. (154) is

$$L \left(\frac{d}{dt} + a \right) \left(\frac{d}{dt} + a \right) i = 0. \tag{157}$$

We verify that $ct\epsilon^{-at}$ is a second solution by noting that

$$\left(\frac{d}{dt} + a \right) t\epsilon^{-at} = \epsilon^{-at},$$

$$L \left(\frac{d}{dt} + a \right)^2 t\epsilon^{-at} = L \left(\frac{d}{dt} + a \right) \epsilon^{-at} = 0. \tag{158}$$

If R^2C is less than $4L$, the first radicand in Eq. (156) is negative, so that we use the second form. With

$$a = \frac{R}{2L}, \quad -\frac{R^2}{4L^2} + \frac{1}{LC} = b^2, \quad r = -a + bj. \tag{159}$$

This leads to solutions of Eq. (154) which are multiples of

$$\epsilon^{rt} = \epsilon^{-at+jbt} = \epsilon^{-at} \cos bt + j\epsilon^{-at} \sin bt. \tag{160}$$

Since the right member of Eq. (154) is $0 = 0 + 0j$, the real and imaginary parts of the last expression in Eq. (160) must each separately be solutions, giving two real expressions.

The discussion just given shows that the *complementary function* for Eq. (145) may be written

$$c_1\epsilon^{-ft} + c_2\epsilon^{-gt} \qquad \text{when } R^2C > 4L, \qquad (161)$$
$$c_1\epsilon^{-at} + c_2t\epsilon^{-at} \qquad \text{when } R^2C = 4L, \qquad (162)$$
$$c_1\epsilon^{-at} \cos bt + c_2\epsilon^{-at} \sin bt \qquad \text{when } R^2C < 4L. \qquad (163)$$

And the complete solution of Eq. (145) is obtained by adding to the particular integral of Eq. (153) or Eq. (152) the appropriate form of the complementary function.

In an application to a specific situation, the values of the constants c_1 and c_2 could be found from two facts about the circuit, for example, the current at some one time i_1 at t_1 and the charge on the condenser at some one time q_2 at t_2. In this case, putting $t = t_1$ in the complete solution, and equating the result to i_1 would give one equation in c_1 and c_2. The second condition could be found by putting $t = t_2$ in the complete solution and its derivative, using the values so obtained for i and di/dt in Eq. (144), and replacing the integral in that equation by q_2. For example, if we knew i_0 the value of the current at $t = 0$, and the complementary function was given by the third form, Eq. (163), the first condition would be

$$\frac{E}{|Z|} \sin (\phi - \theta_z) + c_1 = i_0. \qquad (164)$$

And if at the same time $t = 0$ the charge on the condenser was zero, the second condition would be

$$\frac{L\omega E}{|Z|} \cos (\phi - \theta_z) - aLc_1 + bLc_2 + \frac{RE}{|Z|} \sin (\phi - \theta_z) + Rc_1$$
$$= E \sin \phi. \qquad (165)$$

For a real and positive, ϵ^{at} and ϵ^{at}/t become infinite when t becomes infinite. Hence ϵ^{-at} and $t\epsilon^{-at}$ approach zero and all the terms in the complementary function become small when t is very large.   In fact, even after a fairly short time these terms become negligible in many applications.   Thus the important part of the solution in such cases is the particular integral, which represents the *steady-state*, or permanent, current.   The complementary function represents the *transient current*.   A convenient method of calculating transient currents will be given in Chap. 5.   To find the steady-state solution, we may proceed as follows.

Define *complex current* as the complex exponential term whose imaginary part is the actual simple harmonic steady-state current.   And define *complex* emf as the complex exponential term whose imaginary part is the actual applied simple harmonic emf, the left member of Eq. (141).   The impedance of the element, Z, for the frequency ω is defined in terms of L, R, C, and ω by Eq. (149).   Thus, for a given element, impedance is a complex variable which is a function of a real parameter, the frequency. Then, by Eq. (152), we have

$$\text{complex } i = \frac{\text{complex } e}{Z}, \qquad \text{or} \qquad iZ = e. \qquad (166)$$

In the second form we write i and e, allowing their complex character to be inferred from the context, or the presence of the complex factor Z.   Equation (166) is similar in form to Ohm's law for direct currents.   It reduces the problem of finding the steady-state current in a single circuit to the problem of dividing two complex numbers and of taking the imaginary part of the quotient to obtain the real current.

The real part of the complex current, or quotient in Eq. (166), is the steady-state current due to an applied emf $E \cos (\omega t + \phi)$.

The similarity of Eq. (136) to Eq. (132) shows that if we define the *impedance Z* for the mechanical circuit by

$$Z = mj\omega + \beta + \frac{k}{j\omega} = \beta + j\left(m - \frac{k}{\omega}\right), \qquad (167)$$

for frequency ω of the applied force

$$F = F_0 \sin (\omega t + \phi) = \text{Im } F_0 \epsilon^{j(\omega t + \phi)}. \qquad (168)$$

The steady-state value of the velocity for the resulting forced vibration will be

$$v = \text{Im} \frac{\text{complex } F}{Z} = \frac{F_0}{|Z|} \sin (\omega t + \phi - \theta_z). \qquad (169)$$

Here the polar coordinates of Z are found from Eq. (167) to be

$$Z = \sqrt{\beta^2 + \left(m - \frac{k}{\omega}\right)^2}, \qquad \tan \theta_z = \frac{m - \dfrac{k}{\omega}}{\beta}. \qquad (170)$$

For the displacement s, we use a denominator built up from Eq. (135) with $j\omega$ in place of d/dt. Thus

$$s = \text{Im} \frac{\text{complex } F}{j\omega Z} = -\frac{F_0}{\omega|Z|} \cos (\omega t + \phi - \theta_z)$$

$$= \frac{F_0}{\omega|Z|} \sin \left(\omega t + \phi - \theta_z - \frac{\pi}{2}\right). \qquad (171)$$

13. Electric Networks

In an electric network consisting of several elements, the total drop in emf for each element may be expressed in terms of the current through that element, the constants for the element, and the applied emf in the element. For example, in Fig. 15 if element BC, numbered 1, has resistance R_1, inductance L_1, and capacity C_1 and the applied emf e_1 the potential at B minus that at C, e_{d1} is found as in Eq. (130) to be

$$e_{d1} = L_1 \frac{di_1}{dt} + R_1 i_1 + \frac{q_1}{C_1} - e_1. \qquad (172)$$

The currents in the various elements of any network are related by Kirchhoff's first law, which states that

I. For all the elements which meet at any junction point, the algebraic sum of the currents, taken positive when toward the point, negative otherwise, is zero. This follows from the fact that, since current is conserved, as much goes out from any junction point as comes in.

The emfs in the various elements of any network are related by Kirchhoff's second law.   This states that

II. For all the elements which make up any closed circuit, the algebraic sum of all the voltage drops for individual elements or differences of potential for successive junction points is zero.   For a plane network, it is convenient to go around the circuit clockwise.

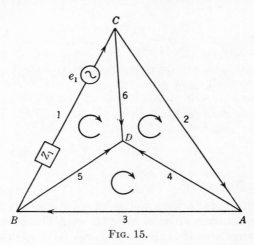

FIG. 15.

The second law expresses the fact that the total drop in emf must be zero when we return to the starting point.

To illustrate the application of these laws, consider the network of Fig. 15, with junction points A, B, C, D. We assign numbers to the elements, and positive directions, as indicated by the numbers and arrows in the figure.   For the first element we have Eq. (172).   And we may write five similar equations for the remaining elements by replacing the subscript 1 by 2, 3, 4, 5, or 6.

On applying law I to the points A, B, C, we find

$$i_2 - i_4 - i_3 = 0,$$
$$i_3 - i_5 - i_1 = 0,$$
$$i_1 - i_6 - i_2 = 0. \qquad (173)$$

The three circuits marked by curved arrows in the figure are *fundamental* in the sense that any other circuit is a combination of one or more of them, with common elements traversed in opposite directions suppressed.   On applying law II to them, we find

$$e_{d2} + e_{d4} - e_{d6} = 0,$$
$$e_{d3} + e_{d5} - e_{d4} = 0,$$
$$e_{d1} + e_{d6} - e_{d5} = 0. \tag{174}$$

It is possible, by introducing the impedances of the elements, to obtain the steady-state currents directly from Eqs. (173) and (174), as we shall show presently.   However, to lead up to this short method, as well as to understand better the nature of these equations, we shall carry out certain further reductions.   We first solve for i_4, i_5, and i_6 from Eq. (173), obtaining

$$i_4 = i_2 - i_3, \qquad i_5 = i_3 - i_1, \qquad i_6 = i_1 - i_2. \tag{175}$$

Now replace each of the six terms e_1 to e_6 in Eq. (174) by its value as given by Eq. (172) and the five similar equations. Next eliminate i_4, i_5, and i_6 by Eq. (175).   And eliminate q_4, q_5, q_6 by equations similar in form to Eq. (175), obtained from it by integration from t_0 the time at which all condensers were discharged to t.   Then Eq. (174) becomes

$$(L_2 + L_4 + L_6)\frac{di_2}{dt} + (R_2 + R_4 + R_6)i_2 + \left(\frac{1}{C_2} + \frac{1}{C_4} + \frac{1}{C_6}\right) q_2$$
$$-L_4\frac{di_3}{dt} - R_4 i_3 - \frac{1}{C_4} q_3 - L_6\frac{di_1}{dt} - R_6 i_1 - \frac{1}{C_6} q_1$$
$$= e_2 + e_4 - e_6, \quad (176)$$

and two other relations of similar form.   Differentiating these equations, and replacing dq_1/dt by i_1, dq_2/dt by i_2, and dq_3/dt by i_3, we obtain three second-order differential equations in the currents i_1, i_2, i_3.   After these are solved for these currents, the remaining three may be found from Eq. (175).

The discussion just given for Fig. 15 could be applied to any network.   We would apply law I to all but one of the points of junction, and we would then solve for as many of the currents as we could in terms of the rest. We would then apply law II to any fundamental set of circuits and eliminate the currents for which we solved the equations obtained from law I. The result is reducible to a system of differential equations, each at most of the second order, with as many equations as there are currents to be determined. For such a system the complementary function may be obtained by putting $i_1 = c_1\epsilon^{rt}$, $i_2 = c_2\epsilon^{rt}$, etc., in the equations with right member, or combinations of the e terms, replaced by zero. The term ϵ^{rt} may be divided out, and elimination of the coefficients c_1, c_2, etc. (for example by setting the determinant of the factors multiplying them, equal to zero) leads to an equation $P(r) = 0$, where $P(r)$ is a polynomial. Each root of this equation leads to a set of values of ratios of the coefficients c_1, c_2, etc., and hence to a term of the complementary function for each i of the form kc_1e^{rt} for i_1. The r and c_1, c_2, etc., are fixed, and there is one arbitrary constant k in each i for each root r. For an actual dissipative network, the roots r will either be real and negative, or if complex have a negative real part. Thus the terms in the complementary function, like those of Eqs. (161), (162), and (163), will each become small for t large. Hence they will correspond to transient currents. The process just described is chiefly of theoretical interest, because it is easier to find the transient currents, with the constants evaluated for specific initial conditions, by the method described in Chap. 5.

When only the steady-state solution is needed, we may proceed as follows. For a particular frequency present in one or more of the applied emfs omit all terms not of this frequency. With each applied emf, associate a complex exponential of which it is the imaginary part as

$$\text{complex } e_1 = E_1\underline{/\omega t + \phi_1} = E_1\epsilon^{j(\omega t + \phi_1)}. \tag{177}$$

And, when all the e's of this frequency are applied, if the current response in element 1 is $I_1 \sin(\omega t + \psi_1)$, define

$$\text{complex } i_1 = I_1\underline{/\omega t + \psi_1} = I_1\epsilon^{j(\omega t + \psi_1)}. \tag{178}$$

Similar to Eq. (149), we define the impedance Z_1 by

$$Z_1 = R_1 + j\left(L_1\omega - \frac{1}{\omega C_1}\right). \tag{179}$$

Then by Eq. (172), the complex voltage drop is

$$e_{d1} = Z_1 i_1 - e_1, \qquad e_{d1}, e_1, i_1 \text{ complex.} \tag{180}$$

Definitions and relations for the other elements are similar to these. Now regard the terms of Eq. (174) as complex, and replace each term by its equivalent obtained from Eq. (180) and the equations similar to it. Then consider the terms in Eq. (175) as complex, and use these relations to eliminate the last three complex currents. This leads to

$$(Z_2 + Z_4 + Z_6)i_2 - Z_4 i_3 - Z_6 i_1 = e_2 + e_4 - e_6,$$
$$(Z_3 + Z_5 + Z_4)i_3 - Z_5 i_1 - Z_4 i_2 = e_3 + e_5 - e_4,$$
$$(Z_1 + Z_6 + Z_5)i_1 - Z_6 i_2 - Z_5 i_3 = e_1 + e_6 - e_5. \tag{181}$$

This system may be solved for any one of the currents. For example, in terms of determinants, we find for i_1

$$i_1 = \frac{\begin{vmatrix} e_2 + e_4 - e_6 & Z_2 + Z_4 + Z_6 & -Z_4 \\ e_3 + e_5 - e_4 & -Z_4 & Z_3 + Z_5 + Z_4 \\ e_1 + e_6 - e_5 & -Z_6 & -Z_5 \end{vmatrix}}{\begin{vmatrix} -Z_6 & Z_2 + Z_4 + Z_6 & -Z_4 \\ -Z_5 & -Z_4 & Z_3 + Z_5 + Z_4 \\ Z_1 + Z_6 + Z_5 & -Z_6 & -Z_5 \end{vmatrix}}. \tag{182}$$

For given numerical values of the constants, this could be reduced to a complex constant times $\epsilon^{j\omega t}$, and its imaginary part would give the current response of frequency ω in the first element.

For any network, the introduction of complex currents, complex emfs, and impedance for each element leads to relations like Eq. (180). And these may be combined with the equations obtained from Kirchhoff's laws I and II, regarded as holding for the complex terms, to obtain a system of simultaneous equations of the first degree which may be solved for the complex currents contained in them.

For simple mechanical circuits, the use of complex exponentials and impedance was described in Eqs. (167) to (171). The extension of these notions for more complicated mechanical systems is illustrated in Probs. 24 to 28 of Exercise V.

14. References

In the discussion of complex numbers and complex exponentials the formal side has been emphasized, the rules for manipulating power series being stated without proof.   For a discussion with more emphasis on theoretical questions, the interested reader is referred to Chaps. V, IX, and XIII of the author's *Treatise on Advanced Calculus*.

Tables of hyperbolic functions and of trigonometric functions for arguments in radians are to be found in most mathematical handbooks.   As more extensive than most such tables, H. B. Dwight's *Mathematical Tables* is recommended.

For additional information about the physical applications mentioned here, the reader may consult E. A. Guillemin's *Communication Networks*, S. Timoshenko's *Vibration Problems in Engineering*, or J. P. Den Hartog's *Mechanical Vibrations*.

EXERCISE V

1. Find the transient current when a condenser of capacity 5 microfarads = 5×10^{-6} farad charged with 0.006 coulomb is discharged through a circuit containing a resistance of 3 ohms and an inductance of 10 henrys.

2. Show that the steady-state solution for i given by Eq. (152) or Eq. (153) is always a solution of Eq. (145), but that it is a solution of Eq. (144) only when the term involving t_0, a multiple of $\cos(\omega t_0 + \phi - \theta_Z)$, is zero.

A simple circuit has $R = 60$ ohms, $L = 8$ henrys, and

$$C = 3 \text{ microfarads} = 3 \times 10^{-6} \text{ farad.}$$

Find the steady-state current when the applied emf e is

3. $100 \sin(120\pi t)$.   **4.** $100 \cos(120\pi t)$.

5. $10 \sin (360\pi t + 40°)$.   **6.** $10 \sin (600\pi t - 20°)$.
7. $50 \sin (120\pi t) + 20 \sin (360\pi t + 40°)$.
8. $50 \sin (120\pi t) + 20 \sin (600\pi t - 20°)$.

A simple circuit has resistance R, inductance L, and capacity C. Find the steady-state current if e is

9. $\sin \omega t$.   **10.** $\cos \omega t$.
11. $A \cos \omega t + B \sin \omega t$.   **12.** $\cos (\omega t + \alpha)$.

13. Check Prob. 12, by using Prob. 11 with $A = \cos \alpha$ and $B = -\sin \alpha$.

14. An 8-lb. weight is constrained by a spring which stretches 1 ft. under a 5-lb. pull and a dashpot which offers 1 lb. resistance when the velocity is 1 ft./sec. Find the steady-state forced vibrations when the applied force $F = 20 \sin 4t$.

15. A heavy disk has a radius of gyration 1 ft. and weighs 100 lb. It vibrates about its axis due to an applied moment $M = 0.2 \sin 300t$. If it is constrained by a damper for which B is 10 ft.-lb.-sec. and a torsional constraint for which K is 20 ft.-lb., find the steady-state forced vibrations.

16. For a given frequency, let the elements of Fig. 16 have impedances Z_1, Z_2, Z_3 and applied complex emfs e_1, e_2, e_3. Use

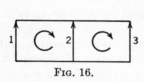

FIG. 16.

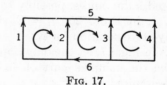

FIG. 17.

Kirchhoff's laws to set up the equations which determine the complex currents.

17. In Prob. 16, let $Z_3 = 0$, $e_1 = 0$, $e_2 = 0$. Solve for i_3 and interpret your result to give the rule for finding the single impedance equivalent to two impedances in parallel,

$$\frac{1}{Z} = \frac{1}{Z_1} + \frac{1}{Z_2}, \quad \text{or} \quad Z = \frac{Z_1 Z_2}{Z_1 + Z_2}.$$

18. In Fig. 17, let the only applied emf be in element 6, and let this be the complex part of e_6. For the frequency of e_6, let the elements have impedances $Z_1, \cdots, Z_6$. Set up the equations which determine the complex currents.

19. Solve the equations of Prob. 18 for i_6, and check by finding the sum of the impedances for Z_1 and Z_2 in parallel, Z_3 and Z_4 in parallel, Z_5, and Z_6 (see Prob. 17).

20. In Fig. 16 let element 1 contain resistance R_1, inductance $(L_1 - M)$, and real applied emf e_1. Also let element 3 contain resistance R_3, inductance $(L_3 - M)$, and real applied emf e_3. If then element 2 contains inductance M, show that the equations for the real currents i_1 and i_2 are

$$e_1 = R_1 i_1 + L_1 \frac{di_1}{dt} + M \frac{di_3}{dt},$$

$$e_3 = R_3 i_3 + L_3 \frac{di_3}{dt} + M \frac{di_1}{dt}.$$

These are the equations for two circuits with mutual inductance M, and the result shows that the presence of mutual inductances in a network does not change the character of the equations. As in this case, a network with mutual inductances can always be replaced by one without them, but with some added elements and changed inductances, possibly to negative values.

21. If in Prob. 20, $e_1 = E_1 \sin t$ and $e_3 = E_3 \sin t$, find the steady-state solution for i_1.

22. In Fig. 17, let the only applied emf be in element 1, and let this be the complex part of e_1. Let the ends of element 6 be short-circuited so that $Z_6 = 0$. And for the frequency of e_1, let the other numbered elements have impedances $Z_1, \cdots, Z_5$. Show that the complex currents i_1, i_2, i_3 satisfy the following system of equations:

$$Z_1 i_1 + Z_4(i_1 - i_2) = e_1,$$
$$Z_4(i_2 - i_1) + Z_2 i_2 + Z_5(i_2 - i_3) = 0,$$
$$Z_5(i_3 - i_2) + Z_3 i_3 = 0.$$

23. Solve the system of Prob. 22 for i_1 and show that the self-impedance of element 1, e_1/i_1, may be written

$$\frac{e_1}{i_1} = Z_1 + \cfrac{1}{\cfrac{1}{Z_4} + \cfrac{1}{Z_2 + \cfrac{1}{\cfrac{1}{Z_3} + \cfrac{1}{Z_5}}}}.$$

Check this by using Prob. 17 twice, first for Z_3, Z_5 in parallel, then this in series with Z_2 taken in parallel with Z_4.

24. The mechanical system of Fig. 18 consists of three vibrating masses, m_1, m_2, m_3, each attached by a spring and dashpot to a fixed base, as indicated by the elements 1, 2, 3. In addition there are spring and dashpot connections between the masses, as indicated by the elements 4 and 5. As in Eq. (167), we define impedances Z_1, Z_2, Z_3 by $Z_1 = m_1 j\omega + \beta_1 + \dfrac{k_1}{j\omega}$, and two similar equations. We also define $Z_4 = \beta_4 + \dfrac{k_4}{j\omega}$, $Z_5 = \beta_5 + \dfrac{k_5}{j\omega}$. The

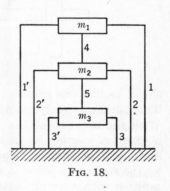

Fig. 18.

only applied force of frequency ω, acts on m_1, and is the complex part of F_1. Show that the complex velocities v_1, v_2, v_3 satisfy the following system of equations:

$$Z_1 v_1 + Z_4(v_1 - v_2) = F_1,$$
$$Z_4(v_2 - v_1) + Z_2 v_2 + Z_5(v_2 - v_3) = 0,$$
$$Z_5(v_3 - v_2) + Z_3 v_3 = 0.$$

25. Observing the similarity of the system of equations of Prob. 24 to that of Prob. 22, deduce from Prob. 23 that, for the complex velocity v_1 and displacement s_1 of m_1 in the mechanical system,

$$\frac{F_1}{v_1} = \frac{F_1}{j\omega s_1} = Z_1 + \cfrac{1}{\cfrac{1}{Z_4} + \cfrac{1}{Z_2 + \cfrac{1}{\cfrac{1}{Z_3} + \cfrac{1}{Z_5}}}}.$$

26. A shaft carrying three disks, Fig. 19, is undergoing tor-

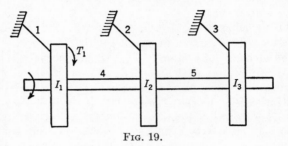

F<small>IG</small>. 19.

sional oscillations caused by a torque applied to the first disk. This torque is of frequency ω and is the complex part of T_1. With the notation of Eq. (138), for the first disk let I_1 be the moment of inertia, the angular displacement be the complex part of θ_1, and the angular velocity be the complex part of Ω_1. And let the element 1 denote a restraining tendency toward a neutral position with a spring constant K_1 and a damping restraint with constant B_1. This leads us to define the impedance

$$Z_1 = I_1 j\omega + B_1 + \frac{K_1}{j\omega}.$$

Similarly for disks 2 and 3, and the restraints indicated by elements 2 and 3, we define Z_2 and Z_3. The elements 4 and 5 denote restraints depending on the relative position and velocity of the disks, so that for them the impedances are $Z_4 = B_4 + \dfrac{K_4}{j\omega}$, $Z_5 = B_5 + \dfrac{K_5}{j\omega}$. Show that Ω_1, Ω_2, Ω_3 satisfy the following system of equations:

$$Z_1\Omega_1 + Z_4(\Omega_1 - \Omega_2) = T_1,$$
$$Z_4(\Omega_2 - \Omega_1) + Z_2\Omega_2 + Z_5(\Omega_2 - \Omega_3) = 0,$$
$$Z_5(\Omega_3 - \Omega_2) + Z_3\Omega_3 = 0.$$

27. Observing the similarity of the system of equations of Prob. 26 to that of Prob. 22, deduce from Prob. 23 that, for the torsional system,

$$\frac{T_1}{\Omega_1} = \frac{T_1}{j\omega\theta_1} = Z_1 + \cfrac{1}{\cfrac{1}{Z_4} + \cfrac{1}{Z_2 + \cfrac{1}{\cfrac{1}{Z_3} + \cfrac{1}{Z_5}}}}.$$

28. Suppose that there are n meshes in Prob. 22, n masses in Prob. 24, or n disks in Prob. 26. Number the connections $n + 1$ from 1 to 2, $N + 2$ from 2 to 3, $\cdots$, $2n - 1$ from $n - 1$ to n. Show that the continued fraction for $\dfrac{e_1}{i_1} = \dfrac{F_1}{v_1} = \dfrac{F_1}{j\omega s_1} = \dfrac{T_1}{\Omega_1} = \dfrac{T_1}{j\omega\theta_1}$ is

$$Z_1 = \cfrac{1}{\cfrac{1}{Z_{n+1}} + \cfrac{1}{Z_2 + \cfrac{1}{\cfrac{1}{Z_{n+2}} + \cdot\cdot}}}$$

$$\cdot\cdot\cdot$$

$$\cdot\cdot\cdot + \cfrac{1}{Z_{n-1} + \cfrac{1}{\cfrac{1}{Z_{2n-1}} + \cfrac{1}{Z_n}}}.$$

CHAPTER 2

FOURIER SERIES AND INTEGRALS

Certain electrical and mechanical problems which lead to linear differential equations were studied in Secs. 11 to 13. In particular, a method of finding the steady-state response to a single sine term was explained. And the response to any linear combination of sine terms is the same linear combination of their responses. In this chapter we shall show how any periodic driving force may be represented exactly by an infinite series of sine terms, its Fourier series, or approximately by a finite sum of sine terms, a harmonic analysis. And many nonrecurrent driving forces may be represented by an integral involving sines, the Fourier integral.

The interpretation of the Fourier series for functions known over a finite range only is explained with a view to the applications to boundary value problems in partial differential equations given in Chap. 4. And we discuss a modification of the Fourier integral, the Laplace transform, upon which we shall base our treatment of Heaviside's operational calculus in Chap. 5.

15. Average. Root Mean Square

Let x be a real variable, and $y = g(x)$ be any function given on the interval a,b. Then $\bar{y}$, the *average* of y with respect to x for the interval a,b is defined by the equation

$$\bar{y} = \frac{1}{b-a} \int_a^b y \, dx = \frac{1}{b-a} \int_a^b f(x) dx. \tag{1}$$

This definition makes

$$(b-a)\bar{y} = \int_a^b y \, dx. \tag{2}$$

When a $< b$ and $\bar{y} > 0$, the left member is the area of a rectangle of base b-a and height $\bar{y}$, while the right member is the area bounded by the graph of $y = f(x)$, the x axis, and the ordinates $x = a$, $x = b$. Thus we may define $\bar{y}$ geometrically as the height of a rectangle between these ordinates whose area equals that under the curve. This leads to a graphic method of estimating averages, for we need only slide a transparent straightedge over the graph parallel to the x axis until the total area between it and the curve above the straightedge appears to be equal to that between it and the curve below the straightedge. This holds whether $\bar{y}$ is positive, as in Fig. 20, or negative, as in Fig. 21.

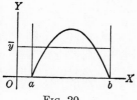

FIG. 20.

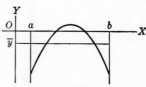

FIG. 21.

The geometric interpretation of Eq. (2) makes it easy to remember the definition.

As a particular example, consider the average of $y = 10x^m$, $m > 0$, with respect to x on the interval 0,1. Since

$$\int_0^1 10x^m \, dx = \frac{10}{m+1} x^{m+1}\Big|_0^1 = \frac{10}{m+1}, \qquad (3)$$

it follows that in this case

$$\bar{y} = \frac{1}{1-0} \cdot \frac{10}{m+1} = \frac{10}{m+1}. \qquad (4)$$

For all values of m, $10x^m$ increases from 0 to 10 as x increases from 0 to 1. And if we take special values of m,

For m =	999	4	1	0.25	$\frac{1}{999}$
$\bar{y}$ =	0.01	2	5	8	9.99

This illustrates that the average always lies between the extreme values of $f(x)$ on a,b, here 0 and 10, but may be quite close to either. Again let y, u, and v be physical quantities related in such a way that

$$y = 10u^{1/999}, \qquad u = v^{(999)^2} \qquad \text{and hence} \qquad y = 10v^{999}, \quad (5)$$

Then if y increased from 0 to 10, u and v would each increase from 0 to 1. And, by the calculation just made, for the interval 0,1 the average of y with respect to u would be 9.99 while the average of y with respect to v would be 0.01. Thus for a physical quantity the average depends on the variable to which we refer it. In most applications this is the time.

The average $\bar{y}$ has the same units as y, and changes like y for a change of scale or units. The average does not depend on the scale or units of x, since a change in these would multiply $b - a$ and dx in Eq. (1) by the same factor.

We define $\bar{\bar{y}}$, the *root mean square* (rms) value of y with respect to x for the interval a,b, by the equation

$$\bar{\bar{y}} = \text{rms } y = \sqrt{\frac{\int_a^b y^2 \, dx}{b - a}} \tag{6}$$

Thus the rms y is the square root of the average of the square of y, and is so defined that

$$(b - a)(\bar{\bar{y}})^2 = \int_a^b y^2 \, dx. \tag{7}$$

This differs from Eq. (2) only in having $(\bar{\bar{y}})^2$ in place of $\bar{y}$, and y^2 in place of y.

Let us again take $y = 10x^m$, $m > 0$, on the interval 0,1. Then

$$\int_0^1 (10x^m)^2 \, dx = \frac{100}{2m + 1} x^{2m+1} \Big|_0^1 = \frac{100}{2m + 1}, \tag{8}$$

so that in this case

$$\bar{\bar{y}} = \sqrt{\frac{1}{1 - 0} \frac{100}{2m + 1}} = \frac{10}{\sqrt{2m + 1}} \tag{9}$$

And if we take special values of m,

For m 999   4   1   0.25 $\dfrac{1}{999}$

$\bar{\bar{y}}$ 0.224 3.333 5.773 8.166 9.99001

This illustrates that the rms value of y always lies between the extreme values of $f(x)$ on a,b, here 0 and 10, but may lie quite close to either. Unless y is constant, $\bar{\bar{y}}$ exceeds $\bar{y}$ as shown in Prob. 30 of Exercise VI. Our tables illustrate this, as do Eqs. (4) and (9) since $(m + 1)^2$ exceeds $2m + 1$.

16. Even Function. Odd Function

The polynomial

$$f(x) = 16 - 8x^2 + x^4 \tag{10}$$

has terms in x to the power 0, 2, 4 all even numbers. Hence its value is unchanged when we replace x by $-x$. That is,

$$f(-x) = f(x). \tag{11}$$

Its graph, Fig. 22, has the y axis as an axis of symmetry. Any function $f(x)$ for which Eq. (11) holds is said to be *even*. We may detect that a function is *even* from the symmetry of its graph about OY, by substituting in Eq. (11), or by observing that it is a combination of a finite or infinite number of terms, each of which has x to an even power. Any of these methods shows that cos x, sec x, cosh x, and sech x are all even functions. If the graph of an even function is known for values on one side of OY, the other half of the graph may

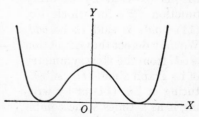

Fig. 22.   An even function.

be obtained by a reflection in OY. For example, $|x|$ is an even function equal to x for positive values of x. Hence its complete graph is as shown in Fig. 23.

For $f(x)$ even, it follows from the symmetry of its graph that

$$\int_{-a}^{0} f(x)dx = \int_{0}^{a} f(x)dx = \frac{1}{2} \int_{-a}^{a} f(x)dx. \tag{12}$$

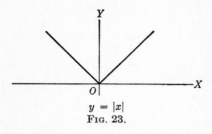

$y = |x|$

FIG. 23.

Dividing each of these by a converts the terms to averages. Hence *the average of an even function is the same for any one of the three intervals* $-a,0$; $0,a$; $-a,a$. This is also a direct consequence of the symmetry and the graphic method of finding averages.

Let us next consider the polynomial

$$f(x) = 4x + 4x^3 + x^5 \tag{13}$$

which has terms in x to the power 1, 3, 5 all odd numbers. Hence it changes sign when we replace x by $-x$. That is,

$$f(-x) = -f(x). \tag{14}$$

Its graph, Fig. 24, has such skew symmetry that for each point P of the graph there is a second point P' in the opposite quadrant for which the chord PP' is bisected by O. Any function $f(x)$ for which Eq. (14) holds is said to be *odd*. We may detect that a function is *odd* from the skew symmetry of its graph about O by substituting in Eq. (14) or by writing it as x times some combination of even powers. In particular the sum of a number of odd powers, or the reciprocal of such a sum, is an odd function. But this is not necessarily true of other combinations of odd powers, for

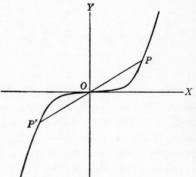

FIG. 24.   An odd function.

example, $(x^3)(x^5)$ which is even and $(x^3)(x^5) + x^7$ which is neither odd nor even. As examples of odd functions other than polynomials in odd powers we may mention sin x, csc x, tan x, cot x, sinh x, csch x, tanh x, and coth x. If the graph of an odd function is known for values on one side of OY, the other half of the graph may be obtained from it by a 180° rotation about O in the xy plane. For example, $(|x| - x^2)/x$, undefined for $x = 0$, is an odd function equal to $1 - x$ for positive values of x. Hence its complete graph is as shown in Fig. 25. As x increases through zero from negative to positive values, this $f(x)$ jumps from $f(0-) = -1$, the

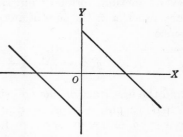

FIG. 25. $y = (|x| - x^2)/x.$

value approached from the left, to $f(0+) = 1$, the value approached from the right. If we put $x = 0$ in Eq. (14), we find

$$f(0) = -f(0), \quad \text{or} \quad 2f(0) = 0, \quad \text{and} \quad f(0) = 0. \quad (15)$$

Hence if we wish our function to be odd and defined for all x, including zero, we must put $f(0) = 0$, or add O to the graph.

For $f(x)$ odd, it follows from the nature of its graph that

$$\int_{-a}^{0} f(x)dx = -\int_{0}^{a} f(x)dx \quad \text{and} \quad \int_{-a}^{a} f(x)dx = 0. \quad (16)$$

Dividing each of these by a or $2a$ converts the terms into averages. Hence *the average of an odd function for the interval* $-a,0$ *is the negative of that for the interval* $0,a$ *and the average for the interval* $-a,a$ *is always zero.* This is also a direct consequence of the skew symmetry and the graphic method of finding averages.

The product of two even functions is even. The product of two odd functions is even. But the product of an odd and an even function is odd.

In particular the square of an even function is even, and the square of an odd function is even. Hence *for any even function, or for any odd function, the root mean square value is the same for any one of the three intervals* $-a,0; 0,a; -a,a.$

The general polynomial or series of powers will be neither odd nor even. However, it may be considered to be the sum of an odd function, formed from the terms with odd powers, and an even function, formed from the terms with even powers. And any function is the sum of an odd function and an even function, since

$$g(x) = \frac{g(x) - g(x)}{2} + \frac{g(x) + g(-x)}{2}, \tag{17}$$

and the first fraction changes sign, while the second is unchanged, when we put $-x$ for x. Starting with e^x which is neither odd nor even, either the series or Eq. (17) would lead to

$$e^x = \sinh x + \cosh x,$$

and thus to $\sinh x$ as the odd component and $\cosh x$ as the even component of e^x.

EXERCISE VI

Find the average of each of the following functions for the interval 1,3:

1. $2 - 4x.$ **2.** $6x^2 + 8x^3.$ **3.** $2e^{-x}.$ **4.** $5 \ln x.$

Find the rms value of each of the following functions for the interval 2,6:

5. $4 - x.$ **6.** $3e^{2x}.$ **7.** $\dfrac{1}{x - 1}.$ **8.** $1 + x^2.$

Verify that each of the following functions is even and so has the same average value for the intervals $-2,0; 0,2; -2,2.$ Compute this average. Also compute the rms for these intervals.

9. $5.$ **10.** $2x^2.$ **11.** $3x^4.$ **12.** $\cos x.$

Verify that each of the following functions is odd and thus has its average value 0 for the interval $-2,2.$ Compute the average for the interval 0,2. Also compute the common value of the rms for the intervals $-2,0$; $0,2$; $-2,2$.

13. $4x$.   **14.** $8x^3$.   **15.** $\sin x$.   **16.** $\sin x \cos x$.

By inspection, find the average value over the interval $-5,5$ of each of the following functions:

17. $\sin^3 2x$.   **18.** $\sin x \cos^5 x + 4$.
19. $\sin 2x \cos^2 x + 2$.   **20.** $2x \cos 4x - 5$.

21. Find the average and rms value over the interval 0,4 of a function which is $2x$ when $0 < x < 2$ and is $8 - 2x$ when $2 < x < 4$ by the following methods: (*a*) by calculating the integral over 0,4 as that over 0,2 plus that over 2,4, and (*b*) by deducing from the graph that the average and rms for 0,4 is the same as that for 0,2.

By calculating the integral over 0, $2\pi/\omega$ as the sum of that over 0, π/ω plus that over π/ω, $2\pi/\omega$ find for one cycle 0, $2\pi/\omega$ the average and rms value for

22. $E |\sin \omega t|$, the output of a full-wave rectifier.

23. $f(t) = E \sin \omega t$, when $0 < t < \pi/\omega$ and $f(t) = 0$ when $\pi/\omega < t < 2\pi/\omega$, the output of a half-wave rectifier.

24. If for y variable $du/dx = ky$, show that when x increases from a to b, u increases by the same amount as for $du/dx = k\bar{y}$, where $\bar{y}$ is the constant of Eq. (1).

25. From $F = m \, dv/dt$ and Prob. 24 deduce that in any interval t_1, t_2 the average force times the increase in time equals the gain in monentum, $\bar{F}(t_2 - t_1) = mv_2 - mv_1$.

26. In the definition of velocity, an "average" velocity $\dfrac{s_2 - s_1}{t_2 - t_2}$ is used. Show that this equals $\bar{v}$ for the interval t_1, t_2. Hint: Use $v = ds/dt$ and Prob. 24.

27. Let the interval a,b be divided into n equal parts by x_1, x_2, $\cdots$, x_{n-1}. As in Fig. 26, label the ordinates of the graph of $y = f(x)$ at these points $y_1, y_2, \cdots , y_{n-1}$, and that at b label y_n. The "average" of these n ordinates is

$$\bar{y}_n = (y_1 + y_2 + \cdots + y_n)/n.$$

Prove that as n becomes infinite, $\bar{y}_n \to \bar{y}$, the average defined by Eq. (1).

28. If for y variable $du/dx = ky^2$, show that when x increases from a to b, u increases by the same amount as for

$$du/dx = k(\bar{y})^2,$$

where $\bar{y}$ is the constant of Eq. (6).

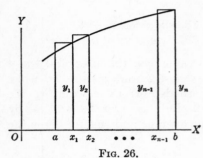

FIG. 26.

29. If after t sec. H cal. of heat are generated by a current of i amperes flowing through a resistance of R ohms,

$$dH/dt = 0.24i^2R.$$

From this and Prob. 27 deduce that for any interval t_2, t_1 the calories generated $H_2 - H_1 = 0.24(\bar{i})^2R$.

30. For current i amperes the power P watts transferred to a load causing a drop in emf of e volts is $P = ei$. If the load has reactance $X = 0$, Sec. 12, $e = iR$, show that $P = \bar{e} \cdot \bar{i}$. But whenever the ratio e/i is not constant throughout the interval t_1, t_2 show that for this interval $P < \bar{e} \cdot \bar{i}$. HINT: Consider

$$\frac{1}{t_2 - t_1} \int_{t_1}^{t_2} (ix - e)^2 dt = \bar{i}^2 x^2 - 2\bar{P}x + \bar{e}^2,$$

where x is any real constant. Since the integral is positive, the same is true of the quadratic expression in x. Hence when equated to zero, the solution for x cannot be real, and the quantity under the radical $(-2\bar{P})^2 - 4(\bar{i}^2)(\bar{e}^2)$ is negative.

31. Prove that unless y is constant in a, b, $\bar{\bar{y}} > \bar{y}$. HINT: If $i = 1$ in Prob. 30, $i = 1$, $P = e$ and $e/i = e$. Hence when e is not constant in t_1, t_2, $\bar{e} < \bar{\bar{e}}$.

If $y = c_1 f_1(x) + c_2 f_2(x)$, and $g = f_1 f_2$, show that for a, b.

32. The average $\bar{y} = c_1\bar{f}_1 + c_2\bar{f}_2$.

33. The rms $\bar{\bar{y}} = \sqrt{c_1\bar{\bar{f}}_1{}^2 + 2c_1c_2\bar{g} + c_2\bar{\bar{f}}_2{}^2}$.

If the subscripts denote the interval over which the average or rms value of $y = f(x)$ is taken, show that

34. $\bar{y}_{ac} = \dfrac{(b - a)\bar{y}_{ab} + (c - b)\bar{y}_{bc}}{(c - a)}$.

35. $\bar{\bar{y}}_{ac} = \sqrt{\dfrac{(b - a)\bar{\bar{y}}_{ab}{}^2 + (c - b)\bar{\bar{y}}_{bc}{}^2}{(c - a)}}$.

A rod of variable density has length L and total mass M. It covers the interval $0,L$ of the x axis. Let $m = f(x)$ be the amount of mass on the interval $0,x$ and $x = f^{-1}(m)$ be the inverse function so that $f^{-1}(0) = 0$ and $f^{-1}(M) = L$. Show that

36. The distance of the center of gravity of the rod from 0 is $\bar{x}$, the average of $x = f^{-1}(m)$ on the interval $0,M$.

37. The radius of gyration of the rod about the y axis is $\bar{\bar{x}}$, the rms value of $x = f^{-1}(m)$ on the interval $0,M$.

17. Averages of Periodic Functions

A function $f(x)$ is said to be *periodic*, of period p, if

$$f(x + p) = f(x). \qquad (18)$$

The graph of every function with period p, like that of Fig. 27, consists of a series of identical pieces such as those for the intervals $-p,0$; $0,p$; $p,2p$. It follows from Eq. (18) that

$$f(x + np) = f(x), \qquad n = 1, 2, \cdots \text{ or } -1, -2, \cdots. \qquad (19)$$

Hence $f(x)$ is necessarily also of period np.

For any number a, the interval $a,a + p$ includes a point $b = 0$ or np. And the parts of the graph for a,b and $b,a + p$ are identical with the parts for c,p and $0,c$, where $c = a + p - b$.

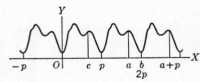

FIG. 27.   A periodic function.

Hence we have

$$\int_a^{a+p} f(x)dx = \int_0^p f(x)dx. \qquad (20)$$

By dividing the intervals $0,np$ or $a, a + np$, where $n > 0$, $p > 0$, into n equal parts each of length p, and applying Eq. (20) to each part, we find

$$\frac{1}{n} \int_0^{np} f(x)dx = \frac{1}{n} \int_a^{a+np} f(x)dx = \int_0^p f(x)dx. \qquad (21)$$

Dividing by p converts each term of Eqs. (20) and (21) into an average, and proves that: *The average of a function of period p for any interval of length p or np is the same as that for the interval $0,p$.*

As shown in Prob. 39 of Exercise VII, for any interval which is very large as compared with the smallest period we get nearly the same value as for the interval $0,p$.

The periodic functions met in applications such as mechanical vibrations, alternating currents, or emfs are often functions of the time. And they are frequently known either exactly or approximately as sums of sine or cosine terms. In calculating rms values, we average e^2 and i^2, while for the average power we form the product ei and average. Thus we are led to averages of squares and products of sine and cosine terms. There are a few simple rules for calculating these special averages which we proceed to derive.

By Sec. 2, the complex function of the real variable x

$$e^{i(\omega x + \phi)} = \cos(\omega x + \phi) + i \sin(\omega x + \phi). \qquad (22)$$

The phase ϕ may have any value, but we assume that the frequency $\omega > 0$. Like its real and imaginary parts, the complex function is of period $p = 2\pi/\omega$. This could be verified directly from the exponential form by using

$$e^{i\omega p} = e^{2\pi i} = \cos 2\pi + i \sin 2\pi = 1. \qquad (23)$$

For, on putting $x + p$ for x in the exponential, we find

$$e^{i[\omega(x+p)+\phi]} = e^{i(\omega x + \phi)} \cdot e^{i\omega p} = e^{i(\omega x + \phi)}, \qquad (24)$$

so that Eq. (18) is satisfied.   Again, the integral

$$\int_0^p e^{i(\omega x+\phi)}\, dx = \frac{1}{\omega i}\, e^{i(\omega x+\phi)}\Big|_0^p = 0, \tag{25}$$

since by Sec. 3 the expression for the indefinite integral, obtained by the rule for real exponentials, has the integrand as its derivative and assumes the same value at the two limits by Eq. (24). Dividing by p converts the integral into an average, with real and imaginary parts averages of cosine and sine terms by Eq. (22). This proves our first rule:

I. *If* $\omega > 0$, *and* $p = 2\pi/\omega$, *the average of* $\cos (\omega x + \phi)$ *or* $\sin (\omega x + \phi)$ *for the interval* $0,p$ *is zero.*   Since the functions are all of period p, the average is zero for any interval of length p or np with n a positive integer.

Let us next consider two positive frequencies ω_1, ω_2 whose ratio is a rational fraction n_1/n_2, the quotient of two positive integers. Then

$$\frac{\omega_1}{\omega_2} = \frac{n_1}{n_2}, \quad \text{so that} \quad \omega = \frac{\omega_1}{n_1} = \frac{\omega_2}{n_2}, \quad \omega_1 = n_1\omega, \quad \omega_2 = n_2\omega. \tag{26}$$

where ω is defined as the common value of the two equal fractions. The periods for frequencies ω, ω_1, ω_2 are

$$p = \frac{2\pi}{\omega}, \quad p_1 = \frac{2\pi}{\omega_1}, \quad p_2 = \frac{2\pi}{\omega_2}, \quad \text{and} \quad p = n_1 p_1 = n_2 p_2. \tag{27}$$

The product $\sin (\omega_1 x + \phi_1) \cos (\omega_2 + \phi_2)$ is necessarily periodic, of period p, since the first factor has p_1 and hence $n_1 p_1$ as a period while the second has p_2 and hence $n_2 p_2$.   To find the average of the product for $0,p$, we first express each of the factors in terms of complex exponentials.   By Sec. 2,

$$\sin (\omega_1 x + \phi_1) = \frac{e^{i(\omega_1 x+\phi_1)} - e^{-i(\omega_1 x+\phi_1)}}{2i}, \tag{28}$$

$$\cos (\omega_2 x + \phi_2) = \frac{e^{i(\omega_2 x+\phi_2)} + e^{-i(\omega_2 x+\phi_2)}}{2}. \tag{29}$$

The product will expand into four terms having in the exponent as coefficients of ix either $\omega_1 + \omega_2$, $\omega_1 - \omega_2$ or the negatives of these quantities. Assume that $\omega_1 > \omega_2$, and decompose each of the exponentials by Sec. 2 into real and imaginary parts. This can lead only to a combination of sine and cosine terms with frequencies $\omega_3 = \omega_1 + \omega_2$ or $\omega_4 = \omega_1 - \omega_2$. The corresponding periods are

$$p_3 = \frac{2\pi}{\omega_1 + \omega_2} = \frac{p}{n_1 + n_2}, \qquad p_4 = \frac{2\pi}{\omega_1 - \omega_2} = \frac{p}{n_1 - n_2}, \qquad (30)$$

where the second form is found by using the last two equalities of Eq. (26), and the first relation of Eq. (27). Since n_1 and n_2 are positive integers, and $\omega_1 > \omega_2$ implies $n_1 > n_2$, $n_3 = n_1 + n_2$ and $n_4 = n_1 - n_2$ are each positive integers. The averages of the sine and cosine terms with frequency ω_3, are zero for the interval $0,p_3$ by rule I, or for $0,n_3p_3$ and hence for $0,p$, since $p = n_3p_3$ by Eq. (30). Similarly for the terms with frequency ω_4 for $0,p$, since $p = n_4p_4$ by Eq. (30). And the argument just given leads to the same conclusion if $\omega_2 < \omega_1$ or if we replace the sine in the product by a cosine, or the cosine by a sine. Thus we have proved the second rule:

II. *Let* $\omega_1 > 0$, $p_1 = 2\pi/\omega_1$, $\omega_2 > 0$, $p_2 = 2\pi/\omega_2$ *and*

$$p = n_1p_1 = n_2p_2.$$

Then if $\omega_1 \neq \omega_2$, *the average of the product of the sine or cosine of* $(\omega_1x + \phi_1)$ *times the sine or cosine of* $(\omega_2x + \phi_2)$ *for the interval* $0,p$ *is zero.* Since each of these products is of period p, the average is zero for any interval of length p or np with n a positive integer.

If the frequencies ω_1 and ω_2 are equal, we may omit the subscripts and write the product $\sin(\omega x + \phi_1) \cos(\omega x + \phi_2)$. The previous argument still holds for the terms with frequency $\omega_1 + \omega_2 = 2\omega$, but the terms which were of frequency $\omega_1 - \omega_2$ are now the constant

$$\frac{e^{i(\phi_1-\phi_2)} - e^{-i(\phi_1-\phi_2)}}{2 \cdot 2i} = \frac{1}{2}\sin(\phi_1 - \phi_2), \qquad (31)$$

where the left member is obtained by putting $\omega_1 = \omega$ and $\omega_2 = \omega$ in Eqs. (28) and (29) and picking out the two exponential terms with a zero coefficient for x, while the reduction to the right member follows from Sec. 2. Since the average of a constant is the constant itself, this proves the third rule:

III. *If $\omega > 0$, and $p = 2\pi/\omega$, the average of the product*

$$\sin (\omega x + \phi_1) \cos (\omega x + \phi_2)$$

for the interval $0,p$ is equal to

$$\tfrac{1}{2} \sin (\phi_1 - \phi_2).$$

Since the product is of period p, the average has this same value for any interval of length p or np.

For the product $\sin (\omega x + \phi_1) \sin (\omega x + \phi_2)$, we use Eq. (28) with $\omega_1 = \omega$ and then with ϕ_1 replaced by ϕ_2 as well. The terms of the product constant in this case are equal to

$$\frac{e^{i(\phi_1-\phi_2)} + e^{-i(\phi_1-\phi_2)}}{2 \cdot 2} = \frac{1}{2} \cos (\phi_1 - \phi_2). \qquad (32)$$

And this same constant is obtained for the product of two cosines $\cos (\omega x + \phi_1) \cos (\omega x + \phi_2)$ by use of Eq. (29). This proves the fourth rule:

IV. *If $\omega > 0$, and $p = 2\pi/\omega$, the average of the product*

$$\sin (\omega x + \phi_1) \sin (\omega x + \phi_2)$$

or

$$\cos (\omega x + \phi_1) \cos (\omega x + \phi_2)$$

for the interval $0,p$ is equal to $\tfrac{1}{2} \cos (\phi_1 - \phi_2)$. Since each of these products is of period p, the average has this same value for any interval of length p or np.

When $\phi_2 = \phi_1$, or in particular $\phi_1 = 0$ and $\phi_2 = 0$, the value given by rule IV is $\tfrac{1}{2} \cos 0 = \tfrac{1}{2}$. Hence we may state the fifth rule:

V. *If $\omega > 0$, and $p = 2\pi/\omega$, the average of the square*

$$\sin^2 (\omega x + \phi), \cos^2 (\omega x + \phi), \sin^2 \omega x, \text{ or } \cos^2 \omega x$$

for the interval $0,p$ *is equal to* $\frac{1}{2}$.

When $\phi_1 = 0$ and $\phi_2 = 0$, the value given by rule III is $\frac{1}{2} \sin 0 = 0$. We may combine this with rule II to give the sixth rule:

VI. *Let* $\omega_1 > 0$, $p_1 = 2\pi/\omega_1$, $\omega_2 > 0$, $p_2 = 2\pi/\omega_2$ *and*

$$p = n_1 p_1 = n_2 p_2.$$

Then if the product of $\sin \omega_1 x$ *or* $\cos \omega_1 x$ *times* $\sin \omega_2 x$ *or* $\cos \omega_2 x$ *is not a square, its average for the interval* $0,p$ *is zero.* For the square, both factors sines or both cosines and $\omega_2 = \omega_1$, the average is $\frac{1}{2}$ by rule V.

To illustrate the use of these rules, suppose that a load has such impedance that an impressed emf of e volts, where

$$e = 150.9 \sin 120\pi t - 31.33 \sin 360\pi t \tag{33}$$

causes a current of i amperes to flow through the load, where

$$i = 14 \sin (120\pi t - 21.9°) - 2 \sin (360\pi t - 50.33°). \tag{34}$$

For frequency $\omega = 120\pi$, $p = 2\pi/\omega = \frac{1}{60}$. And for frequency $\omega_1 = 360 = 3\omega$, $p_1 = 2\pi/(3\omega) = p/3$. Hence $P = \frac{1}{60} = 3p_1$ is a period for each term separately and therefore for the sums, so that we are dealing here with 60-cycle alternating current.

The power transferred to the load is $P = ei$. Let us calculate $\bar{P}$, the average value of P for the interval $0, \frac{1}{60}$. Using Eqs. (33) and (34), with ω for 120π, we may write

$$P = ei = 150.9 \times 14 \sin \omega t \sin (\omega t - 21.9°)$$
$$+ (-31.33)(-2) \sin 3\omega t \sin (3\omega t - 50.33°) + \cdots \tag{35}$$

where the dots stand for products of terms of different frequency ω, 3ω whose average is zero by rule II. For the terms written, the average is found by rule IV. Hence

$$\bar{P} = 150.9 \times 14 \times \frac{1}{2} \cos 21.9° + 31.33 \times 2 \times \frac{1}{2} \cos 50.33°$$
$$= 980 + 20 = 1,000 \text{ watts.} \tag{36}$$

If the rms value of i were required, we would write

$$i^2 = 14^2 \sin^2 (\omega t - 21.9°)$$
$$+ (-2)^2 \sin^2 (3\omega t - 50.33°) + \cdots , \quad (37)$$

using rule II for the omitted term, and find by rule V that

$$\overline{i^2} = (\bar{i})^2 = 14^2 \times \tfrac{1}{2} + 2^2 = 98 + 2 = 100. \quad (38)$$

Hence $\bar{i} = 100^{\frac{1}{2}} = 10$ amperes.   We note that a similar calculation for e gives $\bar{e} = 154.1$ volts, so that $\bar{e} \cdot \bar{i} = 1,541$ exceeds $\bar{P}$. By Prob. 29 of Exercise VI, $\bar{e} \cdot \bar{i}$ must exceed P since the ratio of e/i changes with the time.   The values just found for the interval $0, \frac{1}{60}$ are exact for any interval which is an integral number of cycles, for example, 5 min. which equals $18,000p$. Since any time interval larger than 5 min. is large compared with p, the averages for such an interval will be very close to those found for $0, \frac{1}{60}$ (see Prob. 40 of Exercise VII).

It is sometimes convenient to reduce all the terms to terms of zero phase.   Thus if we expand the sines in Eq. (34) by the addition theorem, Eq. (11) of Sec. 2, it becomes

$$i = 12.990 \sin 120\omega t - 5.222 \cos 120\omega t - 1.277 \sin 360\omega t$$
$$+ 1.540 \cos 360\omega t. \quad (39)$$

From this and Eq. (33), using rules VI and V, we could find $\bar{P}$

$$P = 150.9 \times 12.990 \times \tfrac{1}{2} + (-31.33)(-1.277) \times \tfrac{1}{2}$$
$$= 980 + 20 = 1,000 \text{ watts.} \quad (40)$$

EXERCISE VII

1. Show that the function $f(x) = c$, a constant, is periodic, of period p, for any value of p.

Show that each of the following functions is periodic, and find the smallest possible value of the period p:

2. $7 \sin 5\pi x + 6 \sin 10\pi x + 2 \sin 15\pi x + 2 \sin 20\pi x$.

3. $24 - 13 \cos 20\pi x + 11 \cos 80\pi x - \cos 120\pi x$.

4. $8 \sin 12\pi x + 5 \sin 16\pi x$.   **5.** $6 \cos 12\pi x - 4 \cos 15\pi x$.

6. $10 \sin \dfrac{\pi x}{3} + 7 \sin \dfrac{\pi x}{2}.$ **7.** $9 \cos \dfrac{\pi x}{3} - 4 \cos \dfrac{\pi x}{5}.$

If $f(x) = x^2$ when $0 < x < 1$, and $f(x) = 2 - x$ when $1 < x < 2$, sketch the graph of $y = f(x)$ for $-6 < x < 6$ if

8. $f(x)$ is periodic, of period 2.

9. $f(x)$ is an even function and periodic, of period 4.

10. $f(x)$ is an odd function and periodic, of period 4.

11. If $f(x) = 4x - 4x^2$ when $0 < x < 1$, and $f(x)$ is periodic of period 1, show that $f(x)$ is an even function.

12. If $f(x) = x^3 - 3x^2 + 2x$ when $0 < x < 2$, and $f(x)$ is periodic of period 2, show that $f(x)$ is an odd function.

In each case, find the rms value for an interval equal to a complete period of the sum:

13. $e = 200 \cos 120\pi t - 100 \sin 120\pi t + 30 \sin 360\pi t$.

14. $i = 160 \cos 120\pi t - 80 \sin 120\pi t + 24 \sin 360\pi t$.

15. $e = 240 \cos 60\pi t + 48 \cos 180\pi t$.

16. $i = 2.74 \cos (60\pi t - 31°) + 0.42 \cos (180\pi t - 61°)$.

17. $e = 250 \sin (50\pi t + 78.67°) + 50 \sin (150\pi t - 2.83°)$.

18. $i = 20 \sin 50\pi t + 3 \cos 150\pi t$.

19. $e = 400 \cos (120\pi t + 50°) - 70 \sin (360\pi t + 42°)$.

20. $i = 2.56 \sin (120\pi t + 88.83°) - 0.187 \sin (360\pi t - 33.5°)$.

21. $e = 25 \sin \left(\dfrac{\pi t}{30} + 75°\right) + 5 \sin \left(\dfrac{\pi t}{10} - 75°\right)$.

22. $i = 25 \sin \left(\dfrac{\pi t}{30} + 73.17°\right) + 5 \sin \left(\dfrac{\pi t}{10} - 80.67°\right)$.

Find the average power for a complete period transferred by a current of i amperes due to an emf of e volts given in

23. Probs. 13 and 14.   **24.** Probs. 15 and 16.

25. Probs. 17 and 18.   **26.** Probs. 19 and 20.

27. Probs. 21 and 22.

28. Show that 1 sec. is a possible period for each of the sums given in Probs. 13 to 20, and find the number of cycles per second in each case.

29. If $i = I_1 \sin (\omega t + a_1) + I_3 \sin (3\omega t + a_3)$ and $e = E_1 \sin (\omega t + b_1) + E_3 \sin (3\omega t + b_3)$, show that for a complete cycle the average value of the power P is

$$\bar{P} = \tfrac{1}{2}[E_1I_1 \cos(a_1 - b_1) + E_3I_3 \cos(a_3 - b_3)]$$

and that the rms values are $\bar{i} = \sqrt{\tfrac{1}{2}(I_1{}^2 + I_3{}^2)}$ and

$$\bar{e} = \sqrt{\tfrac{1}{2}(E_1{}^2 + E_3{}^2)}.$$

The results are similar if there are additional terms each with subscript n and frequency $n\omega$, for n some positive integer.

30. Show that the results of Prob. 29 hold if in i and e we replace the sines by cosines.

31. If $i = A_1 \cos \omega t + C_1 \sin \omega t + A_3 \cos 3\omega t + C_3 \sin 3\omega t$ and $e = B_1 \cos \omega t + D_1 \sin \omega t + B_3 \cos 3\omega t + D_3 \sin 3\omega t$, show that for a complete cycle the average value of the power P is $\bar{P} = \tfrac{1}{2}(A_1B_1 + C_1D_1 + A_3B_3 + C_3D_3)$ and that the rms values are $\bar{i} = \sqrt{\tfrac{1}{2}(A_1{}^2 + C_1{}^2 + A_3{}^2 + C_3{}^2)}$,

$$\bar{e} = \sqrt{\tfrac{1}{2}(B_1{}^2 + D_1{}^2 + B_3{}^2 + D_3{}^2)}.$$

The results are similar if there are additional terms each with subscript n and frequency $n\omega$, for n some positive integer.

32. Show that the equations $A_n + I_n \sin a_n$, $C_n = I_n \cos a_n$ are solved by $I_n = \sqrt{A_n{}^2 + C_n{}^2}$, $\tan a_n = \dfrac{A_n}{C_n}$ without canceling minus signs as in Sec. 6. Assume that these equations as well as those with I, a, A, C replaced by E, b, B, D hold for each n present in the sums of Prob. 29 or 31. Deduce that this makes the given i and e, as well as the conclusions identical. Such relations may be used to convert either given form into the other.

33. Show that the equations $A_n = I_n \cos a_n$, $C_n = -I_n \sin a_n$ are solved by $I_n = \sqrt{A_n{}^2 + C_n{}^2}$, $\tan a_n = -\dfrac{C_n}{A_n}$ without canceling minus signs as in Sec. 6. Assume that these equations as well as those with I, a, A, C replaced by E, b, B, D hold for each n present in the sums of Probs. 30 or 31. Deduce that this makes the given i and e, as well as the conclusions, identical. Such relations may be used to convert either given form into the other.

34. Use Prob. 32 to convert Eq. (34) into Eq. (39).

35. Use Prob. 32 to convert Eq. (39) into Eq. (34).

36. Show that if in Eq. (26) n_1 and n_2 are both odd integers the products of rule II, or when $n_1 = n_2 = 1$ the squares of rule V, are of period π/ω, one-half the p used in the rules.

Verify the following illustrations of Prob. 36:

37. $\sin 3\pi x \cos 5\pi x$, $n_1 = 3$, $n_2 = 5$, $2\pi/\omega = 2$, but 1 is a period.

38. $\sin^2 4\pi x$, $2\pi/4 = \frac{1}{2}$, but $\frac{1}{4}$ is a period.

39. Let $f(x)$ satisfy Eq. (18), with $p > 0$. Then any number L large compared with p can be written $L = np + c$, where n is a large positive integer and $0 \leqq c < p$. Show that

$$L\bar{f}_L = np\bar{f}_p + c\bar{f}_c,$$

where the intervals for the averages are a, $a + L$ for $\bar{f}_L$, $0,p$ for $\bar{f}_p$ and $0,c$ for $\bar{f}_c$. Deduce that

$$\bar{f}_L - \bar{f}_p = \frac{np\bar{f}_p + c\bar{f}_c}{np + c} - \bar{f}_p = \frac{c(\bar{f}_c - \bar{f}_p)}{np + c} < \frac{\bar{f}_c - \bar{f}_p}{n}$$

which is numerically less than $2M/n$, where M is the maximum or largest extreme value of $|f(x)|$. This proves that for any interval of length L, so large compared with p that its ratio to p is large compared with the values of $|f(x)|$, the average $\bar{f}_L$ is nearly the same as $\bar{f}_p$ that for $0,p$.

40. In Prob. 40 take $f(x) = A \sin \omega x$, $p = 2\pi/\omega$ and $c = p/2$, or $L = (n + \frac{1}{2})p$. Verify that $f_c = 0.707A$, $\bar{f}_p = 0$, and $\bar{f}_L - \bar{f}_p = \dfrac{0.707A}{2n + 1}$. With x the time in seconds and $\omega = 120\pi$, $p = \frac{1}{60}$ sec. And $\bar{f}_L - \bar{f}_p = 0.006A$ for $n = 60$, or $0.00002A$ for $n = 18,000$, which are good indications of the possible departure of $\bar{f}_L$ from $\bar{f}_p = 0$ for times exceeding 1 sec. or 5 min.

18. Fourier's Theorem for Periodic Functions

If $\omega = 2\pi/p$, so that $p = 2\pi/\omega$, and n is any integer, the function

$$e^{in\omega x} = \cos n\omega x + i \sin n\omega x \tag{41}$$

is periodic of period p. For, on putting $x + p$ for x, we find

$$e^{in\omega(x+p)} = e^{in\omega x} \cdot (e^{i\omega p})^n = e^{in\omega x},$$

by Eq. (23), so that Eq. (18) is satisfied. Hence any sum or series of terms each of which is a constant times $e^{in\omega x}$, its real part $\cos n\omega x$, or its imaginary part $\sin n\omega x$, will be of period p. In particular, if the infinite series

$$a + a_1 \cos \omega x + b_1 \sin \omega x + a_2 \cos 2\omega x + b_2 \sin 2\omega x + \cdots$$
$$+ a_n \cos n\omega x + b_b \sin n\omega x + \cdots \quad (42)$$

or

$$a + \sum_{k=1}^{\infty} (a_k \cos k\omega x + b_k \sin k\omega x) \quad (43)$$

is convergent, it represents a periodic function of period p where

$$p = \frac{2\pi}{\omega} \quad \text{or} \quad \omega = \frac{2\pi}{p}. \quad (44)$$

If a function $f(x)$ is single-valued and continuous on a finite interval and its graph on this interval has finite arc length, we call the function or its graph *regular*. We call a single-valued function $f(x)$ *piecewise regular* if its graph on any finite interval is made up of a finite number of pieces, each of which is a regular arc or an isolated point.

For example, on the interval $0 \leqq x < 8$, the relations

$$f(0) = 1, \quad f(x) = 2 \quad \text{if } 0 < x < 2, \quad f(2) = 1,$$
$$f(x) = 0 \quad \text{if } 2 < x < 8, \quad (45)$$

define a piecewise regular function. And, if we add the condition

$$f(x + 8) = f(x), \quad (46)$$

the function is defined for all values of x as a piecewise regular function of period 8. Its graph is shown in Fig. 28. We use the notation $f(x-)$ to mean the value at x approached from the left and $f(x+)$ to mean the value at x approached from the right. Thus at $x = 2$ these values are $f(2-) = 2$ and $f(2+) = 0$. If x is the time with a suitable submultiple of a second as the unit, this $f(x)$ would represent a rectangular pulse, repeated at an interval four times its duration, of a type often used in testing receiving apparatus.

Suppose that $f(x)$ is any piecewise regular periodic function of period p. Then it may be proved that there are coefficients for which the series (43), with $\omega = 2\pi/p$, converges to $f(x)$ at all points of continuity, and to $\frac{1}{2}[f(x+) + f(x-)]$ at the points of discontinuity. This series is called the *Fourier series of the*

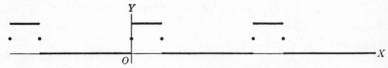

FIG. 28.   A piecewise regular periodic function.

periodic function $f(x)$. Furthermore, correct relations will be obtained from the equation

$$f(x) = a + \sum_{k=1}^{\infty} (a_k \cos k\omega x + b_k \sin k\omega x), \qquad (47)$$

by termwise integration after multiplication by any function of x.

Let us use as multipliers 1, $\cos n\omega x$, $\sin n\omega x$, respectively, where n is any positive integer, and integrate from c to $c + p$, where c is any constant. Dividing by p converts the integrals into averages which may be found for the terms on the right by the rules of Sec. 17. For 1 we find

$$\frac{1}{p} \int_c^{c+p} f(x)dx = a, \qquad \text{or} \qquad a = \frac{1}{p} \int_c^{c+p} f(x)dx \qquad (48)$$

by rule I. For $\cos n\omega x$ and $\sin n\omega x$ we find by rules VI and V

$$\frac{1}{p} \int_c^{c+p} f(x) \cos n\omega x \, dx = \frac{a_n}{2}, \qquad \text{or}$$

$$a_n = \frac{2}{p} \int_c^{c+p} f(x) \cos n\omega x \, dx, \qquad (49)$$

$$\frac{1}{p} \int_c^{c+p} f(x) \sin n\omega x \, dx = \frac{b_n}{2}, \qquad \text{or}$$

$$b_n = \frac{2}{p} \int_c^{c+p} f(x) \sin n\omega x \, dx. \qquad (50)$$

To recapitulate, if $f(x)$ is any piecewise regular periodic function of period p; and a, the a_n, and the b_n are found from Eqs. (48) to (50), then the series (43), with $\omega = 2\pi/p$, will converge to $f(x)$ at all points of continuity, and to $\frac{1}{2}[f(x+) + f(x-)]$ at all points of discontinuity. This is known as *Fourier's theorem for periodic functions*.

Let us illustrate the procedure for the function defined by the relations (45) and (46). Here $p = 8$, $\omega = \pi/4$. We take $c = 0$ and, since the expression for the function changes at 2, calculate the integrals from 0 to 8 as the sum of those from 0 to 2 and from 2 to 8. Thus we find

$$a = \tfrac{1}{8} \left(\int_0^2 2dx + \int_2^8 0dx \right) = \tfrac{1}{8}(4 + 0) = \tfrac{1}{2}. \tag{51}$$

$$a_n = \frac{2}{8} \left(\int_0^2 2 \cos n\omega x \, dx + \int_2^8 0 \cos n\omega x \, dx \right)$$

$$= \frac{1}{4}\left(\frac{2}{n\omega} \sin n\omega x \Big|_0^2 + 0 \right) = \frac{\sin 2n\omega}{2n\omega} = \frac{2}{n\pi} \sin \frac{n\pi}{2}. \tag{52}$$

$$b_n = \frac{2}{8} \left(\int_0^2 2 \sin n\omega x \, dx + \int_2^8 0 \sin n\omega x \, dx \right)$$

$$= \frac{1}{4}\left(-\frac{2}{n\omega} \cos n\omega x \Big|_0^2 + 0 \right) = -\frac{\cos 2n\omega - 1}{2n\omega}$$

$$= \frac{2}{n\pi}\left(1 - \cos \frac{n\pi}{2} \right). \tag{53}$$

To save writing we carry the calculation as far as possible before replacing ω by its value, here $\pi/4$. Putting n successively equal to 1, 2, 3, etc., we find from Eqs. (51) to (53) that the Fourier series for the function $f(x)$ of (45) and (46) is

$$\frac{1}{2} + \frac{2}{\pi}\left(\cos \omega x - \frac{1}{3} \cos 3\omega x + \frac{1}{5} \cos 5\omega x - \cdots \right)$$

$$+ \frac{2}{\pi}\left(\sin \omega x + \frac{2}{2} \sin 2\omega x + \frac{1}{3} \sin 3\omega x + {}^* + \frac{1}{5} \sin 5\omega x + \cdots \right) \tag{54}$$

where $\omega = \pi/4$.

Not all rearrangements of the terms of a Fourier series will give a convergent series, but it is always allowable to group the sine

terms together and the cosine terms together into two separate
series as we have done here.

The defining relations (45) and (46) happen to make the value
of the function equal to $\frac{1}{2}[f(x+) + f(x-)]$ at the points of discontinuity. For example, $f(8) = \frac{1}{2}[f(8+) + f(8-)]$, since
$1 = \frac{1}{2}(2 + 0)$. Hence Fig. 28 is the graph of the sum of the
series (54) for all values of x. Had we taken other values for
$f(x)$ as the definition at the points of discontinuity, we would
still have found the same Fourier series since the values $f(0)$ and
$f(2)$ were not used in Eqs. (51) to (53). We may always obtain
the graph of the Fourier series which represents any piecewise
regular function by plotting the regular arcs, together with the
mid-points of the vertical segments determined by consecutive
arcs. In Fourier series problems, we shall frequently define the
regular arcs only and give no values at the discontinuities, since
these last do not affect the Fourier series.

The full curve of Fig. 29 is the graph of the sum of the terms

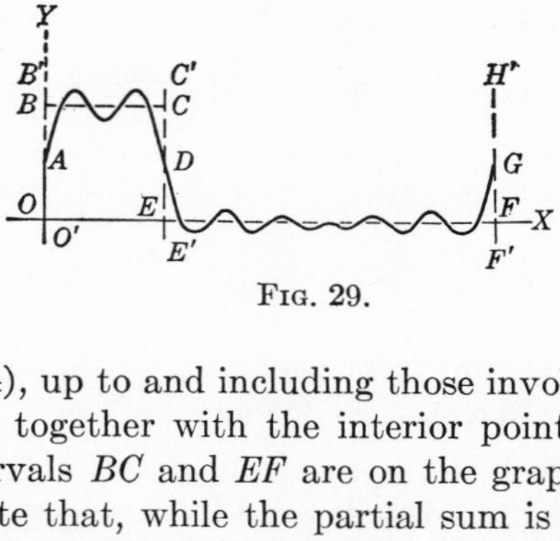

Fig. 29.

of the series (54), up to and including those involving $7\omega x$. The
points A, D, G together with the interior points of the dotted
horizontal intervals BC and EF are on the graph of the sum of
the series. Note that, while the partial sum is almost equal to
$f(x)$ for $x = 0, 2, 8$ where $f(x)$ has a discontinuity, and is a fair
approximation to $f(x)$ for x well inside the intervals 0,2 and 2,8,
the approximation is poor for values of x near but not at 0, 2, 8.
The distance from the minimum nearest 2 to the maximum nearest 2 is greater than the jump of the function at 2. This excess
persists for all the sums, so that if we plotted the sum for a very

large number of terms it would be indistinguishable from the set of dotted segments $O'B'$, BC, $C'E'$, EF, $F'H'$. This is typical of the behavior of sums of Fourier series near points of discontinuity. The sum for a large number of terms is always indistinguishable from the regular arcs, together with the vertical segments joining their ends extended by about 18 per cent. That is, to a segment like EC we add EE' and CC', each 9 per cent of EC. The overshooting of the jumps in this way is known as *Gibbs's phenomenon*.

EXERCISE VIII

Find the Fourier series of a function which is of period 2π and is defined in the interval $-\pi < x < \pi$ as equal to

1. x. **2.** x^2. **3.** x^3. **4.** e^x. **5.** $x \sin x$. **6.** $x \cos x$.

7. $f(x) = \pi$ if $-\pi < x < 0$ and $f(x) = 0$ if $0 < x < \pi$.

8. $f(x) = x$ if $-\pi < x < 0$ and $f(x) = 0$ if $0 < x < \pi$.

Find the Fourier series of a function which is of period 2π and is defined in the interval $0 < x < 2\pi$ as equal to

9. x. **10.** x^2. **11.** x^3 **12.** e^x. **13.** $x \sin x$. **14.** $x \cos x$.

15. $f(x) = \pi$ if $0 < x < \pi$ and $f(x) = 0$ if $\pi < x < 2\pi$.

16. $f(x) = x$ if $0 < x < \pi$ and $f(x) = 0$ if $\pi < x < 2\pi$.

Find the Fourier series of a function $f(x)$ which is of period 10, and such that $f(x) = 0$ if $-5 < x < 0$, and if $0 < x < 5$, $f(x)$ is equal to

17. 10. **18.** x. **19.** e^x. **20.** $\sin x$. **21.** $\cos x$.

22. Show that the Fourier series for a rectangular pulse of unit height, duration w, on from c to $c + w$ and repeated at intervals $2\pi/\omega$, Fig. 30, may be written

$$\frac{\omega w}{2\pi} + \frac{2}{\pi} \sum_{n=1}^{\infty} \frac{1}{n} \sin \frac{n\omega w}{2} \cos n\omega \left(x - c - \frac{w}{2} \right).$$

23. Use Prob. 22 to check Probs. 7, 15, and 17 and Eq. (54).

24. Show that the Fourier series for a function of period $2\pi/\omega$ which equals x for $c < x < c + 2\pi/\omega$ may be written

$$x = c + \frac{\pi}{\omega} - \frac{2}{\omega} \sum_{n=1}^{\infty} \frac{1}{n} \sin n\omega(x - c), \ c < x < c + \frac{2\pi}{\omega}.$$

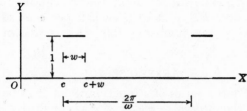

FIG. 30.   A rectangular pulse.

25. Use Prob. 24 to check Probs. 1 and 9.

26. Show that the Fourier series for a function $f(x)$ of period $2\pi/\omega$ such that

$$f(x) = 0 \text{ if } c - \frac{\pi}{\omega} < x < c, f(x) = x \text{ if } c < x < c + \frac{\pi}{\omega},$$

may be written

$$\frac{c}{2} + \frac{\pi}{4\omega} + \left(\frac{2c}{\pi} + \frac{1}{\omega}\right) \sum_{n=1}^{\infty} \frac{\sin n\omega \ (x - c)}{n} - \frac{2}{\pi\omega} \sum_{n=1}^{\infty} \frac{\cos n\omega \ (x - c)}{n^2}.$$

27. Use Prob. 26 to check Probs. 8, 16, and 18.

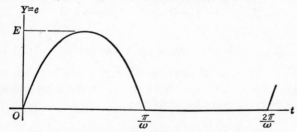

FIG. 31.   Output voltage of a half-wave rectifier.

28. When an emf $E \sin \omega t$ is impressed on a half-wave rectifier, the output voltage e, Fig. 31, of period $2\pi/\omega$, is zero from

$t = -\pi/\omega$ to $t = 0$ and $e = E \sin \omega t$ if $0 < t < \pi/\omega$. Show that

$$e = E \left(\frac{1}{\pi} + \frac{1}{2} \sin \omega t - \frac{2}{\pi} \sum_{n=1}^{\infty} \frac{\cos 2n\omega t}{4n^2 - 1} \right)$$

$$= \frac{E}{\pi} (1 + 1.57 \sin \omega t - 0.67 \cos 2\omega t - 0.13 \cos 4\omega t$$

$$- 0.06 \cos 6\omega t - \cdots).$$

29. Use Prob. 28 to check Prob. 20.

19. Half-range Fourier Series

For *any* given function $f(x)$, Eqs. (48) to (50) and Eq. (44) may be used to find a *Fourier series of period p*, Eq. (43), which represents $f(x)$ for $c < x < c + p$, where $c, c + p$ is any interval on which $f(x)$ is piecewise regular. For, from $f(x)$ on $c, c + p$ we may form a function of period p equal to the given function for $c < x < c + p$. The series (43) and (44) with coefficients calculated by Eqs. (48) to (50) will then represent the periodic function for all x. Hence in particular it will represent the given $f(x)$ for $c < x < c + p$.

The interval $c, c + p$ reduces to $-L, L$ with center at the origin if $c = -L$ and $p = 2L$. With these values Eqs. (48) to (50) and Eq. (44) become

$$a = \frac{1}{2L} \int_{-L}^{L} f(x)dx, \qquad a_n = \frac{1}{L} \int_{-L}^{L} f(x) \cos n\omega x \, dx,$$

$$b_n = \frac{1}{L} \int_{-L}^{L} f(x) \sin n\omega x \, dx, \qquad \omega = \frac{\pi}{L}. \tag{55}$$

Let $f(x)$ be an even function as defined in Sec. 16. Then the integrands $f(x)$ and $f(x) \cos n\omega x$ are each even, while $f(x) \sin n\omega x$ is odd. From Eqs. (12), (16), and (55) we may conclude that $b_n = 0$ and that

$$a = \frac{1}{L} \int_{0}^{L} f(x)dx, \qquad a_n = \frac{2}{L} \int_{0}^{L} f(x) \cos n\omega x \, dx. \tag{56}$$

Hence with these values, for any *even* $f(x)$ of period $2L$, and all x,

$$f(x) = a + \sum_{k=1}^{\infty} a_k \cos n\omega x, \qquad \text{where } \omega = \frac{\pi}{L}. \tag{57}$$

For *any* given function $f(x)$, piecewise regular on $0,L$, Eqs. (56) and (57) may be used to find a *Fourier cosine series of period $2L$* which represents $f(x)$ in $0 < x < L$. For, from $f(x)$ on $0,L$ we may form an even function of period $2L$ equal to the given function for $0 < x < L$. The series (57) with coefficients calculated by Eq. (56) will then represent the even periodic function

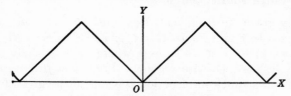

Fig. 32.   An even function.

for all x. Hence in particular it will represent the given $f(x)$ for $0 < x < L$.

We illustrate the procedure by finding the Fourier cosine series of period 2π which represents x in the interval $0 < x < \pi$. On putting $f(x) = x$ and $L = \pi$, $\omega = 1$ in Eq. (56), we find

$$a = \frac{1}{\pi} \int_0^\pi x \, dx = \frac{1}{\pi} \frac{x^2}{2} \Big|_0^\pi = \frac{\pi}{2}. \tag{58}$$

$$a_n = \frac{2}{\pi} \int_0^\pi x \cos nx \, dx = \frac{2}{\pi} \left(\frac{x \sin nx}{n} + \frac{\cos nx}{n^2} \right) \Big|_0^\pi$$

$$= \frac{2}{\pi n^2} (\cos n\pi - 1). \tag{59}$$

It follows from these values and Eq. (57) that, for $0 < x < \pi$,

$$x = \frac{\pi}{2} - \frac{4}{\pi} \left(\cos x + \frac{1}{3^2} \cos 3x + \frac{1}{5^2} \cos 5x + \cdots \right). \tag{60}$$

The graph of the even periodic function with this as its Fourier series is as shown in Fig. 32. Hence Eq. (60) holds for $x = 0$, or $x = \pi$ but not for $x < 0$ or $x > \pi$. The full curve of Fig. 33 is the graph of the sum of the terms of the series (60), up to and including that in $5x$. Comparison with the sum of the series, shown as a dotted curve, shows that we have a fair approximation at all points.

Next suppose that $f(x)$ is an odd function as defined in Sec. 16. Then in Eq. (55) the integrands $f(x)$ and $f(x) \cos n\omega x$ are each odd, so that by Eq. (16) $a = a_n = 0$. But $f(x) \sin n\omega x$ is even,

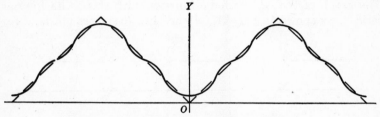

FIG. 33.   Partial sum of a Fourier series.

and we may conclude from Eqs. (55) and (12) that

$$b_n = \frac{2}{L} \int_0^L f(x) \sin n\omega x \, dx. \tag{61}$$

Hence with these values, for any *odd* $f(x)$ of period $2L$, and all x,

$$f(x) = \sum_{k=1}^{\infty} b_k \sin k\omega x, \qquad \text{where } \omega = \frac{\pi}{L}. \tag{62}$$

For *any* given function $f(x)$, piecewise regular on $0,L$, Eqs. (61) and (62) may be used to find a *Fourier sine series of period* $2L$ which represents $f(x)$ in $0 < x < L$. For, from $f(x)$ on $0,L$ we may form an odd function of period $2L$ equal to the given function for $0 < x < L$. The series (62) with coefficients calculated by Eq. (61) will then represent the odd periodic function for all x. Hence in particular it will represent the given $f(x)$ for $0 < x < L$.

We illustrate the procedure by finding the Fourier sine series of period 2π which represents $\pi/2$ in the interval $0 < x < \pi$.

On putting $f(x) = \pi/2$ and $L = \pi$, $\omega = 1$ in Eq. (61), we find

$$b_n = \frac{2}{\pi} \int_0^\pi \frac{\pi}{2} \sin nx \, dx = -\frac{1}{n} \cos nx \Big|_0^\pi = \frac{1 - \cos n\pi}{n}. \quad (63)$$

It follows from these values and Eq. (62) that, for $0 < x < \pi$,

$$\frac{\pi}{2} = 2 \left(\sin x + \frac{1}{3} \sin 3x + \frac{1}{5} \sin 5x + \cdots \right). \quad (64)$$

The graph of the odd periodic function with this as its Fourier series is as shown in Fig. 34.   Hence Eq. (64) does not hold for

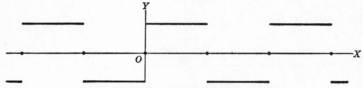

FIG. 34.   An odd function.

$x = 0$ or $x = \pi$.

For the period $p = 2L$, a function $f(x)$ is called *odd-harmonic* if

$$f(x + L) = -f(x). \quad (65)$$

Such a function is necessarily periodic, of period p, since

$$f(x + p) = f[(x + L) + L] = -f(x + L) = f(x). \quad (66)$$

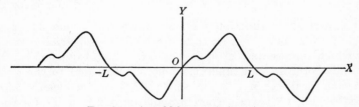

FIG. 35.   An odd-harmonic function.

And as Fig. 35 illustrates for the graph of $f(x)$, the piece for any interval of length L can be obtained from the piece for the preceding interval of length L by reflecting in the x axis and advancing a distance L. It follows that

$$\int_{-L}^{0} f(x)dx = -\int_{0}^{L} f(x)dx \quad \text{and} \quad \int_{-L}^{L} f(x)dx = 0. \quad (67)$$

The oscillographs of many of the emfs generated in practice exhibit the odd-harmonic property.

Equation (65) suggests that we study the related property

$$f(x + L) = f(x). \quad (68)$$

Any function $f(x)$ for which Eq. (68) holds is said to be *even-harmonic* for the period $p = 2L$. Such a function is periodic, of period L, by Eq. (18), and hence of period $2L$ by Eq. (19). And from Eq. (21),

$$\frac{1}{2}\int_{-L}^{L} f(x)dx = \int_{0}^{L} f(x)dx. \quad (69)$$

Let $\omega = 2\pi/p = \pi/L$, so that $L = \pi/\omega$. Then

$$e^{i\omega L} = e^{i\pi} = \cos \pi + i \sin \pi = -1. \quad (70)$$

It follows from this that

$$e^{in\omega(x+L)} = e^{in\omega x} \cdot (e^{i\omega L})^n = (-1)^n e^{in\omega x} \quad (71)$$

$$= \begin{cases} e^{in\omega x}, & \text{if } n = 0, 2, 4, 6, \cdots. \quad (72) \\ -e^{in\omega x}, & \text{if } n = 1, 3, 5, \cdots. \quad (73) \end{cases}$$

This shows that $e^{in\omega x}$, and hence its real and imaginary parts $\cos n\omega x$ and $\sin n\omega x$ by Eq. (40), is even-harmonic for the period $2L$ when n is 0 or an even integer, but is odd-harmonic for the period $2L$ when n is an odd integer.

Now let $f(x)$ in Eq. (55) be odd-harmonic for the period $2L$. Since the product of an odd-harmonic function and an even-harmonic function is odd-harmonic, for n an even integer the integrands $f(x) \cos n\omega x$ and $f(x) \sin n\omega x$ are odd-harmonic. Hence by Eq. (57) the integrals in Eq. (55) are zero, and

$$a = 0, \quad a_2 = 0, \quad b_2 = 0, \quad a_4 = 0, \quad b_4 = 0, \quad \cdots. \quad (74)$$

But the product of two odd-harmonic functions is even-harmonic. Hence for n an odd integer, the integrands $f(x) \cos n\omega x$ and $f(x) \sin n\omega x$ are even-harmonic, and we may use Eq. (69) to transform the integrals. Thus

$$a_m = \frac{2}{L} \int_0^L f(x) \cos m\omega x \, dx, \qquad b_m = \frac{2}{L} \int_0^L f(x) \sin m\omega x \, dx,$$
$$m = 1, 3, 5, \cdots . \tag{75}$$

With these values, for any $f(x)$ which is odd-harmonic for the period $2L$, for all x,

$$f(x) = \Sigma(a_m \cos m\omega x + b_m \sin m\omega x), \tag{76}$$

where the sum is taken over all odd integers, $m = 1, 3, 5, \cdots$.

For *any* given function $f(x)$, piecewise regular on $0,L$, Eqs. (75) and (76) may be used to find an *odd-harmonic Fourier series of period* $2L$ which represents $f(x)$ in $0 < x < L$. For, from $f(x)$ on $0,L$ we may form a function which is odd-harmonic for the period $2L$ equal to the given function for $0 < x < L$. The series (76) with coefficients calculated by Eq. (75) will then represent the odd-harmonic function for all x. Hence in particular it will represent the given $f(x)$ for $0 < x < L$.

We illustrate the procedure by finding the odd-harmonic Fourier series of period 2π which represents x in the interval $0 < x < \pi$. On putting $f(x) = x$ and $L = \pi$, $\omega = 1$ in Eq. (75), we find

$$a_m = \frac{2}{\pi} \int_0^\pi x \cos mx \, dx = \frac{2}{\pi} \left(\frac{x \sin mx}{m} + \frac{\cos mx}{m^2} \right) \Big|_0^\pi$$
$$= -\frac{4}{\pi m^2}. \tag{77}$$

$$b_m = \frac{2}{\pi} \int_0^\pi x \sin mx \, dx = \frac{2}{\pi} \left(-\frac{x \cos mx}{m} + \frac{\sin mx}{m^2} \right) \Big|_0^\pi = \frac{2}{m}. \tag{78}$$

It follows from these values and Eq. (76) that for $0 < x < \pi$,

$$x = -\frac{4}{\pi} \sum \frac{1}{m^2} \cos mx + 2 \sum \frac{1}{m} \sin mx,$$
$$m = 1, 3, 5, \cdots . \tag{79}$$

The graph of the odd-harmonic function with this as its Fourier

series is as shown in Fig. 36.   Hence Eq. (79) does not hold for
$x = 0$ or $x = \pi$.   If we replace the $\pi/2$ in Eq. (60) by the
right member of Eq. (64), and note that the terms in parentheses
are the expansions of the summations in Eq. (79), we see that our
three series are consistent for $0 < x < \pi$.

The simplified formulas for the coefficients given in Eqs. (56),
(61), and (75) may be used to find the series of restricted form
of period $p = 2L$ with specified values on the half-range $0,L$, as

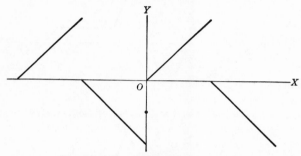

Fig. 36.   An odd-harmonic function.

we have shown.   And this is their principal application.   However, when a function of period $2L$ is to take on specified values
on some full range as $-L,L$ or $0,2L$ we may still use one of these
equations in place of Eq. (48) to (50) if the values are such that
the periodic function is even, odd, or odd-harmonic.   For
example, if our problem was to find a series of period $2L$ represent-
ing $|x|$ in the interval $-L < x < L$, we might notice from its
graph, Fig. 32, that the periodic function is even, and thus compute the coefficients from Eq. (56) as in Eqs. (58) and (59).   Or
we might notice that if the line $y = \pi/2$ were taken as a new x
axis, the graph of Fig. 32 would be odd-harmonic as well as even.
Hence the series for $|x|$ equals the constant $\pi/2$ plus terms
$a_m \cos mx$, whose coefficients could be found from Eq. (75) as in
Eq. (77).   Either method would be simpler than the use of Eq.
(55), since the integrals for $|x|$ from $-L$ to L would have to be
taken for $-x$ from $-L$ to 0, and for x from 0 to L.

To detect from its graph that a function is even, odd, even-harmonic, or odd-harmonic one must recall that the graph for $-L,0$ comes from that for $0,L$ by a displacement for an even-harmonic function, by a displacement together with a reflection in the x axis for an odd-harmonic function, by a reflection about the y axis for an even function, and a reflection about the y axis

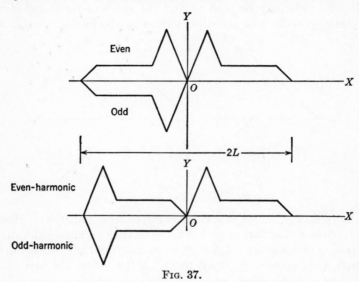

Fig. 37.

together with a reflection about the x axis for an odd function. These geometric relations are summarized in Fig. 37.

EXERCISE IX

Verify that each of the following functions is an even function of period π, and find its Fourier series:

1. $|\sin x|$.   **2.** $|\cos x|$.   **3.** $\sin^2 x$.   **4.** $\cos^2 x$.

Verify that each of the following functions is odd and also odd-harmonic of period 2π, and find its Fourier series:

5. $\sin x\, |\sin x|$.   **6.** $\sin x\, |\cos x|$.   **7.** $\sin^3 x$.   **8.** $\sin x \cos^2 x$.

Verify that each of the following functions is even and also odd-harmonic of period 2π, and find its Fourier series:

9. $\cos x \,|\sin x|$.   **10.** $\cos x \,|\cos x|$.   **11.** $\cos x \sin^2 x$.   **12.** $\cos^3 x$.

Find the Fourier cosine series of period 8 which represents $f(x)$ in the interval $0 < x < 4$ when

13. $f(x) = x$ if $0 < x < 4$.   **14.** $f(x) = 2 - x$ if $0 < x < 4$.
15. $f(x) = 0$ if $0 < x < 2$ and $f(x) = 4$ if $2 < x < 4$.
16. $f(x) = x$ if $0 < x < 2$ and $f(x) = 2$ if $2 < x < 4$.

Find the Fourier sine series of period 8 which in the interval $0 < x < 4$ represents the function given in

17. Prob. 13.   **18.** Prob. 14.   **19.** Prob. 15.   **20.** Prob. 16.

Verify that for $0 < x < L$, with $\omega = \pi/L$,

21. $1 = \dfrac{4}{\pi}\left(\sin \omega x + \dfrac{1}{3}\sin 3\omega x + \dfrac{1}{5}\sin 5\omega x + \cdots\right)$.

22. $x = \dfrac{2L}{\pi}\left(\sin \omega x - \dfrac{1}{2}\sin 2\omega x + \dfrac{1}{3}\sin 3\omega x - \cdots\right)$.

23. $x = \dfrac{L}{2} - \dfrac{4L}{\pi^2}\left(\cos \omega x + \dfrac{1}{3^2}\cos 3\omega x + \dfrac{1}{5^2}\cos 5\omega x + \cdots\right)$.

24. From Probs. 21 and 22, deduce that for $0 < x < L$,

$$Ax + B = \frac{1}{\pi}\left[(4B + 2LA)\sin \omega x - \frac{2LA}{2}\sin 2\omega x \right.$$
$$\left. + \frac{4B + 2LA}{3}\sin 3\omega x - \frac{2LA}{4}\sin 4\omega x + \cdots\right].$$

25. Show that the Fourier cosine series of period $2\pi/\omega$ which represents the function $f(x) = 1$ if $0 < x < w/2$ and $f(x) = 0$ if
$$w/2 < x < 2\pi/\omega$$
is
$$\frac{\omega w}{2\pi} + \frac{2}{\pi}\sum_{n=1}^{\infty}\frac{1}{n}\sin\frac{n\omega w}{2}\cos n\omega x.$$

26. When an emf $E \sin \omega t$ with $E > 0$ is impressed on a full-wave rectifier, the output voltage $e = E\,|\sin \omega t|$. Show that

$$e = E \sin \omega t + E \left(\frac{2}{\pi} - \frac{4}{\pi} \sum_{n=1}^{\infty} \frac{\cos 2n\omega t}{4n^2 - 1} \right)$$

$$= \frac{2E}{\pi} (1 - 0.67 \cos 2\omega t - 0.13 \cos 4\omega t - 0.06 \cos 6\omega t$$

$$- \cdots).$$

27. Show that the output of a half-wave rectifier, the e of Fig. 29, is $\frac{1}{2}E \sin \omega t + \frac{1}{2}E |\sin \omega t|$, and use this and Prob. 26 to check Prob. 28 of Exercise VIII.

28. Check the terms of Prob. 23, other than the constant term, by integrating the terms of Prob. 21.

Use Prob. 24 to show that the following expansions hold for $0 < x < \pi$:

29. $\dfrac{\pi}{4} = \sin x + \dfrac{\sin 3x}{3} + \dfrac{\sin 5x}{5} + \dfrac{\sin 7x}{7} + \cdots .$

30. $-\dfrac{x}{2} + \dfrac{\pi}{4} = \dfrac{\sin 2x}{2} + \dfrac{\sin 4x}{4} + \dfrac{\sin 6x}{6} + \cdots .$

Check the terms in x by integration as in Prob. 28, then find the constant term by using Eq. (56) with $L = \pi$, and so derive for $0 < x < \pi$:

31. $-\dfrac{\pi x}{4} + \dfrac{\pi^2}{8} = \cos x + \dfrac{\cos 3x}{3^2} + \dfrac{\cos 5x}{5^2} + \dfrac{\cos 7x}{7^2} + \cdots$, by integrating the terms of Prob. 29.

32. $\dfrac{x^2}{4} - \dfrac{\pi x}{4} + \dfrac{\pi^2}{24} = \dfrac{\cos 2x}{2^2} + \dfrac{\cos 4x}{4^2} + \dfrac{\cos 6x}{6^2} + \cdots$, by integrating the terms of Prob. 30.

Show that the following expansions hold for $0 < x < \pi$:

33. $-\dfrac{\pi x^2}{8} + \dfrac{\pi^2 x}{8} = \sin x + \dfrac{\sin 3x}{3^3} + \dfrac{\sin 5x}{5^3} + \dfrac{\sin 7x}{7^3} + \cdots$, by integrating the terms of Prob. 31 from 0 to x.

34. $\dfrac{x^3}{12} - \dfrac{\pi x^2}{8} + \dfrac{\pi^2 x}{24} = \dfrac{\sin 2x}{3^3} + \dfrac{\sin 4x}{4^3} + \dfrac{\sin 6x}{6^3} + \cdots$, by integrating the terms of Prob. 32 from 0 to x.

35. Square both sides of Eq. (47), and take averages for the interval $-L,L$ where $L = \pi/\omega$, and so deduce that

$$\frac{1}{2L} \int_{-L}^{L} [f(x)]^2 dx = a^2 + \frac{1}{2} (a_1{}^2 + b_1{}^2 + a_2{}^2 + b_2{}^2 + a_3{}^2 + b_3{}^2$$
$$+ \cdots).$$

36. Show that if $f(x)$ is odd, even, odd-harmonic for the period $2L$ or even-harmonic for the period $2L$ we may replace the left member in Prob. 35 by $\frac{1}{L} \int_0^L [f(x)]^2 \, dx$, and in the right member omit those terms which equal zero.

37. By using Probs. 29 and 36 deduce the validity of the equation $\frac{\pi^2}{8} = \frac{1}{1^2} + \frac{1}{3^2} + \frac{1}{5^2} + \cdots$. Check by putting $x = 0$ in Prob. 31.

38. By using Probs. 30 and 36 deduce the validity of the equation $\frac{\pi^2}{6} = \frac{1}{1^2} + \frac{1}{2^2} + \frac{1}{3^2} + \frac{1}{4^2} + \cdots$. Check by putting $x = 0$ in Prob. 32.

39. By using Probs. 33 and 36 deduce the validity of the equation $\frac{\pi^4}{96} = \frac{1}{1^4} + \frac{1}{3^4} + \frac{1}{5^4} + \cdots$.

20. Harmonic Analysis

One of the early applications of Fourier expansions concerned the resolution of a musical note into its fundamental and overtones, or harmonics. For this reason the determination of the Fourier coefficients of a given function is often called *harmonic analysis*. When the function $f(x)$ is complicated, or given by a graph or tabulation, it is not practical to evaluate the integrals in Eqs. (48), (49), and (50) by the usual elementary methods. If available, harmonic analyzers may be used. These are instruments somewhat similar to planimeters by which the coefficients a_n and b_n can be obtained from a plot, to suitable scale, of $f(x)$ itself. There are also approximate numerical methods, one of which we proceed to explain.

Let $y = f(x)$ be of period p. Select some small positive integer r. Divide the interval $0,p$ into $2r + 1$ equal intervals with end points $0 = x_0,\ x_1,\ x_2,\ \cdots,\ x_{2r} = p$. Find the corresponding values $y_0,\ y_1,\ y_2,\ \cdots,\ y_{2r}$ such that $y_s = f(x_s)$. We shall obtain our harmonic analysis of $f(x)$, or approximation to the Fourier series for $f(x)$, by selecting the coefficients $A,\ A_1,\ A_2,\ \cdots A_r$, and $B_1,\ B_2,\ \cdots,\ B_{r-1}$ so that the equation

$$y = A + \sum_{k=1}^{r} A_k \cos k\omega x + \sum_{k=1}^{r-1} B_k \sin k\omega x, \tag{80}$$

with $\omega = 2\pi/p$, makes $y = y_s$ when $x = x_s$ for $s = 0,\ 1,\ 2,\ \cdots,\ 2r$.

We have omitted the term $B_r \sin r\omega x$. At the points we are considering, $x_s = sp/2r = s\pi/r\omega$. Hence $r\omega x_s = 2\pi$, so that $\sin r\omega x_s = 0$. Thus our conditions would in no way determine B_r.

The right member of Eq. (80) takes the same value for $x_{2r} = p$ as for $x_0 = 0$, since $p\omega = 2\pi$. But since $f(x)$ is of period p, $y_{2r} = y_0$. Hence if Eq. (80) makes $y = y_0$ when $x = x_0$, it will necessarily make $y = y_{2r}$ when $x = x_{2r}$. And we have imposed essentially $2r$ conditions:

$$y_s = A + \sum_{k=1}^{r} A_k \cos k\omega x_s + \sum_{k=1}^{r-1} B_k \sin k\omega x_s,$$
$$s = 0,\ 1,\ 2,\ \cdots,\ 2r - 1. \tag{81}$$

The values of the $2r$ unknown coefficients $A,\ A_1,\ \cdots,\ A_r$, $B_1,\ \cdots,\ B_{r-1}$ are determined by these $2r$ simultaneous first-degree equations. They may be found by a procedure similar to that of Sec. 18, using sums in place of integrals. That is, we multiply the $2r$ equations, Eqs. (81), in turn by 1, $\sin q\omega x_s$, $\cos q\omega x_s$ and add the resulting equations for the $2r$ values of s in each case.

For the multiplier 1, on using the summations

$$\sum_{s=0}^{r-1} \cos k\omega x_s = 0, \qquad \text{when } k = 1,\ 2,\ \cdots,\ r, \tag{82}$$

$$\sum_{s=0}^{r-1} \sin k\omega x_s = 0 \qquad \text{when } k = 1,\ 2,\ \cdots,\ r - 1, \tag{83}$$

found in Probs. 2 and 3 of Exercise X, we obtain the result

$$\sum_{s=0}^{r-1} y_s = 2rA, \quad \text{or} \quad A = \frac{1}{2r} \sum_{s=0}^{r-1} y_s. \quad (84)$$

For the multiplier $\sin q\omega x_s$, on using Eq. (83) and

$$\sum_{s=0}^{r-1} \sin k\omega x_s \sin q\omega x_s = 0 \quad \text{when } k \neq q,$$
$$= r \quad \text{when } k = q \text{ and } k \neq r, \quad (85)$$
$$\sum_{s=0}^{r-1} \cos k\omega x_s \sin q\omega x_s = 0, \quad (86)$$

found in Probs. 4 and 6 of Exercise X, we obtain the result

$$\sum_{s=0}^{r-1} y_s \sin q\omega x_s = rB_q, \quad \text{or} \quad B_q = \frac{1}{r} \sum_{s=0}^{r-1} y_s \sin q\omega x_s. \quad (87)$$

For the multiplier $\cos q\omega x_s$, on using Eqs. (82), (86), and

$$\sum_{s=0}^{r-1} \cos k\omega x_s \cos q\omega x_s = 0 \quad \text{when } k \neq q,$$
$$= r \quad \text{when } k = q \text{ and } k \neq r,$$
$$= 2r \quad \text{when } k = q = r, \quad (88)$$

found in Prob. 5 of Exercise X, we obtain the results

$$\sum_{s=0}^{r-1} y_s \cos q\omega x_s = rA_q \quad \text{when } q = 1, 2, \cdots, r - 1$$
$$= 2rA_r \quad \text{when } q = r. \quad (89)$$

When solved for the coefficients, these become

$$A_r = \frac{1}{2r} \sum_{s=0}^{r-1} y_s \cos r\omega x_s, \quad A_q = \frac{1}{r} \sum_{s=0}^{r-1} y_s \cos q\omega x_s \text{ for } q \neq r. \quad (90)$$

Compact schematic arrangements for computing the coefficients from the values of y_s by Eqs. (84), (87), and (90) have been worked out.   For example, when $r = 6$, we may use the following

SCHEDULE OF HARMONIC ANALYSIS FOR TWELVE ORDINATES

1. Arrange the twelve values y_1, y_2, $\cdots$, $y_{12} = y_0$ as shown,
add the two lines for the sums, U_0 to U_6, and subtract the second
line from the first for the differences, u_1 to u_5.

	y_1	y_2	y_3	y_4	y_5	y_6	
	y_{12}	y_{11}	y_{10}	y_9	y_8	y_7	
Sum	U_0	U_1	U_2	U_3	U_4	U_5	U_6
Difference		u_1	u_2	u_3	u_4	u_5	

2. Arrange the numbers U_0 to U_6 and u_1 to u_5 as shown, and
again add the two lines for the sums, and subtract the second line
from the first for the differences.

	U_0	U_1	U_2	U_3		u_1	u_2	u_3
	U_6	U_5	U_4			u_5	u_4	
Sum	V_0	V_1	V_2	V_3		W_1	W_2	W_3
Difference	v_0	v_1	v_2			w_1	w_2	

3. The coefficients are found from the numbers just obtained
by the calculations indicated in the following tables:

TABLE FOR SINE COEFFICIENTS

Multiply by						
0.500	W_1					
0.866		W_2	w_1	w_2		
1.000	W_3				W_1	W_3
Add products	I	II	I	II	I	II
I + II	$6B_1$		$6B_2$			
I − II	$6B_5$		$6B_4$		$6B_3$	

TABLE FOR CONSTANT AND COSINE COEFFICIENTS

Multiply by								
0.500			v_2		$-V_2$	V_1		
0.866				v_1				
1.000	$V_0 + V_2$	$V_1 + V_3$	v_0		V_0	$-V_3$	v_0	v_2
Add products	I	II	I	II	I	II	I	II
I + II	12A		6A_1		6A_2			
I − II	12A_6		6A_5		6A_4		6A_3	

In these tables, the multipliers are $0.500 = \sin 30°$,

$$0.866 = \sin 60°,$$

$1.000 = \sin 90°$, and because of relations like

$$\sin 30° = \sin 150° = -\sin 210° = -\sin 330°$$
$$= \cos 60° = -\cos 120° = -\cos 240° = \cos 300°,$$

the effect of the schedule is to work out the sums in Eqs. (84), (87), and (90) for $r = 6$.

If the function to be analyzed has a discontinuity at one of the points, x_s, y_s should be taken as $\frac{1}{2}[f(x_s-) + f(x_s+)]$. In particular, when representing a continuous function $f(x)$ with $f(p)$ not equal to $f(0)$ by a Fourier expansion of period p, one should set $y_0 = y_{2r} = \frac{1}{2}[f(0) + f(p)]$.

The computation of the coefficients may be checked by testing Eq. (81) with $r = 6$, $\omega x_s = s30°$, for some of the values $s = 0$ to 11.

EXERCISE X

1. Let $x_s = sp/2r = s\pi/r\omega$ and N be 0 or a positive or negative integer. Show that the sum $\displaystyle\sum_{s=0}^{2r-1} e^{iN\omega x_s} = 2r$ when N is 0, 2r,

$-2r$, or some integral multiple of $2r$ but that the sum is zero when N is not divisible by $2r$. HINT: Note that all the terms are powers of $e^{2\pi i} = 1$ in the first case, and in the second case recall that the sum of the geometric progression $\sum\limits_{s=0}^{2r-1} R^s = \dfrac{R^{2r} - 1}{R - 1}$ if $R \neq 1$.

In Probs. 2 through 6, $x_s = sp/2r = s\pi/r\omega$, and all the sums are on s from $s = 0$ to $s = 2r - 1$. The letters k and q are some one of the integers $0, 1, 2, \cdots, 2r$. By expressing the sines and cosines in terms of complex exponentials and using Prob. 1, verify that

2. $\Sigma \cos k\omega x_s = 2r$ when $k = 0$ or $k = 2r$. and
$\qquad\qquad = 0$ when $k \neq 0$ or $2r$.

3. $\Sigma \sin k\omega x_s = 0$.

4. $\Sigma \sin k\omega x_s \sin q\omega x_s = r$ when $k = q$, but $k \neq r$,
$\qquad\qquad = 0$ when $k \neq q$, or when $k = q = r$.

5. $\Sigma \cos k\omega x_s \cos q\omega x_s = r$ when $k = q$, but $k \neq r$
$\qquad\qquad = 2r$ when $k = q = r$, and
$\qquad\qquad = 0$ when $k \neq q$.

6. $\Sigma \cos k\omega x_s \sin q\omega x_s = 0$.

7. If $f(x)$ is an odd function of period p, show that the sums $U_0, \cdots, U_6$ and hence the cosine coefficients obtained from the twelve-ordinate scheme of the text will all be zero. Also show that in this case we may replace the differences u_1 to u_5 by $2y_1$ to $2y_5$.

Use Prob. 7. to find approximate values of A_1 to A_5 in each of the following cases. Each function is assumed to be odd and of period $p = 2\pi/\omega$, and the values are given for $x_s = ps/12$.

x	$p/12$	$2p/12$	$3p/12$	$4p/12$	$5p/12$
8. y	0.1	0.2	0.3	0.4	0.5
9. y	1.0	1.0	1.0	1.0	1.0
10. y	0.2	0.4	0.6	0.4	0.2
11. y	2.00	6.93	10.00	6.93	2.00

12. If an emf $e = E_0 \sin \omega t$ is impressed on a tube whose characteristic output can be represented by $i = ae + be^3$, show that the output current $i = E_0(a + \frac{3}{4}b) \sin \omega t - \frac{1}{4}E_0 b \sin 3\omega t$.

13. Use Prob. 12, with $E_0 = 1$, $a = 2$, $b = 8$ to check Prob. 11.

14. When an emf $e = E_0 \sin \omega t$ is impressed on a certain tube, its characteristic output current i is an odd and odd-harmonic function. If for $t = 0, 30°, 60°, 90°$ the values of i are $0, a, b, c$, respectively, show that the harmonic analysis of i is

$$i = \frac{a + c + b\sqrt{3}}{3} \sin \omega t + \frac{2a - c}{3} \sin 3\omega t$$
$$+ \frac{a + c - b\sqrt{3}}{3} \sin 5\omega t.$$

15. Use Prob. 14 to check Probs. 9, 10, and 11.

21. Complex Fourier Series

It is often convenient to write the Fourier series (47) in complex form. We note from Sec. 2 that

$$\cos k\omega x = \frac{1}{2}(e^{i\omega x} + e^{-i\omega x}), \qquad \sin k\omega x = \frac{1}{2i}(e^{i\omega x} - e^{-i\omega x}). \quad (91)$$

It follows from these equations that

$$a_k \cos k\omega x + b_k \sin k\omega x = C_k e^{ik\omega x} + C_{-k} e^{-ik\omega x}, \quad (92)$$

provided that we define

$$C_k = \frac{a_k - ib_k}{2}, \qquad C_{-k} = \frac{a_k + ib_k}{2}. \quad (93)$$

If we further define $C_0 = a$, by combining Eqs. (92) and (47), we obtain the compact expression for the Fourier series for $f(x)$

$$f(x) = \sum_{k=-\infty}^{\infty} C_k e^{ik\omega x}. \quad (94)$$

This represents $f(x)$ in the interval $c, c + p$ in such a way that correct relations may be obtained from this equation by termwise integration after multiplication by any function of x. If we use $e^{in\omega x}$ as the multiplier, where n is 0 or any positive or negative integer, integrate from c to $c + p$, and use the result of Prob. 2 of Exercise XI, we find that

$$C_n = \frac{1}{p} \int_c^{c+p} f(x)e^{-in\omega x}\, dx. \tag{95}$$

The right member of Eq. (94) is called the *complex Fourier series* for the real function $f(x)$, and Eq. (95) is the *complex Fourier coefficient formula*. Since

$$e^{-in\omega x} = \cos n\omega x - i \sin n\omega x, \tag{96}$$

for real $f(x)$ the real and imaginary parts of Eq. (95) reduce to Eqs. (48), (49), and (50). Here C_n and C_{-n} are conjugate complex numbers.

If we applied Eqs. (94) and (95) to a complex function of the real variable $x, f = f_1 + if_2$, our expansion would be equivalent to the ordinary Fourier series for f_1 plus i times that for f_2.

Let $g(x)$ be a second real function of period p, whose complex Fourier series is

$$g(x) = \sum_{k=-\infty}^{\infty} D_k e^{ik\omega x}. \tag{97}$$

Then by using the result of Prob. 2 of Exercise XI we find for the average value of the product $f(x)g(x)$ over the interval $0,p$

$$\frac{1}{p} \int_0^p f(x)g(x)dx = \sum_{k=-\infty}^{\infty} C_k D_{-k}. \tag{98}$$

And in particular

$$\frac{1}{p} \int_0^p [f(x)]^2\, dx = \sum_{k=-\infty}^{\infty} C_k C_{-k}. \tag{99}$$

These results can be used in finding the average power or the rms values when the currents and emfs are expressed as complex Fourier series.

22. The Fourier Integral

Let $f(x)$ be a real function defined for all values of x and piece-wise regular on any finite interval. Instead of requiring $f(x)$ to be periodic, we are here considering functions which are small for numerically large values of x, so that they approach zero when x tends to plus infinity or to minus infinity. As in Sec. 19, for any value of L we may find a Fourier series of period $2L$ which represents $f(x)$ on the interval $-L$ to L. Its complex form, as in Eq. (94), is

$$f(x) = \sum_{k=-\infty}^{\infty} C_k e^{ik\omega x}, \qquad -L < x < L, \qquad (100)$$

where

$$C_k = \frac{1}{2L} \int_{-L}^{L} f(t) e^{-ik\omega t}\, dt, \qquad \omega = \frac{\pi}{L} \qquad (101)$$

which is Eq. (95) with p, c, n, x replaced by $2L$, $-L$, k, t, respectively. We may think of the infinite series in Eq. (100) as the limit of the finite sum from $-n$ to n when n tends to infinity. This leads us to write

$$f(x) = \lim_{n \to \infty} S_n \qquad (102)$$

and to study the partial sum S_n given by

$$S_n = \sum_{k=-n}^{n} C_k e^{ik\omega x} = \sum_{k=-n}^{n} \left[\frac{1}{2L} \int_{-L}^{L} f(t) e^{-ik\omega t}\, dt \right] e^{ik\omega x}. \qquad (103)$$

When we interchange the order of finite summation and integration, and bring the exponential in x inside the integral, this becomes

$$S_n = \frac{1}{2L} \int_{-L}^{L} \left[\sum_{k=-n}^{n} e^{ik\omega(x-t)} \right] f(t)\, dt \qquad (104)$$

We now introduce the notation

$$k\omega = u_k, \qquad \Delta u_k = \omega = \frac{\pi}{L} \qquad (105)$$

Then the expression for the partial sum S_n may be written

$$\frac{1}{2\pi} \sum_{k=-n}^{n} \Delta u_k \int_{-L}^{L} e^{iu_k(x-t)} f(t) dt. \tag{106}$$

We next put $n = AL/\pi$, and let L become infinite. Then this makes $\Delta u_k \to 0$, and the expression (106) suggests the integral

$$\frac{1}{2\pi} \int_{-A}^{A} du \int_{-\infty}^{\infty} e^{iu(x-t)} f(t) dt. \tag{107}$$

In fact, if we let n and L increase in such a way that $A = n\pi/L$ remained constant, the expression (106) would approach the repeated integral (107) as a limit.

By Eq. (102) the limit of the expression (106) as $n \to \infty$ with L fixed is $f(x)$ in the interval $-L$ to L. Since this makes $n\pi/L$ tend to infinity, we are led to take the limit of the expression (107) as A tends to infinity and to conjecture that under suitable conditions

$$f(x) = \lim_{A \to \infty} \frac{1}{2\pi} \int_{-A}^{A} du \int_{-\infty}^{\infty} e^{iu(x-t)} f(t) dt. \tag{108}$$

As a matter of fact, if

$$\int_{-\infty}^{\infty} |f(x)| \, dx \text{ is finite,} \tag{109}$$

$f(x)$ is piecewise regular, and is so defined at points of discontinuity that

$$f(x) = \frac{f(x+) + f(x-)}{2}, \tag{110}$$

then it may be proved that Eq. (108) holds for all values of x. This is the complex form of the *Fourier integral theorem*.

Our discussion made Eq. (108) plausible if the extension from $-A$ to A gave the same result as a slightly different limiting process, and the proof which we omit consists in showing that the contributions from $-\infty$ to $-A$ and from A to ∞ have no effect on the limiting situation when Eq. (109) holds. As we have stated it, the theorem holds if $f = f_1 + if_2$ is a complex function of the real variable x.

When $f(x)$ is a real function, the imaginary part of the right member of Eq. (108) is zero, since we take the integral from $-A$ to A of a function of u which is odd because of the presence of the factor $\sin u(x - t)$. Taking real parts leads to

$$f(x) = \lim_{A \to \infty} \frac{1}{2\pi} \int_{-A}^{A} du \int_{-\infty}^{\infty} \cos u(x - t) f(t) dt$$
$$= \frac{1}{\pi} \int_{0}^{\infty} du \int_{-\infty}^{\infty} \cos u(x - t) f(t) dt, \quad (111)$$

since the presence of $\cos u(x - t)$ makes the first integral an even function of u. This is the real form of the *Fourier integral theorem*.

23. Fourier Transforms

For a function satisfying the conditions imposed on $f(x)$ in the preceding section, we define the *Fourier transform* by the relation

$$F(u) = \int_{-\infty}^{\infty} e^{-iut} f(t) dt. \quad (112)$$

The function $f(x)$ may be recovered from its transform since by Eq. (108)

$$f(x) = \lim_{A \to \infty} \frac{1}{2\pi} \int_{-A}^{A} e^{iux} F(u) du. \quad (113)$$

This relation expresses $f(x)$ in terms of functions e^{iux} of frequency u by an integration on u, over a continuous range of values. It is somewhat analogous to the expression of a periodic function in terms of functions $e^{ik\omega x}$ by a sum on k, Eq. (94), and thus for a discrete set of frequencies k.

For many linear systems, the response $R(x,u)$ to a single complex exponential e^{iux} is known or can be found easily. For such systems, the response to the function $f(x)$ of Eqs. (112) and (113) may be found by building up a function $R(x)$ from $R(x,u)$ by the same process that $f(x)$ comes from e^{iux} in Eq. (113). Thus

$$R(x) = \lim_{A \to \infty} \frac{1}{2\pi} \int_{-A}^{A} R(x,u) F(u) du. \quad (114)$$

The direct exact evaluation of the infinite integrals involved in this process is usually not practicable, but in some cases their evaluation may be reduced to cases already tabulated. In a number of applications, it is more convenient to use the modification to Laplace transforms instead of the Fourier transforms. The Laplace transforms are discussed in the following section.

24. Laplace Transforms

If a constant voltage is impressed on a circuit, starting at $t = 0$, we may think of the impressed emf as the function of the time

$$e(t) = 0 \quad \text{for } t = 0 \quad \text{and} \quad e(t) = E_0 \quad \text{for } t > 0. \quad (115)$$

or, for a suddenly impressed alternating emf

$$e(t) = 0 \quad \text{for } t = 0 \quad \text{and} \quad e(t) = E_0 \sin \omega t \quad \text{for } t > 0 \quad (116)$$

These functions, which are zero for negative values and whose numerical value is at most a constant, E_0, are special cases of functions $g(x)$ satisfying the following conditions:

$$g(x) = 0 \quad \text{for } x < 0, \quad |g(x)| < e^{ax} \quad \text{for } x > x_1, \quad a > 0, \quad (117)$$

and $g(x)$ is piecewise regular.

These functions need not satisfy the condition (109) and thus the definition of a Fourier transform (112) may not be directly applicable to them. For example, the function $g(x)$ corresponding to Eq. (115) with $E_0 = 1$ is

$$g(x) = 0 \quad \text{for } x < 0 \quad \text{and} \quad g(x) = 1 \quad \text{for } x > 0, \quad (118)$$

and for this function

$$\int_{-\infty}^{\infty} g(x)dx = \lim_{M \to \infty} \int_0^M 1dx = \lim_{M \to \infty} M = \infty, \quad (119)$$

so that Eq. (109) does not hold. Also

$$\int_{-\infty}^{\infty} e^{-iut}g(t)dt = \int_0^{\infty} e^{-iut}1dt = \frac{e^{-iut}}{-iu}\Big|_0^{\infty}$$

$$= \lim_{M \to \infty} \frac{1}{u}[\sin Mu + i(\cos Mu - 1)] \quad (120)$$

which oscillates and so diverges. However, for the modified function

$$f(x) = g(x)e^{-bx}, \qquad b > a, \tag{121}$$

condition (109) will necessarily hold, and we may form

$$F(u) = \int_{-\infty}^{\infty} e^{-iut}f(t)dt = \int_{0}^{\infty} e^{-(b+iu)t}g(t)dt. \tag{122}$$

Let us put $p = b + iu$, and denote the resulting function of p as derived from $g(x)$ by $G(p)$. Then

$$G(p) = \int_{0}^{\infty} e^{-pt}g(t)dt. \tag{123}$$

The function $G(p)$ so defined is called the *Laplace transform* of $g(x)$. The variable p is complex, but when its real part b is greater than some possible a for which Eq. (117) holds, $G(p)$ is an analytic function of p. Hence we may often find the form of $G(p)$ by assuming that p is real and sufficiently large for the integral in Eq. (123) to converge and calculating that integral.

Some examples and properties of Laplace transforms are given in Exercise XI. Additional examples and their application will be found in Chap. 5. In these applications we solve problems by operations which eventually determine the Laplace transform of the solution. Hence it is necessary to know to what extent $G(p)$ determines $g(x)$. We assume that $g(x)$ is piecewise regular and satisfies the condition (117). The solutions to the problems of the type we consider always have these properties. Thus the $f(x)$ of Eq. (121) is a function for which the Fourier integral theorem or Eqs. (112) and (113) hold. And for the $F(u)$ of Eq. (122) we have

$$g(x)e^{-bx} = f(x) = \lim_{A \to \infty} \frac{1}{2\pi} \int_{-A}^{A} e^{iux}F(u)du. \tag{124}$$

Put $p = b + iu$. Then $F(u)$ equals the $G(p)$ of Eq. (123). Also $dp = i\ du$, and $p = b + iA$ when $u = A$, $p = b - iA$ when $u = \cdot \cdot A$. If we multiply by e^{bx} and use these relations, Eq. (124) becomes

$$g(x) = \lim_{A \to \infty} \frac{1}{2\pi i} \int_{b-iA}^{b+iA} e^{px} G(p)dp. \tag{125}$$

This relation necessarily holds for x corresponding to an interior point of one of the regular arcs. If there are points of discontinuity, the relation would hold at these points if

$$g(x) = \frac{g(x+) + g(x-)}{2}. \tag{126}$$

It follows that, if the Laplace transform $G(p)$ is given, the function $g(x)$, required to satisfy Eq. (126), is uniquely determined at all points.

In practice, the actual values of $g(x)$ at the points of discontinuity are not important. Sometimes we take them as $g(x+)$ or $g(x-)$. More often we leave them undefined. They have no effect on the value of $G(p)$ as determined by Eq. (123). And the values of $g(x)$ on the regular arcs are uniquely determined by $G(p)$.

The right member of Eq. (125) is the same for all sufficiently large values of b. In some cases it can be found by the method of residues from the theory of functions of a complex variable. However, in our problems we will determine the correspondence of $G(p)$ to $g(x)$ by Eq. (123) combined with a few general principles for a few simple functions, tabulate the results, and find $g(x)$ from $G(p)$ by reading the table backward. Thus we need Eq. (125) only to justify this process by showing that there is just one $g(x)$ for a given $G(p)$.

25. References

Alternative elementary discussions of Fourier series will be found in Churchill's *Fourier Series and Boundary Value Problems*, and in Chaps. II and VIII of the author's *Differential Equations for Electrical Engineers*.

For an extended discussion of harmonic analysis, the reader may consult Lipka's *Graphical and Mechanical Computation*, Vol. II, or Scarborough's *Numerical Analysis*.

Derivations of most of the results which we have stated without proof will be found in Carslaw's *Theory of Fourier Series and Integrals,* or in Chap. XIV of the author's *Treatise on Advanced Calculus.*

EXERCISE XI

1. By the procedure used to derive Eq. (25), show that the integral $\int_c^{c+p} e^{ik\omega x}\, dx = p$ if $k = 0$, and $= 0$ if k is an integer, positive or negative, where $p = 2\pi/\omega$.

2. With the notation of Prob. 1, deduce from Prob. 1 that the integral $\int_c^{c+p} e^{i(k-n)\omega x}\, dx = p$ if $n = k$, and $= 0$ if n is 0 or a positive or negative integer with $n \neq k$.

3. By expressing the sines in terms of complex exponentials, deduce the result of Prob. 29 of Exercise VII from Eqs. (98) and (99).

4. Let $f(x) = 0$ for $x < -a$, $f(x) = 1$ for $-a < x < a$, $f(x) = 0$ for $x > a$. Show that for this function the Fourier transform $F(u)$ of Eq. (112) is $F(u) = \dfrac{2}{u} \sin au$.

5. If $f(x)$ is a real even function of x, show that the Fourier transform of Eq. (112) is the real even function of u, given by the expression $F(u) = \int_{-\infty}^{\infty} \cos ut\, f(t) dt = 2\int_0^{\infty} \cos ut\, f(t) dt$.

6. Use Prob. 5 to check Prob. 4.

7. When the conditions of Prob. 5 hold, so that $F(u)$ is real and even, show that Eq. (113) is equivalent to

$$f(x) = \frac{1}{\pi}\int_0^{\infty} \cos ux\, F(u) du.$$

8. By applying the result of Prob. 7 to the function of Prob. 4, with $x = 0$, show that $\int_0^{\infty} \dfrac{\sin au}{u}\, du = \dfrac{\pi}{2}$, if $a > 0$.

9. Show that $\int_0^{\infty} \dfrac{\sin au}{u}\, du = \dfrac{\pi}{2}$ for $a > 0$, $= 0$ for $a = 0$, and $= -\dfrac{\pi}{2}$ for $a < 0$. HINT: Note that the integrand is zero when $a = 0$ and reverses sign when a reverses sign, and use Prob. 8.

10. Let $f(x) = 0$ for $x < a$, $f(x) = 1$ for $a < x < b$, $f(x) = 0$ for $x > a$. Show that for this function the Fourier transform $F(u)$ of Eq. (112) is $F(u) = (e^{-iua} - e^{-iub})/iu$. Also show that Eq. (113) is equivalent to

$$ f(x) = \frac{1}{\pi} \int_0^\infty \left[\frac{\sin u(x - a)}{u} - \frac{\sin u(x - b)}{u} \right] du. $$

11. Use Prob. 9 to verify directly that in the result of Prob. 10 the right member equals $\frac{1}{2}$ for $x = a$ or $x = b$ and for other values of x equals the values given in the definition of $f(x)$.

12. Let c_1 and c_2 be constants, $G_1(p)$ be the Laplace transform of $g_1(x)$ and $G_2(p)$ be the Laplace transform of $g_2(x)$. Show that the Laplace transform of $c_1g_1(x) + c_2g_2(x)$ is $c_1G_1(p) + c_2G_2(p)$.

13. If $g(x) = 0$ for $x < 0$ and $g(x) = 1$ for $x > 0$, show that the Laplace transform $G(p) = 1/p$.

14. If $g(x) = 0$ for $x < 0$ and $g(x) = e^{kx}$ for $x > 0$, show that the Laplace transform $G(p) = 1/(p - k)$.

15. The *convolution* or *faltung* of two functions $f_1(x)$ and $f_2(x)$ is defined by $h(x) = \int_{-\infty}^\infty f_1(y)f_2(x - y)dy$. By putting $y = x - z$, show that $h(x) = \int_{-\infty}^\infty f_2(z)f_1(x - z)dz$ so that the order of the functions is unimportant.

16. If $g_1(x)$ and $g_2(x)$ are each $= 0$ for $x < 0$, show that their convolution as defined in Prob. 15 is $h(x) = \int_0^x g_1(y)g_2(x - y)dy$.

17. The Laplace transform $H(p)$ of the function $h(x)$ of Prob. 16 is $H(p) = \int_0^\infty e^{-pt} dt \int_0^t g_1(y)g_2(t - y)dy$. Since $g_1(y) = 0$ when $y < 0$, and $g_2(t - y) = 0$ when $y > t$ or when $t < 0$ and $y > 0$, this is equal to

$$ \int_{-\infty}^\infty e^{-pt} dt \int_{-\infty}^\infty g_1(y)g_2(t - y)dy $$
$$ = \int_{-\infty}^\infty g_1(y)dy \int_{-\infty}^\infty e^{-pt} g_2(t - y)dt. $$

By putting $z = t - y$, $t = z + y$ in the integral in t, deduce that $H(p) = \int_{-\infty}^\infty e^{-py}g_1(y)dy \int_{-\infty}^\infty e^{-pz}g_2(z)dz = G_1(p)G_2(p)$. When the functions $g_1(x)$ and $g_2(x)$ each satisfy the conditions (117), all the integrals converge and the change of order of integration is legitimate, so that the Laplace transform of the convolution is the product of the separate Laplace transforms.

18. Let $g_1(x) = 0$ for $x < 0$ and $g_1(x) = e^x$ for $x > 0$. Also let $g_2(x) = 0$ for $x < 0$ and $g_2(x) = e^{2x}$ for $x > 0$. Show that the convolution $h(x)$ of Probs. 15 and 16 is $e^{2x} - e^x$.

19. By Prob. 14, the Laplace transforms of the functions in Prob. 18 are $G_1(p) = 1/(p - 1)$ and $G_2(p) = 1/(p - 2)$. The Laplace transforms of their convolution $h(x)$, or $H(p)$ is $G_1(p)G_2(p)$ by Prob. 17, and is $G_2(p) - G_1(p)$ by Probs. 12 and 18. Show that these are equal.

CHAPTER 3

PARTIAL DIFFERENTIAL EQUATIONS

In many situations it is necessary to study physical quantities which depend on more than one independent variable. Consideration of the effect of changing these independent variables one at a time leads to the notion of partial derivatives. And known physical principles may be formulated in equations that involve partial derivatives of the unknown functions. Such equations are called partial differential equations.

As a typical example of how these equations arise in engineering or physical problems, we shall discuss in detail the derivation of the equation governing the flow of heat. We shall also describe the equations which dominate a number of other fields, explaining the significance of the quantities which occur in them and giving some indication of the physical laws of which they are the mathematical interpretation.

For some partial differential equations it is possible to find a general solution containing arbitrary functions. We illustrate this, and show how it is also possible to form partial differential equations from an assumed general solution of special type. Finally we explain how to find a form of particular solution which will prove useful in solving the boundary value problems of Chap. 4.

26. Heat Flow

Let us study the flow of heat in a long, thin, uniform rod whose sides are insulated. At any cross section C, Fig. 38, the temperature $U°C$. will depend only on the distance $OC = x$ cm. and the time t sec. Consider a small segment of the rod CC', of length Δx. Then the rate at which heat flows into the segment through the cross section at C is $-KA \dfrac{\partial U}{\partial x}$ cal./sec. The constant K

is the thermal conductivity in calories per cm. per second per degree centigrade. A is the area of the cross section in square centimeters. And $\dfrac{\partial U}{\partial x}$ is evaluated at x to give the rate of increase of temperature in a direction perpendicular to the cross section, and into the segment. The minus sign is due to the fact that heat flows from a higher to a lower temperature. Similarly the rate of flow of heat out of the segment through the cross section at C' is

$-KA \left.\dfrac{\partial U}{\partial x}\right|_{x+\Delta x}$, where the subscript indicates that $\dfrac{\partial U}{\partial x}$ is evalu-

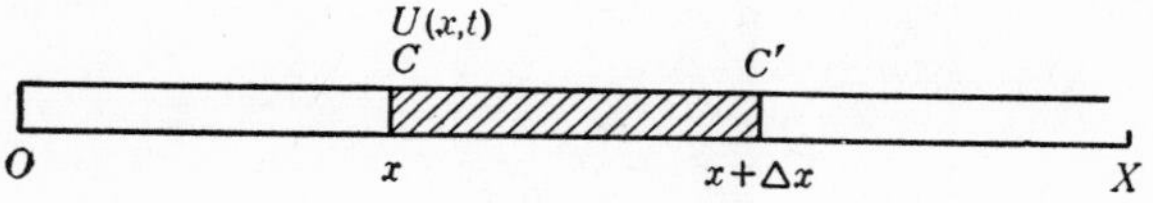

FIG. 38.

ated with x replaced by $x + \Delta x$. The income rate minus the outgo rate is

$$KA \left(\left.\frac{\partial U}{\partial x}\right|_{x+\Delta x} - \left.\frac{\partial U}{\partial x}\right|_{x} \right). \tag{1}$$

This is the rate at which heat is absorbed by the segment.

Let c cal./gm. °C. be the specific heat and D gm./cm.³ be the density. Then the rate at which heat is absorbed by the segment of volume $A \, \Delta x$ cm.³, owing to changing temperature, is $cDA \, \Delta x \left.\dfrac{\partial U}{\partial t}\right|_{x'}$ cal./sec. The rate $\dfrac{\partial U}{\partial t}$ should be an average for the whole segment, and this average will be reached at some point x' between x and $x + \Delta x$. If we equate the expression just found to that obtained in Eq. (1), and divide both sides by $KA \, \Delta x$, the result is

$$\frac{cD}{K} \left.\frac{\partial U}{\partial t}\right|_{x'} = \frac{\left.\dfrac{\partial U}{\partial x}\right|_{x+\Delta x} - \left.\dfrac{\partial U}{\partial x}\right|_{x}}{\Delta x}. \tag{2}$$

Now let Δx approach zero. Then x', between x and $x + \Delta x$, approaches x. And in the right member we may put $\dfrac{\partial U}{\partial x} = F(x,t)$

to obtain

$$\lim_{\Delta x \to 0} \frac{F(x + \Delta x, t) - F(x,t)}{\Delta x} = \frac{\partial F}{\partial x} = \frac{\partial}{\partial x}\left(\frac{\partial U}{\partial x}\right) = \frac{\partial^2 U}{\partial x^2}, \quad (3)$$

by the definition of the partial derivative of $F(x,t)$ with respect to x. Hence the limiting form of Eq. (2) is

$$\frac{cD}{K}\frac{\partial U}{\partial t} = \frac{\partial^2 U}{\partial x^2}. \quad (4)$$

We need no subscripts since all the derivatives are evaluated at x. If we replace $K/(cD)$ by a^2 cm.^{2}/sec., the equation for heat flow in the rod may be written

$$\frac{\partial U}{\partial t} = a^2\frac{\partial^2 U}{\partial x^2}. \quad (5)$$

If the rod were of homogeneous material, but of variable cross section, we would have to keep A with $\frac{\partial U}{\partial x}$ to be evaluated at x and $x + \Delta x$ in (1). And in this case the final equation would be

$$\frac{\partial U}{\partial t} = a^2\frac{1}{A}\frac{\partial}{\partial x}\left(A\frac{\partial U}{\partial x}\right), \quad (6)$$

for a rod of variable cross section $A(x)$.

For flow in three dimensions, a similar analysis for a rectangular element with dimensions Δx, Δy, Δz would lead to an income minus outgo term for each direction. And the final equation analogous to Eq. (5) would be

$$\frac{\partial U}{\partial t} = a^2\left(\frac{\partial^2 U}{\partial x^2} + \frac{\partial^2 U}{\partial y^2} + \frac{\partial^2 U}{\partial z^2}\right). \quad (7)$$

This same equation holds for diffusion, whether of a solid through a solution, a liquid through a porous material, or one fluid through another. In fact, if U is the concentration of the diffused substance, and a^2 cm.^{2}/sec. is the diffusivity, Eq. (7) is the equation governing diffusion phenomena.

For steady flow of heat the temperature U does not vary with the time.   Hence $\dfrac{\partial U}{\partial t} = 0$ in Eq. (7) and

$$\frac{\partial^2 U}{\partial^2 x} + \frac{\partial^2 U}{\partial y^2} + \frac{\partial^2 U}{\partial z^2} = 0, \tag{8}$$

Laplace's equation, is satisfied by the steady-state temperature.

Next consider the steady flow of heat in a rod of variable cross section $A(x)$.   Then $\dfrac{\partial U}{\partial t} = 0$ in Eq. (6), and since U is now a function of a single variable x, the partial derivatives reduce to ordinary derivatives, and we may write $\dfrac{d}{dx}$ in place of $\dfrac{\partial}{\partial x}$. Consequently we have

$$0 = a^2 \frac{1}{A} \frac{d}{dx}\left(A \frac{dU}{dx}\right) \quad \text{or} \quad \frac{d}{dx}\left(A \frac{dU}{dx}\right) = 0. \tag{9}$$

This admits the integral

$$A \frac{dU}{dx} = c_1, \quad \text{or} \quad dU = c_1 A \, dx. \tag{10}$$

The physical meaning of the first relation is that the rate at which heat flows through any cross section,

$$Q = -KA \frac{dU}{dx} = -Kc_1, \tag{11}$$

is constant for steady flow.   The second relation (10) may be integrated to give

$$U - U_1 = c_1 \int_{x_1}^{x} A \, dx. \tag{12}$$

If the temperature difference for two points on the rod is known, c_1 may be found from Eq. (12) and then the rate of flow through any section Q may be found from Eq. (11).

EXERCISE XII

1. A rod of uniform cross section has temperature U_1 at a point $x = x_1$ and a temperature U_2 at a point $x = x_2$.   Show that the rate of flow through any cross section of area A is

$$Q = -KA \frac{U_2 - U_1}{x_2 - x_1}.$$

2. Compute the heat loss per day through 50 m². of brick wall ($K = 0.0020$), if the wall is 30 cm. thick, the inner face is at 20°C., and the outer face is at 0°C. If the combustion of coal is 7000 cal./gm., and the efficiency of the furnace is 60 per cent, how much coal must be consumed daily to compensate for this loss?

3. A refrigerator with walls 8 cm. thick has as its outside dimensions 108 by 108 by 58 cm. The temperature inside is 10°C., and that outside is 25°C., while $K = 0.0002$ is an average value for the walls. Assume that there is uniform flow, and neglect the effects at the edges and corners. That is, regard the heat gain as that for a single wall equal in area to the surface halfway between the inner and outer surfaces or the surface of a box 100 by 100 by 50 cm. Find the heat gain per day.

4. If ice is used in the box of Prob. 3, find the number of kilograms required per day, recalling that a gram of ice, in melting, absorbs 80 cal. and the specific heat of water is 1, and assuming that the water from the ice is at 5°C. when it leaves the box.

5. Suppose that a mechanical refrigerating unit is used in the box of Prob. 3. Assume that it pumps 50 per cent as much heat outside the refrigerator as the same electrical energy would generate in a heating coil for which case each watt would produce 0.24 cal./sec. Find the number of kilowatt hours used per day.

6. Carry out the analysis of the text for flow in a rod for which c, D, K, and A, though constant for each cross section, vary with x, and derive the equation for this case

$$c(x) \, D(x) \, A(x) \, \frac{\partial U}{\partial x} = \frac{\partial}{\partial x} \left[K(x) \, A(x) \, \frac{\partial U}{\partial x} \right].$$

7. For the flow of heat along the radii normal to a set of concentric cylinders, deduce the equation:

$$\frac{\partial U}{\partial t} = a^2 \frac{1}{r} \frac{\partial}{\partial r} \left(r \frac{\partial U}{\partial r} \right).$$

8. If the flow of Prob. 7 is steady, show that the rate of flow through a cylindrical surface of radius r and length L is

$$Q = -K2\pi rL \frac{dU}{dr}.$$

9. If in Prob. 8 the temperature is U_1 for $r = r_1$ and U_2 for $r = r_2$, show that the rate of flow in calories per second through any cylindrical section of length L is given by

$$Q = -2\pi KL \frac{U_2 - U_1}{\ln r_2 - \ln r_1}.$$

10. A steam pipe 30 cm. in diameter is insulated by a layer of concrete $(K = 0.0025)$ 10 cm. thick. The outer surface is at 25°C., and the inner surface is at 155°C. Compute the heat loss in calories per day for 40 m. of pipe. HINT: Use Prob. 8.

11. For the flow of heat along the radii normal to a set of concentric spheres, deduce the equation

$$\frac{\partial U}{\partial t} = a^2 \frac{1}{r^2} \frac{\partial}{\partial r}\left(r^2 \frac{\partial U}{\partial r}\right).$$

12. If the flow in Prob. 11 is steady show that the rate of flow through a spherical surface of radius r is

$$Q = -4\pi Kr^2 \frac{dU}{dr}.$$

13. If in Prob. 12 the temperature is U_1 for $r = r_1$ and U_2 for $r = r_2$, show that the rate of flow in calories per second through any spherical section of radius r is given by

$$Q = 4\pi Kr_1 r_2 \frac{U_2 - U_1}{r_2 - r_1}.$$

14. A hollow lead sphere whose inner and outer diameters are 2 cm. and 8 cm. is heated by a small resistance coil placed inside. At what rate must heat be supplied to keep the inner surface at a temperature 15°C. higher than that of the outside surface if $K = 0.0827$ for lead?

15. A spherical shell for which $K = 0.0025$ of inner radius 24 cm. and outer radius 26 cm. has its inner surface 40°C. higher than its outer one. Compute the rate in calories per second at which heat must be supplied by using Prob. 12.

16. Check Prob. 15 by considering the loss as equal to that for a single wall equal in area to the midsurface of the shell, a sphere of radius 25 cm.

17. A long cylindrical shell of material for which $K = 0.003$ of inner radius 100 cm. and outer radius 102 cm. has its inner surface 50°C. higher than its outer one. Compute the rate of heat loss in calories per second, per meter length of the shell, by using Prob. 8.

18. Check Prob. 17 by considering the loss as equal to that for a single wall equal in area to the midsurface of the shell, or lateral surface of a cylinder 101 cm. in radius and 100 cm. in height.

27. Direct Integration

The solution of certain partial differential equations may be obtained by integrating with respect to a single variable, keeping the outer independent variable fixed. For example, consider

$$\frac{\partial z}{\partial x} = 4y, \tag{13}$$

where z is a function of x and y. Keeping y fixed, and integrating with respect to x leads to

$$z = 4xy + f(y). \tag{14}$$

Since y is kept fixed, the "constant" of integration may involve y and therefore is written as an arbitrary function of y, or $f(y)$.

Similarly to solve the equation

$$\frac{\partial^2 z}{\partial y^2} = 4y, \tag{15}$$

we would integrate twice with respect to y, keeping x fixed. The results would be

$$\frac{\partial z}{\partial y} = 2y^2 + f(x) \qquad \text{and} \qquad z = \frac{2}{3}y^3 + yf(x) + g(x). \quad (16)$$

For the equation

$$\frac{\partial^2 z}{\partial x\,\partial y} = 4y, \qquad \text{or} \qquad \frac{\partial}{\partial x}\left(\frac{\partial z}{\partial y}\right) = 4y, \quad (17)$$

an integration with respect to x gives

$$\frac{\partial z}{\partial y} = 4xy + F(y), \quad (18)$$

and a second integration with respect to y gives

$$z = 2xy^2 + \int^y F(y)dy + g(x) \text{ or } z = 2xy^2 + f(y) + g(x). \quad (19)$$

We may use the simplified notation $f(y)$, since if $F(y)$ is an arbitrary function of y, so is its integral. The omission of a lower limit means that any indefinite integral is to be used.

In a few cases, the solutions of partial differential equations may be found from their similarity to ordinary differential equations of solvable type. Thus consider

$$\frac{\partial^2 z}{\partial x^2} = -y^2 z. \quad (20)$$

If y were a constant k, this would be

$$\frac{d^2 z}{dx^2} = -k^2 z, \qquad \text{with solution } z = c_1 \sin kx + c_2 \cos kx. \quad (21)$$

Replacing c_1 and c_2 by functions of y, and with $k = y$, we find

$$z = f(y) \sin xy + g(y) \cos xy \quad (22)$$

as the solution of Eq. (20).

Suppose we have a system of simultaneous partial differential equations. If any one of them can be solved by the methods just discussed, the restrictions on the arbitrary functions in the solution may be found by substituting the solution in the other equations of the system. If inconsistencies arise, the system has no solution.

As an example, suppose that we have the equations

$$\frac{\partial^2 z}{\partial x^2} = 0, \qquad \frac{\partial^2 z}{\partial y^2} = 0, \qquad (23)$$

which hold simultaneously. By integrating the first equation with respect to x twice, we find that its solution is

$$z = xf(y) + g(y). \qquad (24)$$

We next substitute this solution in the second equation, obtaining

$$xf''(y) + g''(y) = 0. \qquad (25)$$

For this to be true for all values of x, we must have

$$f''(y) = \frac{d^2 f}{dy^2} = 0 \qquad \text{and} \qquad g''(y) = \frac{d^2 g}{dy^2} = 0. \qquad (26)$$

The solutions of these ordinary differential equations are

$$f(y) = c_1 y + c_2, \qquad g(y) = c_3 y + c_4, \qquad (27)$$

respectively. From Eqs. (27) and (24) it follows that

$$z = c_1 xy + c_2 x + c_3 y + c_4. \qquad (28)$$

This is the solution of the system (23). Thus the solution involves arbitrary constants, but no arbitrary functions. If the second equation had been $\dfrac{\partial^2 z}{dy^2} = 2x^3$, the system would not have had any solution.

EXERCISE XIII

Integrate each of the following partial differential equations:

1. $\dfrac{\partial z}{\partial x} = 0.$ **2.** $\dfrac{\partial z}{\partial x} = 4xy.$ **3.** $\dfrac{\partial z}{\partial y} = 0.$

4. $\dfrac{\partial z}{\partial y} = 4y.$ **5.** $\dfrac{\partial z}{\partial x} = 3x^2 + 3y^2.$ **6.** $\dfrac{\partial z}{\partial y} = \cos \dfrac{y}{x}.$

Solve each of the following partial differential equations:

7. $\dfrac{\partial^2 z}{\partial x\,\partial y} = 0.$ **8.** $\dfrac{\partial^2 z}{\partial x\,\partial y} = 2x + 4y.$

9. $\dfrac{\partial^2 z}{\partial x\,\partial y} = e^{2x-y}.$ **10.** $\dfrac{\partial^2 u}{\partial x\,\partial t} = \dfrac{2x}{t}.$

11. $\dfrac{\partial^2 u}{\partial t^2} = 12x^2 t.$ **12.** $\dfrac{\partial^2 u}{\partial x^2} = 16te^{2x}.$

13. $\dfrac{\partial^2 z}{\partial x^2} = \sin\,(2x - 3y).$ **14.** $\dfrac{\partial^2 z}{\partial y^2} = 12xy.$

15. $\dfrac{\partial^2 u}{\partial x\,\partial p} = 12px.$

For each of the following equations, introduce a new variable as indicated. Verify that this reduces the equation to the second form, and by integrating this solve the original equation.

16. $\dfrac{\partial z}{\partial x} = 2xyz.$ $u = \ln z,$ $\dfrac{\partial u}{\partial x} = 2xy.$

17. $z\dfrac{\partial z}{\partial x} = x - y.$ $u = z^2,$ $\dfrac{\partial u}{\partial x} = 2x - 2y.$

18. $\dfrac{\partial z}{\partial x} = ye^z.$ $u = e^{-z},$ $\dfrac{\partial u}{\partial x} = -y.$

Each of the following equations in $u(x,y)$, $u(x,t)$, or $u(x,p)$ involves no differentiation with respect to the second independent variable y, t, or p. Hence if this is treated as a constant, the equation becomes essentially an ordinary differential equation in u and x. Noting that this ordinary equation is linear in u, with constant coefficients, solve each given partial differential equation.

19. $\dfrac{\partial u}{\partial x} - yu = 2x.$ **20.** $\dfrac{\partial u}{\partial x} - u = 2t.$

21. $\dfrac{\partial u}{\partial x} + 2pu = 0.$ **22.** $\dfrac{\partial u}{\partial x} + (4 + 2p)u = 0.$

23. $\dfrac{\partial^2 u}{\partial x^2} - 4y^2 u = 0.$ **24.** $\dfrac{\partial^2 u}{\partial x^2} + 4t^2 u = 0.$

25. $\dfrac{\partial^2 u}{\partial x^2} - \dfrac{p^2}{v^2}\,u = 0.$ **26.** $\dfrac{\partial^2 u}{\partial x^2} + \dfrac{p^2}{v^2}\,u = 0.$

27. Solve the partial differential equation

$$y \frac{\partial^2 z}{\partial x \, \partial y} + \frac{\partial z}{\partial x} = 9x^2 y^2$$

by putting $\frac{\partial z}{\partial x} = p$ and thus reducing the equation to the form

$$y \frac{\partial p}{\partial y} + p = 9x^2 y^2.$$

If x is treated as a constant, this is essentially an ordinary differential equation in y and p.

Show that the system of simultaneous partial differential equations

28. $\frac{\partial z}{\partial x} = 4x - 5y$, $\frac{\partial z}{\partial y} = -5x + 2y$ has as its solution
$z = 2x^2 - 5xy + y^2 + c$.

29. $\frac{\partial z}{\partial x} = y$, $\frac{\partial z}{\partial y} = 2x$ has no solution.

30. $\frac{\partial z}{\partial x} = \cos 2y$, $\frac{\partial z}{\partial y} = -2x \sin 2y$ has as its solution
$z = x \cos 2y + c$.

31. $\frac{\partial z}{\partial x} = 3x^2 y - y^3$, $\frac{\partial z}{\partial y} = x^3 - 3xy^2$ has as its solution
$z = x^3 y - y^3 x + c$.

32. $\frac{\partial^2 z}{\partial x^2} = 0$, $\frac{\partial^2 z}{\partial x \, \partial y} = 0$ has as its solution $z = g(y) + cx$.

33. $\frac{\partial^2 z}{\partial x^2} = 2$, $\frac{\partial^2 z}{\partial x \, \partial y} = 3$, $\frac{\partial^2 z}{\partial y^2} = 4$ has as its solution
$z = x^2 + 3xy + 2y^2 + c_1 x + c_2 y + c_3$.

34. $\frac{\partial^2 z}{\partial x^2} = 4e^{y-2x}$, $\frac{\partial z}{\partial y} = e^{y-2x}$ has as its solution
$z = e^{y-2x} + c_1 x + c_2$.

28. Elimination of Functions

If a given relation between x, y, and z with one or more arbitrary functions is the solution of some partial differential equation, then that equation may be found by differentiation and elimination. Thus from

$$z = f(x^2 + y^2) \tag{29}$$

we find that

$$\frac{\partial z}{\partial x} = 2xf'(x^2 + y^2), \qquad \frac{\partial z}{\partial y} = 2yf'(x^2 + y^2). \tag{30}$$

Here $f'(u)$ means the derivative of $f(u)$ with respect to u, so that if the arbitrary function happened in a particular case to be $f(u) = \sin u$, we would have $f'(u) = \cos u$.

To find the equation satisfied by the z of Eq. (29), with f the arbitrary function, we must eliminate f and f' from Eqs. (29) and (30). In this case it will suffice to multiply $\frac{\partial z}{\partial x}$ by y, $\frac{\partial z}{\partial y}$ by $-x$, add and deduce from Eq. (30) that

$$y \frac{\partial z}{\partial x} - x \frac{\partial z}{\partial y} = 0. \tag{31}$$

When there is just one arbitrary function, f, differentiation with respect to x and y will lead to two equations containing f and f', in the general case. Then from the three equations f and f' can be eliminated to obtain a single first-order partial differential equation of which the given relation is the solution. A method which sometimes enables us to deduce a solution of this type when the partial differential equation is given is described in Probs. 13 and 17 of Exercise XIV.

When there is more than one arbitrary function, we could take higher derivatives. But it is only exceptionally that at any stage we have the right number of functions and equations. For example, if we start with a relation containing two functions f and g, the first derivatives, with the relation, lead to three equations in f, g, f', and g'. And if we take the three second derivatives we have six equations in six quantities. At the next stage we have ten equations in eight quantities, which is one too many. Hence the given relation in f and g will, in general, not be the solution of any single equation but the common part of the solutions of two third-order equations.

To illustrate the exceptional case when elimination is possible and leads to a single equation of lowest order, consider

$$z = f(2x - y) + g(2x + 3y). \tag{32}$$

Differentiation of this leads to

$$\frac{\partial z}{\partial x} = 2f'(2x - y) + 2g'(2x + 3y)$$

$$\frac{\partial z}{\partial y} = -f'(2x - y) + 3g'(2x + 3y) \tag{33}$$

Here the three equations contain four quantities f, g, f', g'. But by omitting the first one we have two equations in two quantities f', g'. There is still one equation lacking; therefore we find

$$\frac{\partial^2 z}{\partial x^2} = 4f''(2x - y) + 4g''(2x + 3y)$$

$$\frac{\partial^2 z}{\partial x\,\partial y} = -2f''(2x - y) + 6g''(2x - 3y)$$

$$\frac{\partial^2 z}{\partial y^2} = f''(2x - y) + 9g''(2x + 3y). \tag{34}$$

From these three equations in the two quantities f'' and g'', we may eliminate f'' and g''. For example, we may solve the first two equations for f'' and g'' and substitute in the third. The result is

$$3\,\frac{\partial^2 z}{\partial x^2} + 4\,\frac{\partial^2 z}{\partial x\,\partial y} - 4\,\frac{\partial^2 z}{\partial y^2} = 0. \tag{35}$$

EXERCISE XIV

In each case form a first-order partial differential equation by eliminating the arbitrary function f.

1. $z = f(2x - 3y)$. **2.** $z = f(x)$. **3.** $z = f(y) + 2xy$.
4. $z = f(xy)$. **5.** $z = yf(x + 2y)$. **6.** $z = xf(y/x)$.

In each case form a second-order partial differential equation by eliminating the arbitrary functions f and g.

7. $z = f(3x + 2y) + g(x - y)$. **8.** $z = f(x) + g(y) + y \ln x$.
9. $z = f(x) + yg(x) + y^2$. **10.** $z = f(y) + g(2x - y)$.
11. $z = f(x - y) + g(x + y)$. **12.** $z = f(x) \cdot g(y)$.

13. In some cases the solution of the equation

$$A \frac{\partial z}{\partial x} + B \frac{\partial z}{\partial y} = C, \tag{a}$$

where A, B, C are given functions of x, y, z, may be found by
setting up the system of ordinary differential equations

$$\frac{dx}{A} = \frac{dy}{B} = \frac{dz}{C}, \tag{b}$$

finding two first integrals of this system in the form

$$U(x,y,z) = c_1, \qquad V(x,y,z) = c_2, \tag{c}$$

with c_1 and c_2 arbitrary constants, and setting

$$U(x,y,z) = f[V(x,y,z)], \tag{d}$$

with f the arbitrary function.

If **i**, **j**, **k** are unit vectors along the axes, the vector

$$\mathbf{N} = \frac{\partial z}{\partial x} \mathbf{i} + \frac{\partial z}{\partial y} \mathbf{j} - \mathbf{k}$$

is normal to the surface $z = z(x,y)$. Since Eq. (a) expresses that
$\mathbf{N} \cdot \mathbf{T} = 0$, where $\mathbf{T} = A\mathbf{i} + B\mathbf{j} + C\mathbf{k}$, **T** is perpendicular to **N**,
and thus must lie in the tangent plane of any surface which is a
solution of Eq. (a). The system (b) defines curves always tangent
to **T**. And for any value of c_1 or c_2 the surfaces, Eq. (c), are each
tangent to **T**. For a particular f, with each c_2, Eq. (d) matches
a $c_1 = f(c_2)$. The one pair c_1,c_2 determine a curve of intersection
of surfaces, Eq. (c), and hence tangent to **T**, which lies on the
surface, Eq. (d). As c_2 varies, the curve of intersection sweeps
out the whole surface, Eq. (d), which accordingly at each of its
points is tangent to **T** for that point, and therefore is a solution.

Apply this method to the particular equation $x \dfrac{\partial z}{\partial x} + y \dfrac{\partial z}{\partial y} = z$,

obtaining successively $\dfrac{dx}{x} = \dfrac{dy}{y} = \dfrac{dz}{z}$, $\ln\ x + \ln\ c_1 = \ln\ z$,

$\ln x + \ln c_2 = \ln y$, or $z/x = c_1$, $y/x = c_2$, $z = xf(y/x)$. Compare Prob. 6 and its solution.

Use the method of Prob. 13 to show that the solution of

14. $4 \dfrac{\partial z}{\partial x} + 3 \dfrac{\partial z}{\partial y} = 8$ is $z = 2x + f(3x - 4y)$.

15. $a \dfrac{\partial z}{\partial x} + b \dfrac{\partial z}{\partial y} = c$ is $az = cx + f(bx - ay)$.

16. $\dfrac{\partial z}{\partial x} + \dfrac{\partial z}{\partial y} = z$ is $z = e^x f(x - y)$.

17. If one or two of the functions A, B, C in Prob. 13 is zero, we understand Eq. (*b*) of Prob. 13 to mean that the corresponding numerator is zero. Apply this to Eq. (31) of the text to obtain successively $\dfrac{dx}{y} = \dfrac{dy}{-x} = \dfrac{dz}{0}$, $dz = 0$, $z = c_1$, $x\,dx + y\,dy = 0$, $x^2 + y^2 = c_2$, $z = f(x^2 + y^2)$ in agreement with Eq. (29).

Use the method of Prob. 13, as modified in Prob. 17, to show that the solution of

18. $5 \dfrac{\partial z}{\partial x} - 7 \dfrac{\partial z}{\partial y} = 0$ is $z = f(7x + 5y)$.

19. $a \dfrac{\partial z}{\partial x} + b \dfrac{\partial z}{\partial y} = 0$ is $z = f(bx - ay)$.

20. $x \dfrac{\partial z}{\partial x} + y \dfrac{\partial z}{\partial y} = 0$ is $z = f\left(\dfrac{y}{x}\right)$.

21. $\dfrac{\partial z}{\partial x} = 0$ is $z = f(y)$, and compare Prob. 1 of Exercise **XIII**.

22. $2x \dfrac{\partial z}{\partial x} - 3y \dfrac{\partial z}{\partial y} = 0$ is $z = f(x^3 y^2)$.

29. Linear Equations

We shall describe a method of solving partial differential equations of the type

$$3 \frac{\partial^2 z}{\partial x^2} + 4 \frac{\partial^2 z}{\partial x \, \partial y} - 4 \frac{\partial^2 z}{\partial y^2} = 0, \tag{36}$$

made up of terms each of which is a partial derivative of $z(x,y)$ to the same order, here the second, multiplied by some constant coefficient. Such equations are *linear*, or have a first-degree character in z. That is, the result of substituting $c_1 z_1 + c_2 z_2$ in the left number, where c_1 and c_2 are any constants, is the result for z_1, times c_1, plus the result for z_2, times c_2. Hence in particular if z_1 and z_2 are both solutions, they make the left member zero, and so does $c_1 z_1 + c_2 z_2$, which is again a solution.

Let us replace the x derivatives by powers of x, and the y derivatives by powers of y, to obtain

$$3x^2 + 4xy - 4y^2 = 0. \tag{37}$$

Solving this as a quadratic equation in x gives the two roots

$$x = -2y \qquad \text{or} \qquad x = \tfrac{2}{3} y \tag{38}$$

which lead to the factorization

$$3x^2 + 4xy - 4y^2 = 3(x + 2y)(x - \tfrac{2}{3} y)$$
$$= (x + 2y)(3x - 2y). \tag{39}$$

This shows that Eq. (36) may be written as

$$\left(\frac{\partial}{\partial x} + 2 \frac{\partial}{\partial y} \right) \left(3 \frac{\partial}{\partial x} - 2 \frac{\partial}{\partial y} \right) z = 0. \tag{40}$$

Hence any solution of either first-order equation

$$\frac{\partial z}{\partial x} + 2 \frac{\partial z}{\partial y} = 0 \qquad \text{or} \qquad 3 \frac{\partial z}{\partial x} - \frac{\partial z}{\partial y} = 0 \tag{41}$$

will solve Eqs. (40) or (36). For a solution of the second equation will lead to zero when we use the right-hand parenthesis in Eq.

(40), and hence will give zero when we let the operation indicated by the first parenthesis act on this zero. To show that the same is true of the first equation, we have merely to interchange the order of the factors in Eqs. (39) and (40).

In Prob. 19 of Exercise XIV we showed that the equation

$$a \frac{\partial z}{\partial x} + b \frac{\partial z}{\partial y} = 0 \qquad \text{had} \qquad z = f(bx - ay) \qquad (42)$$

as its solution. Hence $z_1 = f(2x - y)$ is a solution of the first equation of Eq. (41), and $z_2 = g(2x + 3y)$ is a solution of the second. We have written $2x + 3y$ as it is simpler than $-2x - 3y$ and leads to an equivalent result, since an arbitrary function of u is also a function of $-u$, or of ku for any constant $k \neq 0$.

From the linear character of Eq. (36), and the fact that the z_1 and z_2 just found are solutions, $z = z_1 + z_2$ is also a solution. Thus

$$z = f(2x - y) + g(2x + 3y) \qquad (43)$$

is a solution of Eq. (36). It is the most general solution because it contains two independent terms containing arbitrary functions, and we started with a second-order equation of special type. We have used $z_1 + z_2$ instead of $c_1 z_1 + c_2 z_2$, since the last form is equivalent to the first, with different arbitrary functions $c_1 f$ in place of f and $c_2 g$ in place of g.

We note that our result is in accord with the derivation of Eq. (35) as that which had its solution given by Eq. (32).

When there are equal factors, the above process does not give two independent terms. In this case the general solution is obtained by adding the terms after multiplying one of them by a first-degree factor. Thus consider

$$\frac{\partial^2 z}{\partial x^2} - 4 \frac{\partial^2 z}{\partial x \, \partial y} + 4 \frac{\partial^2 z}{\partial y^2} = \left(\frac{\partial}{\partial x} - 2 \frac{\partial}{\partial y} \right) \left(\frac{\partial}{\partial x} - 2 \frac{\partial}{\partial y} \right) z = 0. \quad (44)$$

Here $z_1 = f(2x + y)$ is a solution, since it leads to zero when acted on by the right-hand parenthesis. But $z_2 = xg(2x + y)$ is also a solution, because the effect of the right-hand parenthesis on this is to annihilate the terms in g' and to give the result of acting on x times g, here 1 times g. And the left-hand parenthesis annihilates this. Thus

$$z = f(2x + y) + xg(2x + y) \tag{45}$$

is the general solution of Eq. (44). In place of the x which multiplies g we could use any first-degree factor in x and y, except a multiple of $2x + y$, since this last would not lead to two independent terms. Usually we use x, unless it multiplies $g(x)$, when we use y to give the simplest solution.

Let us next consider equations with left member of the same special type, but with right member a function of x and y. For example,

$$3 \frac{\partial^2 z}{\partial x^2} + 4 \frac{\partial^2 z}{\partial x \, \partial y} - 4 \frac{\partial^2 z}{\partial y^2} = 16 \sin 2y + 64xy. \tag{46}$$

Since the first term contains y alone, we may find a particular solution for it by using $z = Y(y)$ in the left member. Then

$$-4 \frac{d^2 Y}{dy^2} = 16 \sin 2y, \qquad \frac{dY}{dy} = 2 \cos 2y, \qquad Y = \sin 2y, \tag{47}$$

where we have integrated repeatedly and omitted constants of integration.

We could find a particular solution for $64xy$, a polynomial term, by trying a general polynomial of the fourth degree, and using any set of coefficients which would give $64xy$. But in this case we may also note that the middle term would convert Ax^2y^2 into $16Axy$, and hence $4x^2y^2$ into $64xy$. The other terms would lead to $24y^2$, a function of y alone produced by $-y^4/2$ and to $32x^2$, a function of x alone produced by $8x^4/9$. Thus

$$- \, ^8/_9 x^4 + 4x^2y^2 + \tfrac{1}{2}y^4 \text{ leads to } 64xy. \tag{48}$$

We next replace the right member by zero, and solve the resulting Eq. (36), obtaining the solution (43). Finally we combine this with the particular solutions in Eqs. (47) and (48). The result is

$$z = \sin 2y - \tfrac{3}{9}x^4 + 4x^2y^2 + \tfrac{1}{2}y^4 + f(2x - y)$$
$$+ g(2x + 3y). \quad (49)$$

Since the first two terms produce the right member and the last two terms produce zero, from its linear character Eq. (46) admits this as a solution. But for this special type of equation, when the order is 2, any solution with two independent terms containing arbitrary functions is the general solution. For a proof of this, and a more general method of solution compare Prob. 12 of Exercise XV.

EXERCISE XV

Solve each of the following partial differential equations:

1. $\dfrac{\partial^2 z}{\partial x^2} - 6\dfrac{\partial^2 z}{\partial x\,\partial y} + 5\dfrac{\partial^2 z}{\partial y^2} = 0.$ **2.** $\dfrac{\partial^2 z}{\partial x^2} - 2\dfrac{\partial^2 z}{\partial x\,\partial y} = 0.$

3. $2\dfrac{\partial^2 z}{\partial x^2} + 5\dfrac{\partial^2 z}{\partial x\,\partial y} + 3\dfrac{\partial^2 z}{\partial y^2} = 0.$ **4.** $3\dfrac{\partial^2 z}{\partial x\,\partial y} + \dfrac{\partial^2 z}{\partial y^2} = 0.$

5. $\dfrac{\partial^2 z}{\partial x^2} - 6\dfrac{\partial^2 z}{\partial x\,\partial y} + 9\dfrac{\partial^2 z}{\partial y^2} = 0.$ **6.** $9\dfrac{\partial^2 z}{\partial x^2} + 4\dfrac{\partial^2 z}{\partial y^2} = 0.$

7. $\dfrac{\partial^2 z}{\partial x\,\partial y} - 4\dfrac{\partial^2 z}{\partial y^2} = 16y.$ **8.** $\dfrac{\partial^2 z}{\partial x^2} - 4\dfrac{\partial^2 z}{\partial y^2} = 12x^2.$

9. Show that the general solution of Laplace's equation $\dfrac{\partial^2 U}{\partial x^2} + \dfrac{\partial^2 U}{\partial y^2} = 0$ is $U = f(x + iy) + g(x - iy)$, where $i^2 = -1$.

10. Show that if v is constant and $v \neq 0$, the general solution of the wave equation

$$v^2\frac{\partial^2 u}{\partial x^2} - \frac{\partial^2 u}{\partial t^2} = 0 \quad \text{is} \quad u = f(x - vt) + g(x + vt).$$

11. By the method of the text, show that if $p \neq q$ the solution of

$$\frac{\partial^2 z}{\partial x^2} - (p + q)\frac{\partial^2 z}{\partial x\,\partial y} + pq\frac{\partial^2 z}{\partial z^2} = 0$$

or

$$\left(\frac{\partial}{\partial x} - p\frac{\partial}{\partial y}\right)\left(\frac{\partial}{\partial x} - q\frac{\partial}{\partial y}\right)z = 0$$

is $z = f(px + y) + g(qx + y)$. Now put $u = px + y, v = qx + y,$

verify that

$$\frac{\partial}{\partial x} = p \frac{\partial}{\partial u} + q \frac{\partial}{\partial v}, \qquad \frac{\partial}{\partial y} = \frac{\partial}{\partial x} + \frac{\partial}{\partial y},$$

so that

$$\frac{\partial}{\partial x} - p \frac{\partial}{\partial y} = (q - p) \frac{\partial}{\partial v} \quad \text{and} \quad \frac{\partial}{\partial x} - q \frac{\partial}{\partial y} = (p - q) \frac{\partial}{\partial v}.$$

Hence from the factored form the given equation is equivalent to $-(p - q)^2 \dfrac{\partial^2 z}{\partial v \, \partial u} = 0$, or $\dfrac{\partial^2 z}{\partial v \, \partial u} = 0$. This may be solved by successive integration, as in Sec. 26, to give $z = f(u) + g(v)$ or $z = f(px + y) + g(qx + y)$, which proves that this is the general solution.

12. We may devise a systematic method of solving equations with a right member by the substitution of Prob. 11. Thus to solve $\dfrac{\partial^2 z}{\partial x^2} - (p + q) \dfrac{\partial^2 z}{\partial x \, \partial y} + pq \dfrac{\partial^2 z}{\partial y^2} = F(x,y)$ where $F(x,y)$ is any given function and $p \neq q$, we put $u = px + y$, $v = qx + y$. Using Prob. 11 for the left member, show that the equation becomes $-(p - q)^2 \dfrac{\partial^2 z}{\partial v \, \partial u} = F\left(\dfrac{u - v}{p - q}, \dfrac{pv - qu}{p - q}\right)$, which may be solved as in Sec. 26 to give $z =$ a particular integral $+ f(u) + g(v)$. This process is usually longer than the tentative method used in the text for Eq. (46), but it proves that the complete solution of an equation of this type contains just two arbitrary functions when $p \neq q$.

13. If we let $q = p$ in the equation of Prob. 12, it becomes $\dfrac{\partial^2 z}{\partial x^2} - 2p \dfrac{\partial^2 z}{\partial x \, \partial y} + p^2 \dfrac{\partial^2 z}{\partial y^2} = F(x,y)$. If $p = 0$, this may be solved by successive integration as it stands. When $p \neq 0$, show that we may solve by a procedure similar to that of Prob. 12, if we use the substitution $u = px + y$, $v = y$.

30. Particular Solutions

The solution of a particular physical problem cannot contain any constants or functions which may be given arbitrary values.

If one of the conditions in the mathematical formulation of a problem is a differential equation, there must be auxiliary relations at hand which serve to determine the arbitrary elements in the solution of the differential equation. Sometimes we obtain the specific solution desired by first finding the general solution, including the arbitrary elements, and then determining these elements from the initial conditions, or boundary values. Although this is the usual procedure for elementary problems involving ordinary differential equations, where arbitrary constants appear, it is less often applicable to problems involving partial differential equations because of the difficulty of fitting arbitrary functions to the auxiliary conditions.

An alternative method is to find particular solutions of the partial differential equation which satisfy some of the boundary conditions and then to combine these particular solutions in such a way that all the conditions of the physical problem are met. In this connection, solutions equal to a product of factors, each factor being a function of only one of the independent variables, are useful. Accordingly we shall outline a systematic procedure for finding such particular solutions.

As an example to which our method applies, let us consider Laplace's equation in two variables

$$\frac{\partial^2 U}{\partial x^2} + \frac{\partial^2 U}{\partial y^2} = 0. \tag{50}$$

We wish to find all solutions, if there are any, of the form

$$U = X(x) \cdot Y(y), \quad \text{or} \quad U = XY. \tag{51}$$

In the second form we have written X for $X(x)$ and Y for $Y(y)$, relying on our notation to remind us that X is a function of x alone and Y is a function of y alone. We also use primes for ordinary derivatives so that

$$X' = X'(x) = \frac{dX}{dx} \quad \text{and} \quad X'' = X''(x) = \frac{d^2X}{dx^2}, \tag{52}$$

with similar defining relations for Y' and Y''. Then by successive partial differentiation we find from Eq. (51) that

$$\frac{\partial U}{\partial x} = X'Y, \qquad \frac{\partial^2 U}{\partial x^2} = X''Y,$$

$$\frac{\partial U}{\partial y} = XY', \qquad \frac{\partial^2 U}{\partial y^2} = XY''. \qquad (53)$$

Now insert these values in Eq. (50). The result,

$$X''Y + XY'' = 0 \qquad \text{or} \qquad X''Y = -XY'', \qquad (54)$$

is a condition that the U of Eq. (51) be a solution of the given partial differential equation. We may separate the variables in the last equation, and write it in the form

$$\frac{X''}{X} = -\frac{Y''}{Y}. \qquad (55)$$

Such separation of the variables is not possible for all equations. Our procedure succeeds only when the equation in X, Y and their derivatives is capable of separation.

We now observe that the left member of Eq. (55) does not involve y, and hence cannot change when y changes while x is kept fixed. Similarly the right member does not involve x, and hence cannot change when x changes while y is kept fixed. As the two members are equal, their common value does not change when we change the variables one at a time. Since we may go from any values x_1, y_1 to any other values x_2, y_2 by first changing x_1 to x_2, with $y = y_1$ and then changing y_1 to y_2, with $x = x_2$, the common value is the same at x_2, y_2 as at x_1, y_1 and therefore must be a constant k. Thus we may write

$$\frac{X''}{X} = -\frac{Y''}{Y} = k, \qquad \text{or} \qquad X'' = kX, \qquad Y'' = -kY. \qquad (56)$$

In more familiar notation, the last two equations are

$$\frac{d^2X}{dx^2} - kX = 0, \qquad \frac{d^2Y}{dy^2} + kY = 0. \qquad (57)$$

The form of solution of these linear differential equations

with constant coefficients depends on the roots of the equations $m^2 - k = 0$ and $m^2 + k = 0$. First let k be negative. Then $-k$ is positive, and the roots involve $\sqrt{-k}$. To simplify the writing, put $\sqrt{-k} = a$, or $k = -a^2$. Then the equation $m^2 + a^2 = 0$ has roots ai and $-ai$. And these lead to the solution

$$X = c_1 \sin ax + c_2 \cos ax. \tag{58}$$

The equation $m^2 - a^2$ has roots a and $-a$, which lead to

$$Y = c_3 e^{ay} + c_4 e^{-ay}. \tag{59}$$

Next let $k = 0$. Then each of the two equations in m reduces to $m^2 = 0$, with roots $0,0$ in each case. These lead to

$$X = c_5 + c_2 x \qquad \text{and} \qquad Y = c_7 + c_8 y. \tag{60}$$

Finally let k be positive. Here the roots involve $\sqrt{k}$, and to simplify the writing we put $\sqrt{k} = b$, or $k = b^2$. The first equation is now $m^2 - b^2 = 0$, with roots b and $-b$. These lead to

$$X = c_9 e^{bx} + c_{10} e^{-bx}. \tag{61}$$

The equation $m^2 + b^2 = 0$, with roots bi and $-bi$, leads to

$$Y = c_{11} \sin by + c_{12} \cos by. \tag{62}$$

From Eqs. (58) to (62), and Eq. (51) we find as the desired particular solutions of the given equation, Eq. (50)

$$
\begin{aligned}
U &= (c_1 \sin ax + c_2 \cos ax)(c_3 e^{ay} + c_4 e^{-ay}), \\
U &= (c_5 + c_6 x)(c_7 + c_8 y), \\
U &= (c_9 e^{bx} + c_{10} e^{-bx})(c_{11} \sin by + c_{12} \cos by).
\end{aligned} \tag{63}
$$

Each of these solutions apparently contains four constants c, but really only three independent ones, since one of them may be divided out. For example, in the first form, if $c_1 \neq 0$, we may write

$$
\begin{aligned}
U &= \left(\sin ax + \frac{c_2}{c_1} \cos ax \right)(c_1 c_3 e^{ay} + c_1 c_4 e^{-ay}) \\
&= (\sin ax + c_2' \cos ax)(c_3' e^{by} + c_4' e^{-by}).
\end{aligned} \tag{64}
$$

The advantage of not replacing any of the constants in the solutions (63) by unity as we have just done with c_1, in effect, in obtaining Eq. (64) is that we do not exclude the possibility of any of them being zero.

Since Eq. (50) has a linear character, the sum of any number of solutions is again a solution. Hence if we take any number of solutions of one or more of the forms given in Eq. (63), obtained by giving different values to a, b, and the constants c, and add the results we will have a solution of Eq. (50). We may even combine an infinite number of such terms into an infinite series, provided the series converges in such a way that it may be differentiated termwise twice.

Let us next consider the first-order equation

$$2x \frac{\partial z}{\partial x} - 3y \frac{\partial z}{\partial y} = 0. \tag{65}$$

This will have a solution of the form given in Eq. (51), or

$$z = XY, \tag{66}$$

provided that

$$2xX'Y - 3yXY' = 0, \qquad \text{or} \qquad 2xX'Y = 3yXY'. \tag{67}$$

We may separate the variables by writing this in the form

$$2x \frac{X'}{X} = 3y \frac{Y'}{Y}. \tag{68}$$

The argument used for Eq. (55) shows that each member of this equation must equal a constant k. Consequently,

$$2x \frac{X'}{X} = 3y \frac{Y'}{Y} = k, \qquad \text{or} \qquad 2xX' = kX, \qquad 3yY' = kY. \tag{69}$$

The equation in X, in more familiar notation, is

$$2x \frac{dX}{dx} = kX, \qquad \text{or} \qquad \frac{dX}{X} = \frac{k}{2} \frac{dx}{x}. \tag{70}$$

This has as its integral

$$\ln X = \frac{k}{2} \ln x + c_1, \qquad \text{so that} \qquad X = e^{c_1} x^{k/2}. \qquad (71)$$

The equation in Y is

$$3y \frac{dY}{dy} = kY, \qquad \text{and has} \qquad Y = e^{c_2} y^{k/3} \qquad (72)$$

as its solution. From Eqs. (71), (72), and (66) we find that

$$z = XY = e^{c_1} e^{c_2} x^{k/2} y^{k/3}. \qquad (73)$$

This may be simplified by putting $e^{c_1} e^{c_2} = c$, a new constant, and setting $k = 6a$ to avoid fractions. Thus

$$z = cx^{3a} y^{2a} \qquad (74)$$

is the solution of the given equation of the desired form.

To see how a fairly general solution may be built up out of particular solutions, we recall that in Prob. 22 of Exercise XIV the general solution of Eq. (65) was found to be

$$z = f(x^3 y^2). \qquad (75)$$

Suppose that $f(u)$ is a regular analytic function for $u = 0$, so that it admits of a Maclaurin expansion

$$f(u) = A_0 + A_1 u + A_2 u^2 + \cdots + A_n u^n + \cdots. \qquad (76)$$

Then the solution (75) admits the expansion

$$z = A_0 + A_1 x^3 y^2 + A_2 (x^3 y^2)^2 + \cdots + A_n (x^3 y^2)^n + \cdots, \qquad (77)$$

which is an infinite series of terms each of the form (74), with a equal to 0, 1, 2, 3, $\cdots$, n, $\cdots$ and $c = A_n$ for $a = n$.

EXERCISE XVI

1. The equation for one-dimensional heat flow or diffusion was found in Eq. (5) to be

$$\frac{\partial U}{\partial t} = a^2 \frac{\partial^2 U}{\partial x^2}$$

Show that the only solutions of this equation of the special form $U = X(x) \cdot T(t)$ are of one of the three forms:

$$U = (c_1 e^{kx} + c_2 e^{-kx}) e^{a^2 k^2 t},$$
$$U = (c_3 \sin bx + c_4 \cos bx) e^{-a^2 b^2 t},$$
$$U = c_5 + c_6 x.$$

Find particular solutions of the form $X(x) \cdot Y(y)$ for each of the following partial differential equations:

2. $2 \dfrac{\partial z}{\partial x} - \dfrac{\partial z}{\partial y} = 0.$ **3.** $y \dfrac{\partial z}{\partial x} - x \dfrac{\partial z}{\partial y} = 0.$ **4.** $x \dfrac{\partial z}{\partial x} + y \dfrac{\partial z}{\partial y} = 0.$

5. $e^y \dfrac{\partial z}{\partial x} = e^x \dfrac{\partial z}{\partial y}.$ **6.** $\dfrac{\partial z}{\partial x} + \dfrac{\partial z}{\partial y} = 2z.$ **7.** $y^2 \dfrac{\partial z}{\partial x} + x^2 \dfrac{\partial z}{\partial y} = 0.$

8. $\dfrac{\partial^2 z}{\partial x^2} = 4 \dfrac{\partial^2 z}{\partial y^2}$ **9.** $\dfrac{\partial^2 z}{\partial x\,\partial y} = 2 \dfrac{\partial^2 z}{\partial y^2}.$ **10.** $\dfrac{\partial^2 z}{\partial x^2} = -4 \dfrac{\partial^2 z}{\partial y^2}.$

Find particular solutions of the form $X(x) \cdot T(t)$ for each of the following equations:

11. $\dfrac{\partial^2 U}{\partial x^2} = 9 \dfrac{\partial^2 U}{\partial t^2}.$ **12.** $\dfrac{\partial^2 U}{\partial x^2} = -9 \dfrac{\partial^2 U}{\partial t^2}.$ **13.** $\dfrac{\partial^2 U}{\partial x^2} = 3 \dfrac{\partial^2 U}{\partial x\,\partial t}.$

14. Show that the differential equation

$$r^2 \frac{\partial^2 U}{\partial r^2} + r \frac{\partial U}{\partial r} + \frac{\partial^2 U}{\partial \theta^2} = 0$$

has particular solutions of the form:

$$U = (c_1 r^k + c_2 r^{-k})(c_3 \sin k\theta + c_4 \cos k\theta).$$

15. Show that the differential equation

$$\frac{\partial^2 U}{\partial r^2} + \frac{1}{r^2} \frac{\partial^2 U}{\partial \theta^2} + \frac{1}{r} \frac{\partial U}{\partial r} + a^2 U = 0$$

has particular solutions of the form:

$$U = [c_1 J_n(ar) + c_2 Y_n(ar)](c_3 \sin n\theta + c_4 \cos n\theta),$$

where $J_n(x)$ and $Y_n(x)$ are two independent solutions of the ordinary differential equation known as *Bessel's equation:*

$$\frac{d^2X}{dx^2} + \frac{1}{x}\frac{dX}{dx} + \left(1 - \frac{n^2}{x^2}\right)X = 0.$$

16. For $n = 0$ or a positive integer, *Bessel's function* of order n is defined by

$$J_n(x) = \sum_{k=0}^{\infty} \frac{(-1)^k x^{n+2k}}{2^{n+2k} k!(n+k)!} \qquad \text{with } 0! = 1 \text{ in the first term.}$$

By termwise substitution, verify that this is a solution of Bessel's equation of order n, given at the end of Prob. 15.

17. From Eq. (7) of Sec. 2, deduce that

$$e^{xt/2} = \sum_{r=0}^{\infty} \frac{x^r}{2^r}\frac{1}{r!}t^r \qquad \text{and} \qquad e^{-\frac{x}{2}\frac{1}{t}} = \sum_{s=0}^{\infty} (-1)^s \frac{x^s}{2^s}\frac{1}{s!}t^{-s}.$$

18. Let $J_{-n}(x) = (-1)^n J_n(x)$ for n zero or a positive integer. Multiply the series in Prob. 17 termwise, and by using the expansion of Prob. 16 show that $e^{\frac{x}{2}\left(t - \frac{1}{t}\right)} = \sum_{n=-\infty}^{\infty} J_n(x)t^n$.

19. From Prob. 18, with $t = e^{i\phi}$, deduce that

$$e^{ix\sin\phi} = \sum_{n=-\infty}^{\infty} J_n(x)e^{in\phi}.$$

20. By taking real and imaginary components of the equation of Prob. 19, deduce the expansions

$$\cos(x\sin\phi) = J_0(x) = 2J_2(x)\cos 2\phi$$
$$+ 2J_4(x)\cos 4\phi + \cdots,$$
$$\sin(x\sin\phi) = 2J_1(x)\sin\phi + 2J_3(x)\sin 3\phi$$
$$+ 2J_5(x)\sin 5\phi + \cdots.$$

21. The equation of Prob. 19 is a complex Fourier series for the complex function of the real variable ϕ of period 2π, $e^{ix\sin\phi}$. Apply Eq. (95) of Sec. 21 with c, p, x, ω replaced by $-\pi$, 2π,

ϕ, 1, respectively, to show that

$$J_n(x) = \frac{1}{\pi} \int_0^\pi \cos \,(x \sin \phi - n\phi)d\phi.$$

31. Vibrations. Wave Equations

Let us consider a tightly stretched string, vibrating in a plane. Call the weight per unit of length D (lb./ft.) and the tension T (lb.).   We take x (ft.) as the coordinate along the equilibrium position of the string, the x axis in Fig. 39.   And u (ft.) is the

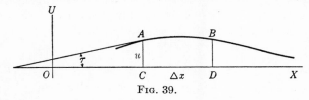

Fig. 39.

distance from a point on the string to its corresponding equilibrium position.   We are thinking of small vibrations, and therefore neglect the small motion parallel to the x axis due to the displaced position of the string not being a straight line.   Thus the mass of the displaced segment AB is taken as that of the segment CD, or $(D/g)\Delta x$.   And for this segment AB, the product of mass times acceleration parallel to the x axis is

$$\frac{D}{g}\, \Delta x\, \frac{\partial^2 u}{\partial t^2}\,\Big|_{x'}, \tag{78}$$

where x' is a suitably chosen value between x and $x + \Delta x$.

We assume that the tension is so large compared with the weight that the effect of gravity is negligible.   Then the effective forces on the segment are due to the tension at the ends.   These are along the tangent to the curve giving the position of the string, whose inclination τ to the x axis is small.   Thus we may neglect the difference between $\sin \tau$ and $\tan \tau = \dfrac{\partial u}{dx}$.   Hence the u component of tension at A is $- T \sin \tau$, or with our approxima-

tion, $-T \tan \tau = -T \left. \dfrac{\partial u}{\partial x} \right|_x$. Similarly for B we find $T \left. \dfrac{\partial u}{dx} \right|_{x+\Delta x}$
And the resultant force parallel to the u axis is

$$T \left(\left. \frac{\partial u}{\partial x} \right|_{x+\Delta x} - \left. \frac{\partial u}{\partial x} \right|_x \right). \tag{79}$$

But force equals mass times acceleration. Hence we may equate the expressions for their u components given in Eqs. (79) and (78). If we do this, divide through by Δx, and take the limit as $\Delta x \to 0$, $x + \Delta x$ and the intermediate value x' will both approach x. Hence we have in the limit

$$\frac{D}{g} \frac{\partial^2 u}{\partial t^2} = T \frac{\partial^2 u}{\partial x^2}. \tag{80}$$

This is the equation for a vibrating string, valid when $\left(\dfrac{\partial u}{\partial x} \right)^2$ is small compared with unity, since the various approximations made all amount to a replacement of the factor

$$\sqrt{1 + \left(\frac{\partial u}{\partial x} \right)^2} = \cos \tau$$

by unity in certain places.

If we replace gT/D by v^2 (ft.²/sec.²), Eq. (80) becomes

$$\frac{\partial^2 u}{\partial t^2} = v^2 \frac{\partial^2 u}{\partial x^2}, \quad \text{or} \quad \frac{1}{v^2} \frac{\partial^2 u}{\partial t^2} = \frac{\partial^2 u}{\partial x^2}. \tag{81}$$

The solution of this equation was found in Prob. 10 of Exercise XV to be $u = f(x - vt) + g(x + vt)$. If we calculate $x - vt$ for a particular value x_1 at time t_1, and then for a time t_0 sec. later but at a position vt_0 to the right, we get the same value. For if

$$t_2 = t_1 + t_0, \quad x_2 = x_1 + vt_0, \quad \text{then } x_2 - vt_2 = x_1 - vt_1. \tag{82}$$

This shows that the term $f(x - vt)$ represents a wave traveling to the right with velocity v. Similarly $g(x + vt)$ represents a wave traveling to the left with velocity v. For this reason, Eq. (81) is called the *wave equation* in one dimension.

We may use any convenient units for u and x, provided that the units of v are the same as those of x/t.

An argument similar to that given for the string may be used for a vibrating stretched membrane such as a drumhead. Since the element is here a small rectangle instead of a small segment, there is a term in $\dfrac{\partial^2 u}{\partial y^2}$ as well as a term in $\dfrac{\partial^2 u}{\partial x^2}$. Thus we find

$$\frac{1}{v^2}\frac{\partial^2 u}{\partial t^2} = \frac{\partial^2 u}{\partial x^2} + \frac{\partial^2 u}{\partial y^2} \tag{83}$$

as the equation for a vibrating membrane when $v^2 = gT/D$, where here T is in pounds per foot and D is in pounds per square foot.

The *wave equation* in three dimensions is

$$\frac{1}{v^2}\frac{\partial^2 u}{\partial t^2} = \frac{\partial^2 u}{\partial x^2} + \frac{\partial^2 u}{\partial y^2} + \frac{\partial^2 u}{\partial z^2} \tag{84}$$

Here t is time, x, y, z are lengths all with the same unit, and v is a velocity having the same units as x/t. For sound waves in a solid or in air, u is a displacement. An equation of this form also holds for electromagnetic waves in empty space. In this case u is one of the three components of the electric field intensity vector, or of the magnetic field intensity vector. See Sec. 36 and in particular Eq. (117).

32. Curvilinear Coordinates

For problems in a plane involving circular symmetry about the origin, it is often convenient to introduce polar coordinates

$$x = r \cos \theta, \qquad y = r \sin \theta. \tag{85}$$

In most discussions of partial differentiation, it is shown as an illustration or application of the theory that

$$\frac{\partial^2 U}{\partial x^2} + \frac{\partial^2 U}{\partial y^2} = \frac{\partial^2 U}{\partial r^2} + \frac{1}{r^2}\frac{\partial^2 U}{\partial \theta^2} + \frac{1}{r}\frac{\partial U}{\partial r} \tag{86}$$

This identity holds whether U is a function of two variables only, first x,y and then r,θ or of these pairs together with other variables such as z and t which remain unchanged. Thus we may use Eq. (86) to transform Laplace's equation, Eq. (8), or the heat equation, Eq. (7), to cylindrical coordinates r, θ, z. For example, the heat equation, Eq. (7), becomes

$$\frac{\partial U}{\partial t} = a^2 \left(\frac{\partial^2 U}{\partial r^2} + \frac{1}{r^2} \frac{\partial^2 U}{\partial \theta^2} + \frac{1}{r} \frac{\partial U}{\partial r} + \frac{\partial^2 U}{\partial z^2} \right). \tag{87}$$

Similarly we find that the wave equation, Eq. (84), becomes

$$\frac{1}{v^2} \frac{\partial^2 u}{\partial t^2} = \frac{\partial^2 u}{\partial r^2} + \frac{1}{r^2} \frac{\partial^2 u}{\partial \theta^2} + \frac{1}{r} \frac{\partial u}{\partial r} + \frac{\partial^2 u}{\partial z^2}. \tag{88}$$

For problems in space involving spherical symmetry about the origin, it is more convenient to introduce spherical coordinates

$$x = r \cos \theta \sin \phi, \qquad y = r \sin \theta \sin \phi, \qquad z = r \cos \phi. \tag{89}$$

Here r is a radial coordinate giving the distance from the origin, θ is an angular coordinate of longitude, and ϕ is a coordinate of colatitude measured down from the z axis. For these coordinates

$$\frac{\partial^2 U}{\partial x^2} + \frac{\partial^2 U}{\partial y^2} + \frac{\partial^2 U}{\partial z^2} = \frac{\partial^2 U}{\partial r^2} + \frac{2}{r} \frac{\partial U}{\partial r} + \frac{1}{r^2 \sin^2 \phi} \frac{\partial^2 U}{\partial \theta^2}$$
$$+ \frac{1}{r^2} \frac{\partial^2 U}{\partial \phi^2} + \frac{\cot \phi}{r^2} \frac{\partial U}{\partial \phi}. \tag{90}$$

This may be derived by a lengthy elementary calculation, or more briefly by methods based on symbolic vector operators or on the calculus of variations. Any partial differential equation in which the space coordinates x, y, z appear in the Laplacian expression only, for example Eqs. (7) and (84), may be expressed in spherical coordinates by means of Eq. (90).

EXERCISE XVII

1. For one choice of the functions f and g in the general solution of Eq. (81) it becomes $u = B \cos b(x - vt) - B \cos b(x + vt)$.

Show that this may be written $u = 2B \sin bx \sin bvt$, and thus has the form $X(x)$ $T(t)$ used in Sec. 29.

2. If the string is of length L and is fixed at both ends, we must have $u(0,t) = 0$ and $u(L,t) = 0$. Show that the second condition will be met if we take $b = n\pi x/L$, where n is any positive integer, in the solution of Prob. 1. With $2B = A$, this gives the harmonic vibrations $u = A \sin \dfrac{n\pi x}{L} \sin \dfrac{n\pi vt}{L}$.

3. The fundamental note of the string is given by the solution of Prob. 2 with $n = 1$. Recalling the definition of $v = \sqrt{gT/D}$, deduce that the pitch of the fundamental note of a musical string is $(1/2L)\sqrt{gT/D}$. Thus the pitch is proportional to the square root of the tension, and is inversely proportional to the length and the square root of the density.

4. For a string whose density and tension vary with position, show that the equation is

$$\frac{D(x)}{g} \frac{\partial^2 u}{\partial t^2} = \frac{\partial}{\partial x} \left[T(x) \frac{\partial u}{\partial x} \right].$$

5. Apply the method of Sec. 30 to Eq. (81), and so deduce that

$$u = (c_1 \sin kx + c_2 \cos kx)(c_3 \sin kvt + c_4 \cos kvt)$$

is a particular solution.

6. For a vibrating string with viscous damping the equation is

$$\frac{\partial^2 u}{\partial t^2} = v^2 \frac{\partial^2 u}{\partial x^2} - b \frac{\partial u}{\partial t}$$

By the method of Sec. 30 deduce that this admits the particular solution

$$u = e^{-bt/2} (c_1 \sin kx + c_2 \cos kx)(c_3 \sin Mt + c_4 \cos Mt)$$

where $M = \sqrt{k^2 v^2 - (b^2/4)}$.

7. Use Eq. (87) to check Prob. 7 of Exercise XII.

8. Use Eqs. (90) and (7) to check Prob. 11 of Exercise XII.

9. Assume that u depends on the spherical r, but not on θ or ϕ.

By combining Eqs. (84) and (90) deduce the equation for spherical waves

$$\frac{1}{v^2}\frac{\partial^2 u}{\partial t^2} = \frac{1}{r^2}\frac{\partial}{\partial r}\left(r^2\frac{\partial u}{\partial r}\right).$$

10. The general solution of the equation of Prob. **9** is

$$u = \frac{1}{r}f(r - vt) + \frac{1}{r}g(r + vt).$$

Verify by direct substitution that this satisfies the equation.

11. Check the solution of Prob. 10 by using the substitution $u(r,t) = U(r,t)/r$ to reduce the equation of Prob. 9 to a wave equation in $U(r,t)$ with constant coefficients.

12. From Eqs. (86) and (83) show that in cylindrical coordinates the equation of a vibrating membrane is

$$\frac{1}{v^2}\frac{\partial^2 u}{\partial t^2} = \frac{\partial^2 u}{\partial r^2} + \frac{1}{r^2}\frac{\partial^2 u}{\partial \theta^2} + \frac{1}{r}\frac{\partial u}{\partial r}.$$

13. We may obtain an expression for the harmonic vibrations of the membrane of Prob. 12 by putting $u(r,\theta,t) = \sin btU(r,\theta)$. Make this substitution, and show that if $b = av$, the equation in U becomes that for which particular solutions were found in Prob. 15 of Exercise XVI.

33. Transmission of Electricity

Let us study the flow of electricity in a long imperfectly insulated cable. In Fig. 40, AB is the cable, and the current flows from the source through AB, then through the load, and back through $B'A'$ to the source. We shall speak of the return path $A'B'$ as the ground, although it may be a second cable. The arrow indicates that the direction from A to B is considered to be positive in measuring current and difference of potential. Compare Secs. 11 and 13. If x (miles) is the distance along the cable from A, the emf e (volts) and the current i (amperes) will depend on x as well as on the time t (seconds).   That is,

$$e = e(x,t), \qquad i = i(x,t). \tag{91}$$

The series resistance R (ohms per mile) and series inductance L (henrys per mile) are so defined that for a short segment of the line from x to $x + \Delta x$, $R \, \Delta x$ and $L \, \Delta x$ have meanings for the segment somewhat similar to the lumped resistance and induct-

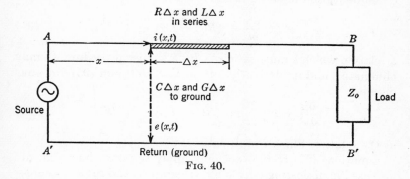

FIG. 40.

ance for an ordinary simple circuit.   And the emf decreases with distance in accord with the relation

$$-\frac{\partial e}{\partial x} = Ri + L \frac{\partial i}{\partial t}. \tag{92}$$

The capacitance to ground C (farads per mile) and conductance to ground G (mhos per mile) are so defined that the decrease in current for the short segment is somewhat similar to that in two parallel circuits, one with lumped capacity $C \, \Delta x$ and one with lumped resistance $1/(G \, \Delta x)$.   And the current decreases with distance in accord with the relation

$$-\frac{\partial i}{\partial x} = Ge + C \frac{\partial e}{\partial t}. \tag{93}$$

The two equations (92) and (93) together determine e and i in terms of x and t.   They are called the *transmission-line equations*.

In some applications, a different convention as to direction is used, and the equations appear without the minus signs.

We may eliminate i from our equations by differentiating Eq. (92) with respect to x. The resulting equation contains $\dfrac{\partial i}{\partial x}$ whose value is given by Eq. (93) as it stands, and $\dfrac{\partial^2 i}{\partial x\, \partial t}$ whose value is obtained from Eq. (93) by differentiation with respect to t. Substitution of these values leads to

$$\frac{\partial^2 e}{\partial x^2} + LC\, \frac{\partial^2 e}{\partial t^2} + (RC + LG)\, \frac{\partial e}{\partial t} + RGe, \qquad (94)$$

a relation which e must satisfy. By a similar procedure we may eliminate e and its derivatives from Eqs. (92) and (93) and thus derive

$$\frac{\partial^2 i}{\partial x^2} + LC\, \frac{\partial^2 i}{\partial t^2} + (RC + LG)\, \frac{\partial i}{\partial t} + RGi \qquad (95)$$

as the relation which i must satisfy.

Equations (92) to (95) not only apply to power lines, but are also used in discussing telephony, telegraphy, and radio antennas. In many applications to telegraph signaling, the leakage is small, and the term for the effect of inductance is negligible, so that we may set $G = 0$ and $L = 0$. Equations (92) to (94) then simplify to

$$-\frac{\partial e}{\partial x} = Ri, \qquad -\frac{\partial i}{\partial x} = C\, \frac{\partial e}{\partial t}, \qquad \frac{\partial^2 e}{\partial x^2} = RC\, \frac{\partial e}{\partial t}. \qquad (96)$$

These are known as the *telegraph* or *cable equations*.

When the frequencies are high, the terms in the time derivatives are large, and some qualitative properties of the solution may be found by neglecting the terms for the losses due to leakage and resistance in comparison with them. For this *lossless line*, $G = 0$ and $R = 0$ so that the simplified equations

$$-\frac{\partial e}{\partial x} = L\, \frac{\partial i}{\partial t}, \qquad -\frac{\partial i}{\partial x} = C\, \frac{\partial e}{\partial t}, \qquad \frac{\partial^2 e}{\partial x^2} = LC\, \frac{\partial^2 e}{\partial t^2} \qquad (97)$$

apply. They are known as the *radio equations*.

EXERCISE XVIII

1. Show that the general solution of the radio equations, Eqs. (97), may be written

$$e = f(x - vt) + g(x + vt),$$

$$i = \sqrt{\frac{C}{L}} [f(x - vt) - g(x + vt)], \qquad \text{where } v = \frac{1}{\sqrt{LC}}.$$

2. By the argument used for Eqs. (81) and (82) interpret the solutions of Prob. 1 as a combination of two waves, one moving to the right and the other to the left, each with velocity $v = 1/\sqrt{LC}$.

3. If e and i are functions of x and t, and k is any constant, the equations of transformation $e = e_1 \epsilon^{-kt}$, $i = i_1 \epsilon^{-kt}$ define e_1 and i_1 as two new functions of x and t. When Eqs. (92) and (93) hold, show that e_1 and i_1 satisfy the equations

$$-\frac{\partial e_1}{\partial x} = (R - kL)i_1 + L \frac{\partial i_1}{\partial t},$$

$$-\frac{\partial i_1}{\partial x} = (G - kC)e_1 + C \frac{\partial e_1}{\partial t}.$$

4. A transmission line whose constants satisfy the relation $LG = RC$ is called a *distortionless line*. In this case $G/C = R/L$. Show that if we transform variables as in Prob. 3, with $k = R/L$, the equations in e_1 and i_1 have the form of Eqs. (97). Use this fact, and Prob. 1, to find the general solution for the distortionless line in the form

$$e = \epsilon^{-kt}[f(x - vt) + G(x + vt)],$$

$$i = \epsilon^{-kt} \sqrt{\frac{C}{L}} [f(x - vt) - g(x + vt)], \qquad \text{where } v = \frac{1}{\sqrt{LC}},$$

$$k = \frac{R}{L} = \frac{G}{C}.$$

5. Interpret the solution of the distortionless line found in Prob. 4 as a combination of waves which preserve their shape, but die down exponentially. Compare Prob. 2.

6. Consider a power line whose source or impressed emf is a single sine term. After the steady state has been reached, the current and emf will involve t through a factor of this same frequency. Thus we may write

$$e = E_m(x) \sin [\omega t + \phi_1(x)], \qquad i = I_m(x) \sin [\omega t + \phi_2(x)].$$

We now define *complex* quantities $F(x)$ and $H(x)$ by the relations

$$F(x) = E_m(x)\epsilon^{j\phi_1(x)}, \qquad H(x) = I_m(x)\epsilon^{j\phi_2(x)}.$$

Then, with Im meaning imaginary component as in sec. 12, we have

$$e = \text{Im complex } e = \text{Im } F(x)\epsilon^{j\omega t},$$
$$i = \text{Im complex } i = \text{Im } H(x)\epsilon^{j\omega t},$$

and the complex e and complex i, abbreviated by e and i, satisfy Eqs. (92) and (93). Show that the condition for this is that $F(x)$ and $H(x)$ are solutions of

$$-\frac{dF}{dx} = (R + j\omega L)H, \qquad -\frac{dH}{dx} = (G + j\omega C)F,$$

a system of simultaneous ordinary differential equations.

7. The following notation is useful in discussing the transmission line of Prob. 6. Let $Z = R + j\omega L$ be the complex series impedance and $Y = G + j\omega C$ be the complex shunt admittance. Define the propagation constant $\gamma = \alpha + j\beta = \sqrt{ZY}$, and the characteristic impedance $Z_K = \sqrt{Z/Y}$. Then the Eqs. of Prob. 6 are $-dF/dx = ZH$, $-dH/dx = YF$. Show that these imply $d^2F/dx^2 = ZYF = \gamma^2 F$. Hence find F, and then H from the first equation, and deduce that

$$\text{complex } e = K_1\epsilon^{\gamma x + j\omega t} + K_2\epsilon^{-\gamma x + j\omega t},$$
$$\text{complex } i = \frac{\text{complex } e}{Z_k},$$

where $K_1 = A\epsilon^{ja}$, $K_2 = B\epsilon^{jb}$ are complex arbitrary constants.

8. Deduce from Prob. 7 that for the real emf,

$$e = A\epsilon^{\alpha x} \sin (\omega t + \beta x + a) + B\epsilon^{-\alpha x} \sin (\omega t - \beta x + b).$$

9. Show that, when $R = 0$ and $G = 0$, the particular complex solutions found in Prob. 7 are special cases of the general solution of the radio equations found in Prob. 1.

10. If the line is of length x_1 and is terminated in a load impedance Z_0, then for the complex values e, i, $e = iZ_0$ when $x = x_1$. If the real input voltage is $E_i \sin \omega t$, then for the complex e, $e = E_i\epsilon^{j\omega t}$ when $x = 0$. Show that these two conditions determine the value of the complex constants K_1, K_2 in Prob. 7.

11. Consider the particular case of Prob. 10 when the line is short-circuited at $x = x_1$, or $Z_0 = 0$. Show that in this case for the real e

$$e = -D[\sinh \alpha(x - x_1) \sin (\omega t - \phi) \cos \beta(x - x_1)$$
$$+ \cosh \alpha(x - x_1) \cos (\omega t - \phi) \sin \beta(x - x_1)],$$

where

$$D = \frac{E_i}{\sqrt{\sinh^2 \alpha x_1 + \sin^2 \alpha x_1}}, \qquad \phi = \tan^{-1} (\tan \beta x_1 \coth \beta x_1),$$

with ϕ in a quadrant such that $\sin \beta x_1$ and $\sin \phi$ have the same sign.

34. Maxwell's Equations

An electromagnetic field may be mathematically characterized by five vectors **E, H, D, B,** and **J.** In terms of the differential operations curl and div (divergence) whose meaning we shall recall in detail later, the differential equations satisfied by these vectors may be written

$$\text{curl } \mathbf{E} = - \frac{\partial \mathbf{B}}{\partial t},$$

$$\text{curl } \mathbf{H} = \mathbf{J} + \frac{\partial \mathbf{D}}{\partial t},$$

$$\text{div } \mathbf{B} = 0,$$

$$\text{div } \mathbf{D} = \rho, \tag{98}$$

In a homogeneous isotropic medium we also have the proportionality relations

$$\mathbf{D} = K\mathbf{E}, \qquad \mathbf{B} = \mu\mathbf{H}, \qquad \mathbf{J} = \sigma\mathbf{E}. \tag{99}$$

Equations (98) and (99) are the fundamental *Maxwell equations* when the MKS rationalized system of units is used. In this case

$\mathbf{E} = E_x\mathbf{i} + E_y\mathbf{j} + E_z\mathbf{k} =$ electric field intensity (volt/meter)

$\mathbf{H} = H_x\mathbf{i} + H_y\mathbf{j} + H_z\mathbf{k}$
$\qquad\qquad = $ magnetic field intensity (ampere-turn/meter)

$\mathbf{D} = D_x\mathbf{i} + \mathbf{D}_y\mathbf{j} + D_z\mathbf{k} =$ electric flux density (coulomb/meter²)

$\mathbf{B} = B_x\mathbf{i} + B_y\mathbf{j} + B_z\mathbf{k} =$ magnetic flux density (weber/meter²)

$\mathbf{J} = J_x\mathbf{i} + J_y\mathbf{j} + J_z\mathbf{k} =$ current density (ampere/meter²)

For each vector the second expression is written in terms of **i, j, k** the unit vectors along the coordinate axes and the scalar components along these axes, indicated by subscripts. For a particular point in the region where the field exists, and a particular instant of time, any one of the five vectors has a definite magnitude and direction, and thus is a vector function of position and time. Thus each component depends on the coordinates *xyz* of the point at which it is to be calculated and on the time *t*. Hence a complete description of the electromagnetic field in terms of the scalar components involves fifteen functions of *x, y, z,* and *t*.

We confine our attention to the case where Eqs. (99) hold with the coefficients *K*, *μ*, *σ* constant throughout the field under consideration. Then we may use these relations to eliminate **D, B,** and **J** from Eqs. (98) which then take the form:

$$\operatorname{curl} \mathbf{E} = -\mu\,\frac{\partial H}{\partial t},$$

$$\operatorname{curl} \mathbf{H} = \sigma\mathbf{E} + K\,\frac{\partial \mathbf{E}}{\partial t},$$

$$\operatorname{div} \mathbf{H} = 0, \tag{100}$$

$$\operatorname{div} \mathbf{E} = \frac{\rho}{K}.$$

The first of these relations is equivalent to the three component equations

$$\frac{\partial E_z}{\partial y} - \frac{\partial E_y}{\partial z} = -\mu \frac{\partial H_x}{\partial t},$$

$$\frac{\partial E_x}{\partial z} - \frac{\partial E_z}{\partial x} = -\mu \frac{\partial H_y}{\partial t}, \qquad (101)$$

$$\frac{\partial E_y}{\partial x} - \frac{\partial E_x}{\partial y} = -\mu \frac{\partial H_z}{\partial t}.$$

The components of curl **H** are analogous to those just written for curl **E**. Thus, for example, the first component of the second equation is

$$\frac{\partial H_z}{\partial y} - \frac{\partial H_y}{\partial z} = \sigma E_x + K \frac{\partial E_x}{\partial t}. \qquad (102)$$

The last two equations, Eqs. (100), when written explicitly in terms of components, become

$$\frac{\partial H_x}{\partial x} + \frac{\partial H_y}{\partial y} + \frac{\partial H_z}{\partial z} = 0,$$

$$\frac{\partial E_x}{\partial x} + \frac{\partial E_y}{\partial y} + \frac{\partial E_z}{\partial z} = \frac{\rho}{K}. \qquad (103)$$

35. Electrostatic Fields

In a static field the current density $\mathbf{J} = \sigma\mathbf{E}$ is zero, and the other four field vectors are independent of the time. Thus $\frac{\partial H}{\partial t} = 0$ and $\frac{\partial E}{\partial t} = 0$, and Eqs. (100) reduce to

$$\text{curl } \mathbf{E} = 0, \quad \text{curl } \mathbf{H} = 0, \quad \text{div } \mathbf{H} = 0, \quad \text{div } \mathbf{E} = \frac{\rho}{K}. \quad (104)$$

But curl $\mathbf{E} = 0$ is the condition that there exists a V_E such that

$$-\mathbf{E} = \text{grad } V_E = \frac{\partial V_E}{\partial x}\mathbf{i} + \frac{\partial V_E}{\partial y}\mathbf{j} + \frac{\partial V_E}{\partial z}\mathbf{k}, \qquad (105)$$

where the last expression shows the meaning of the differential operation grad (gradient). V_E is called the *electric scalar potential function*. For any function V_E, the **E** formed from it by Eq. (105)

will satisfy the first equation of Eq. (104). And the last will be satisfied if

$$\text{div (grad } V_E) = \frac{\partial^2 V_E}{\partial x^2} + \frac{\partial^2 V_E}{\partial y^2} + \frac{\partial^2 V_E}{\partial z^2} = -\frac{\rho}{K}. \quad (106)$$

This is *Poisson's equation*. In general, the charge density ρ is a function of x, y, and z. In a region free of charges, $\rho = 0$, and Eq. (106) reduces to Laplace's equation.

Since curl $\mathbf{H} = 0$, there exists a V_M such that

$$-\mathbf{H} = \text{grad } V_M = \frac{\partial V_M}{\partial x}\mathbf{i} + \frac{\partial V_M}{\partial y}\mathbf{j} + \frac{\partial V_M}{\partial z}\mathbf{k}. \quad (107)$$

V_M is called the *magnetic scalar potential function*. And to make div $\mathbf{H} = 0$, we must have

$$\text{div (grad } V_M) = \frac{\partial^2 V_M}{\partial x^2} + \frac{\partial^2 V_M}{\partial y^2} + \frac{\partial^2 V_M}{\partial z^2} = 0. \quad (108)$$

This is *Laplace's equation*.

If ρ is given, boundary conditions on E or V_E together with Eq. (106) determine V_E, and the electrostatic field E is then found from Eq. (105). Similarly, boundary conditions on H or V_M together with Eq. (108) determine V_M, and the magnetostatic field is then found from Eq. (107). The $\mathbf{E}$ and $\mathbf{H}$ so found will necessarily satisfy the system of Eqs. (104).

36. Electromagnetic Waves. Radiation. Skin Effect

We may eliminate H from the system of Eqs. (100) by the following procedure. Take the curl of both members of the first equation. This gives

$$\text{curl (curl } \mathbf{E}) = \text{curl}\left(-\frac{\partial \mathbf{H}}{\partial t}\right) = -\frac{\partial(\text{curl } \mathbf{H})}{\partial t} \quad (109)$$

Differentiation of the second equation of Eq. (100) leads to

$$\frac{\partial(\text{curl } \mathbf{H})}{\partial t} = \sigma\frac{\partial \mathbf{E}}{\partial t} + K\frac{\partial^2 \mathbf{E}}{\partial t^2}. \quad (110)$$

The left member of Eq. (109) may be transformed by the identity
curl (curl **E**) = grad (div **E**) − ∇²**E**,

$$\text{where } \nabla^2 \mathbf{E} = \frac{\partial^2 \mathbf{E}}{\partial x^2} + \frac{\partial^2 \mathbf{E}}{\partial y^2} + \frac{\partial^2 \mathbf{E}}{\partial z^2}. \quad (111)$$

This holds for any vector function, and could be verified by a
lengthy elementary calculation, or more briefly by using symbolic
vector operators.   Let us use the fourth equation of Eq. (100) to
replace div **E** by ρ/K, and then substitute the values given by
Eqs. (110) and (111) in Eq. (109).   The result is

$$\frac{\text{grad } \rho}{K} - \nabla^2 \mathbf{E} = -\mu\sigma \frac{\partial \mathbf{E}}{\partial t} - \mu K \frac{\partial^2 \mathbf{E}}{\partial t^2}. \quad (112)$$

By a similar procedure which starts with the second equation,
we may eliminate **E** from the system of Eqs. (100).   The result is

$$\nabla^2 \mathbf{H} = \mu\sigma \frac{\partial \mathbf{H}}{\partial t} + \mu K \frac{\partial^2 \mathbf{H}}{\partial t^2}. \quad (113)$$

Let us consider an electromagnetic field in empty space.   Since
there are no electric charges or conduction currents, $\rho = 0$ and
$\sigma = 0$.   We use the subscript 0 to indicate that μ and K have the
values for empty space, $\mu_0 = 4\pi \times 10^{-7} = 1.257 \times 10^{-6}$ henry
per meter and $K_0 = 8.854 \times 10^{-12}$ farad per meter.   Then Eqs.
(100) become

$$\text{curl } \mathbf{E} = -\mu_0 \frac{\partial \mathbf{H}}{\partial t}, \qquad \text{div } \mathbf{E} = 0,$$
$$\text{curl } \mathbf{H} = K_0 \frac{\partial \mathbf{E}}{\partial t}. \qquad \text{div } \mathbf{H} = 0. \quad (114)$$

And we may reduce Eqs. (112) and (113) to the form

$$\nabla^2 \mathbf{E} = \mu_0 K_0 \frac{\partial^2 \mathbf{E}}{\partial t^2}, \qquad \nabla^2 \mathbf{H} = \mu_0 K_0 \frac{\partial^2 \mathbf{H}}{\partial t^2}. \quad (115)$$

Introduce the constant c defined by the relation

$$c = \frac{1}{\sqrt{\mu_0 K_0}} = 2.998 \times 10^8 \text{ m./sec.} \quad (116)$$

Then Eqs. (115) show that each of the components E_x, E_y, E_z, H_x, H_y, H_z satisfies an equation of the form

$$\nabla^2 u = \frac{\partial^2 u}{\partial x^2} + \frac{\partial^2 u}{\partial y^2} + \frac{\partial^2 u}{\partial z^2} = \frac{1}{c^2} \frac{\partial^2 u}{\partial t^2} \qquad (117)$$

This is similar to Eq. (84) with $v = c$. And the discussion of Eq. (81), a special case of Eq. (84), showed that its solutions included representations of waves traveling with velocity $v = c$. Hence Eq. (117) indicates that electric and magnetic disturbances are propagated through empty space with a common velocity c. And the value of c, given in Eq. (116), is numerically equal to the velocity of light in empty space. These facts are basic in the electromagnetic theory of light.

The conditions which hold in empty space are closely approximated in the atmosphere, provided that there are no electric charges, ions and electrons, present. Hence Eqs. (114) to (117) are useful in studying the fields due to radiation from an antenna. These equations are also applicable to the fields inside hollow wave guides of conducting material.

In a conducting medium, ρ is constant so that grad $\rho = 0$. Hence Eq. (112) reduces to

$$\nabla^2 \mathbf{E} = \mu\sigma \frac{\partial \mathbf{E}}{\partial t} + \mu K \frac{\partial^2 \mathbf{E}}{\partial t^2}. \qquad (118)$$

From this and the last equation of Eqs. (99), $J = \sigma E$, we also have

$$\nabla^2 \mathbf{J} = \mu\sigma \frac{\partial \mathbf{J}}{\partial t} + \mu K \frac{\partial^2 \mathbf{J}}{\partial t^2}. \qquad (119)$$

A comparison of Eqs. (113), (118), and (119) shows that in a conducting medium $\mathbf{H}$, $\mathbf{E}$, and $\mathbf{J}$ satisfy equations of the same form.

For ordinary metal conductors, K is much less than 10^{-11} farad per meter and σ is of the order of 10^7 mhos per meter. Hence if the frequency is less than 10^{10} cycles per second, the first term on the right in Eq. (119) is more than 10^8 times the last term. Thus we can neglect the last term, and therefore reduce the equation to

$$\nabla^2 J = \frac{\partial^2 J}{\partial x^2} + \frac{\partial^2 J}{\partial y^2} + \frac{\partial^2 J}{\partial z^2} = \mu\sigma\,\frac{\partial J}{\partial t}. \tag{120}$$

This is the equation governing the skin effect in metal conductors.

37. References

The reader desiring to refresh his knowledge of partial differentiation will find the useful properties of partial derivatives reviewed in Chap. II of the author's *Methods of Advanced Calculus*. And in Chaps. VIII and XII of this same book will be found an introduction to vector analysis and the calculus of variations, which includes the application of these subjects to the derivation and transformation of partial differential equations to which we referred in Secs. 32, 34, and 36.

A fuller discussion of the underlying physical theories is contained in such specialized treatises as H. S. Carslaw's *Mathematical Theory of the Conduction of Heat in Solids*, P. M. Morse's *Vibration and Sound*, and J. A. Stratton's *Electromagnetic Theory*.

EXERCISE XIX

1. Write out that component equation of the second equation of Eq. (100) which contains E_z and $\dfrac{\partial E_z}{\partial t}$.

2. Use Eqs. (86) and (106) to deduce the equation satisfied by the electrostatic potential V_E in cylindrical coordinates:

$$\frac{\partial^2 V_E}{\partial r^2} + \frac{1}{r^2}\frac{\partial^2 V_E}{\partial \theta^2} + \frac{1}{r}\frac{\partial V_E}{\partial r} + \frac{\partial^2 V_E}{\partial z^2} = -\frac{\rho}{K}.$$

3. Put $V_E = \epsilon^{-az}U(r,\theta,z)$ in the equation of Prob. 2, and assume that $\rho = 0$. Show that the resulting equation has the form of that in Prob. 15 of Exercise XVI, and from that problem deduce that

$$V_E = \epsilon^{-az}J_n(ar)(c_3 \sin n\theta + c_4 \cos n\theta)$$

is a particular solution of the equation of Prob. 2 when $\rho = 0$.

4. In the equation of Prob. 2 assume that $\rho = 0$, and that V_E is independent of z.   Deduce from Prob. 14 of Exercise XVI that

$$V_E = (c_1 r^n + c_2 r^{-n})(c_3 \sin n\theta + c_4 \cos n\theta)$$

is a particular solution of the equation of Prob. 2 when $\rho = 0$.

5. In the equation of Prob. 2 assume that V_E is independent of z and θ, so that V_E and ρ are functions of r only.   Show that in this case

$$\frac{1}{r}\frac{d}{dr}\left(r\frac{dV_E}{dr}\right) = -\frac{\rho}{K}.$$

This implies that $dV_E = -\dfrac{dr}{Kr}\left(\int r\rho\,dr + c_1\right)$, so that V_E can be found by a second integration.

6. From Prob. 5 deduce that $V_E = c_1 \ln r + c_2$ is a particular solution of the equation of Prob. 2. when $\rho = 0$.

7. If V_E has the form given in Prob. 6, show that

$$E = -\operatorname{grad} V_E = -\frac{c_1}{r}\mathbf{u}_r,$$

where $\mathbf{u}_r = \cos\theta\,\mathbf{i} + \sin\theta\,\mathbf{j}$ is a unit vector in the direction of increasing r.

8. Show that when $\mathbf{E}$ and $\mathbf{H}$ are functions of x and t only, so that all y and z derivatives are zero, and we expand in terms of components, as in Eqs. (101) and (103), the Eqs. (114) for an electromagnetic field in empty space take the form

$$0 = \frac{\partial H_x}{\partial t}, \qquad \frac{\partial E_z}{\partial x} = \mu_0\frac{\partial H_y}{\partial t}, \qquad \frac{\partial E_y}{\partial x} = -\mu_0\frac{\partial H_z}{\partial t}, \qquad \frac{\partial E_x}{\partial x} = 0,$$

$$0 = \frac{\partial E_x}{\partial t}, \qquad -\frac{\partial H_z}{\partial x} = K_0\frac{\partial E_y}{\partial t}, \qquad \frac{\partial H_y}{\partial x} = K_0\frac{\partial E_z}{\partial t}, \qquad \frac{\partial H_x}{\partial x} = 0$$

9. Under the conditions of Prob. 8, Eq. (117) reduces to the form $\dfrac{\partial^2 u}{\partial x^2} = \dfrac{1}{c^2}\dfrac{\partial^2 u}{\partial t^2}$.   Using Prob. 10 of Exercise XV, show that this has as its general solution $u = f(x - ct) + g(x + ct)$.

10. From Prob. 8 we must have $E_x = \text{const.}$ and $H_x = \text{const.}$, since all their partial derivatives are zero. And from Prob. 9 we must have $E_y = f(x - ct) + g(x + ct)$, and

$$E_z = F(x - ct) + G(x + ct).$$

Show that from these and from Prob. 8 we must have

$$H_y = -K_0 c F(x - ct) + K_0 c G(x + ct) + C_2,$$

and $H_z = K_0 c f(x - ct) - K_0 c g(x + ct) + C_3$, where C_2 and C_3 are constants which may be made zero by redefining the arbitrary functions f, g, F, and G.

11. By direct substitution, and use of the relation (116), show that the values found in Prob. 10 satisfy all the equations of Prob. 8. They give the general solution of the system.

12. By an argument like that used for Eqs. (81) and (82) show that the special case of the solution in Prob. 10 given by $E_x = 0$, $E_y = f(x - ct)$, $E_z = F(x - ct)$, $H_x = 0$, $H_y = -K_0 c F(x - ct)$, $H_z = K_0 c f(x - ct)$ represents a wave moving with velocity c in the direction of the positive x axis.

13. Show that for the advancing transverse plane wave of Prob. 12 the vectors **E** and **H** are perpendicular.

14. Show that $u = U(y,z)[c_1 \cos (\omega t - x) + c_2 \sin (\omega t - x)]$ will be a solution of Eq. (117), provided that

$$\frac{\partial^2 U}{\partial y^2} + \frac{\partial^2 U}{\partial z^2} + \left(\frac{\omega^2}{c^2} - \beta^2\right) U = 0.$$

This equation and vectors **E** and **H,** whose components have the special form which gave rise to it, play a central role in the study of hollow wave guides.

15. Show that if we introduce polar coordinates in the yz plane, and call the constant expression in parentheses a^2, the equation of Prob. 14 takes the form for which particular solutions were found in Prob. 15 of Exercise XVI. These particular solutions are used in studying wave guides with circular cross sections.

16. In a long straight wire carrying alternating current the current density **J** satisfies Eq. (120). If the wire is parallel to the z axis, $J_x = 0$, $J_y = 0$, and J_z is independent of z and θ, where

r, θ, z are cylindrical coordinates. Use Eq. (86) to show that in this case

$$\frac{\partial^2 J_z}{\partial r^2} + \frac{1}{r}\frac{\partial J_z}{\partial r} = \mu\sigma\frac{\partial J_z}{\partial t}.$$

17. If the current in Prob. 16 has the frequency ω, we may write $J_z = u\sin(\omega t + \phi) = \operatorname{Im} Ue^{j\omega t}$. Here Im means imaginary component as in Sec. 12, u is a real function of r only, and $U = ue^{j\phi}$ is a complex function of r only. By substituting in the equation of Prob. 16, derive the ordinary differential equation

$$\frac{d^2 U}{dr^2} + \frac{1}{r}\frac{dU}{dr} - j\omega\mu\sigma U = 0.$$

It follows from Prob. 15 of Exercise XVI, with $n = 0$, that $U = c_1 J_0(ar) + c_2 Y_0(ar)$ will be a solution of this equation if $a^2 = -j\omega\mu\sigma$, or $a = j^{3/2}\sqrt{\omega\mu\sigma}$. If $J_0(x)$ is Bessel's function of order zero defined by the series in Prob. 16 of Exercise XVI, any independent solution $Y_0(x)$ becomes infinite for $x = 0$. This leads us to take $c_2 = 0$ in the present case, and to set

$$U = c_1 J_0(j^{3/2}mr),$$

with $m = \sqrt{\omega\mu\sigma}$. Since $J_0(0) = 1$, at the center of the wire $r = 0$ and $J_z = \operatorname{Im} c_1 e^{j\omega t}$. This determines the complex constant c_1. The real functions ber (Bessel real) and bei (Bessel imaginary) such that $J_0(j^{3/2}x) = \operatorname{ber} x + j\operatorname{bei} x$ are tabulated, as well as the functions $M(x)$, $\theta(x)$ derived from them and the relation ber $x + j$ bei $x = Me^{j\theta}$. Hence if $J_z = u_0\sin(\omega t + \beta)$ at the center of the wire, the required current density is

$$J_z = Mu_0\sin(\omega t + \beta + \theta),$$

where M and θ are found from tables of $M(x)$, $\theta(x)$ with $x = mr$ and $m = \sqrt{\omega\mu\sigma}$.

CHAPTER 4

BOUNDARY VALUE PROBLEMS

In Chap. 3 we saw how partial differential equations arose in
the study of heat, electricity, mechanical vibrations, and other
physical phenomena. For some of the equations, or systems of
equations, general solutions containing arbitrary functions could
be found. In such cases, for any particular physical problem it
must be possible to find auxiliary conditions which determine the
proper choice of the arbitrary functions. Such auxiliary relations
are often equations which hold for some fixed time, as initial
conditions for $t = 0$, or equations which hold for certain fixed
points, as boundary conditions for points on the boundary of a
segment or region. We shall refer to any set of auxiliary relations
as *boundary conditions*. Whether or not the appropriate system
of partial differential equations admits of a general solution, in
addition to this system a specific physical situation must imply
enough auxiliary relations so that there is only one set of values
of the unknown variables which satisfy the boundary conditions
as well as the differential equations. A system of differential
equations combined with a set of boundary conditions which
completely determine a solution constitutes a *boundary value
problem*.

It is often possible to solve a boundary value problem in the
form of a series of terms, each of which satisfies some of the
boundary conditions. In the cases discussed, the sum of the
series satisfies these some boundary conditions for arbitrary
values of certain coefficients. And these coefficients may be
determined so that the remaining boundary conditions are
satisfied. This last step frequently depends on Fourier expansions like those of Chap. 2. In this chapter we shall solve

a number of boundary value problems by the process just described.

38. Laplace's Equation

It was shown in Eq. (8), Sec. 26, that the temperature in a steady-state distribution satisfies *Laplace's equation*

$$\frac{\partial^2 U}{\partial x^2} + \frac{\partial^2 U}{\partial y^2} + \frac{\partial^2 U}{\partial z^2} = 0. \tag{1}$$

This equation is also satisfied by the electric potential function in an electrostatic field in space free of charges, Eq. (106) of Sec. 35, with $\rho = 0$, as well as the magnetic potential function in a magnetostatic field, Eq. (107) of Sec. 35. Similarly Eq. (1) holds for gravitational potential in space free of attracting matter. And in irrotational, steady fluid motion the velocity potential is found to satisfy Laplace's equation, Eq. (1). When seeking steady-state or equilibrium solutions whose time derivatives are zero, Eq. (84) of Sec. 31, Eq. (117) of Sec. 36, and the components of Eqs. (113), (118), and (119) of Sec. 36 all reduce to a form equivalent to Eq. (1).

Since the temperatures on the surface of a body determine the steady-state distribution inside, physical considerations suggest that there is just one solution of Eq. (1) taking on given boundary values and it may be proved mathematically that this is the case if the boundary and boundary values are sufficiently regular.

In temperature distribution or potential problems in a plane, taken as the xy plane, Laplace's equation becomes

$$\frac{\partial^2 U}{\partial x^2} + \frac{\partial^2 U}{\partial y^2} = 0. \tag{2}$$

Although the general solution of this equation was found in Prob. 9 of Exercise XV, it is not easy to find what values of the arbitrary functions will satisfy given boundary conditions. Hence it is more convenient to use the method of combining particular solutions described in Sec. 30. We illustrate this for some particular physical situations. For definiteness, we shall use the language of heat flow.

39. Temperatures in a Rectangular Plate

If a homogeneous plane plate has its faces insulated and its edges kept at prescribed temperatures, its steady-state temperatures will be determined. In particular, consider the rectangle $ABCD$ of Fig. 41, with sides AD and BC so long compared with AB and CD that we may treat them as infinite. Let the prescribed boundary temperatures be $0°$ for AD, DC, and BC and $25°$ along AB, and assume

$$AB = 20 \text{ cm.}$$

Take the origin at A, and the axes of x and y along AB and AD, respectively. Then the boundary conditions are

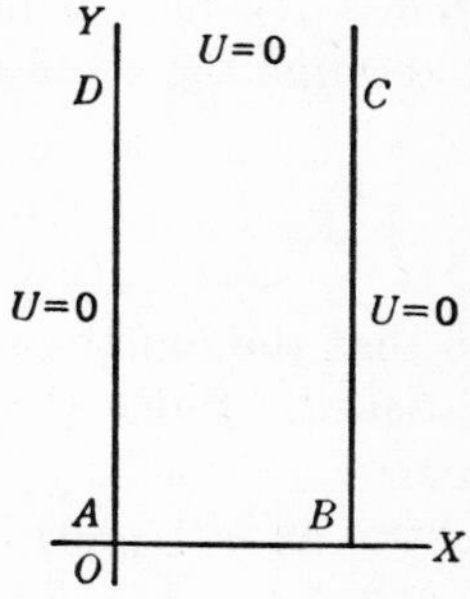

Fig. 41.

$$U(0,y) = 0, \quad U(20,y) = 0, \quad U(x,+\infty) = 0, \quad U(x,0) = 25. \quad (3)$$

Our boundary value problem is to find the solution of Eq. (2) which satisfies the conditions of Eq. (3).

It follows from Eq. (63) of Sec. 30 that Eq. (2) admits

$$U = (c_1 \sin ax + c_2 \cos ax)(c_3 e^{ay} + c_4 e^{-ay}) \quad (4)$$

as a particular solution of the form $X(x) \cdot Y(y)$. By specializing the constants in Eq. (4) we may satisfy the first three conditions of Eq. (3). In fact, if $c_3 = 0$, the second factor will be zero for $y = +\infty$. And if $c_2 = 0$, the first factor will reduce to $c_1 \sin ax$ and thus be zero for $x = 0$. It will also be zero for $x = 20$ if

$$\sin 20a = 0, \quad 20a = n\pi \quad \text{or} \quad a = \frac{n\pi}{20}, \quad (5)$$

where n is any positive integer. If we write B_n for the product

c_1c_4 which goes with a particular n, we have

$$B_n e^{-n\pi y/20} \sin \frac{n\pi x}{20}, \qquad n = 1, 2, 3, \cdots \tag{6}$$

as a set of terms each of which satisfies Eq. (2) and the first three boundary conditions of Eq. (3).

The same will be true of a sum, or infinite series, of such terms. Hence to solve our boundary value problem it merely remains to determine the coefficients of a series

$$U(x,y) = \sum_{n=1}^{\infty} B_n e^{-n\pi y/20} \sin \frac{n\pi x}{20}, \tag{7}$$

so that the fourth and last boundary condition of Eq. (3) will be satisfied. Since $e^0 = 1$, this will be the case if

$$25 = U(x,0) = \sum_{n=1}^{\infty} B_n \sin \frac{n\pi x}{20}, \qquad \text{for } 0 < x < 20. \tag{8}$$

It follows from the discussion of Fourier sine series based on Eqs. (61) and (62) of Sec. 19 that

$$f(x) = \sum_{n=1}^{\infty} b_n \sin \frac{n\pi x}{L}, \qquad \text{for } 0 < x < L \tag{9}$$

for any piecewise regular function $f(x)$, if the b_n are found from

$$b_n = \frac{2}{L} \int_0^L f(x) \sin n\omega x \, dx, \qquad \text{where } \omega = \frac{\pi}{L}. \tag{10}$$

And from Prob. 24 of Exercise IX we may conclude that in particular

$$Ax + B = \frac{1}{\pi} \left(p \sin \frac{\pi x}{L} - \frac{q}{2} \sin \frac{2\pi x}{L} + \frac{p}{3} \sin \frac{3\pi x}{L} \right.$$
$$\left. - \frac{q}{4} \sin \frac{4\pi x}{L} + \cdots \right), \qquad \text{for } \theta < x < L,$$

$$\text{where } p = 4B + 2LA \text{ and } q = 2LA. \tag{11}$$

A comparison of Eq. (8) with Eq. (9) shows that the B_n are the coefficients b_n of the expansion of 25 in a Fourier sine series with frequency $\pi/20 = \pi/L = \omega$ and half-period $L = 20$. The values of b_n could be found from Eq. (10) with $f(x) = 25$. But since $25 = Ax + B$, with $A = 0$, $B = 25$, it is simpler to substitute these values and $L = 20$ in Eq. (11) and so find that $p = 100$, $q = 0$, and

$$25 = \frac{100}{\pi}\left(\sin\frac{\pi x}{20} + \frac{1}{3}\sin\frac{3\pi x}{20} + \frac{1}{5}\sin\frac{5\pi x}{20} + \cdots\right), \quad (12)$$

for $0 < x < 20$.

We may now replace the B_n in Eq. (7) by the values found by identifying Eq. (12) with Eq. (8). An equivalent practical procedure is to multiply each sine term in Eq. (12) by an appropriate exponential factor and thus obtain as the complete solution of our problem

$$U(x,y) = \frac{100}{\pi}\left(e^{-\pi y/20}\sin\frac{\pi x}{20} + \frac{1}{3}e^{-3\pi y/20}\sin\frac{3\pi x}{20}\right.$$
$$\left. + \frac{1}{5}e^{-5\pi y/20}\sin\frac{5\pi x}{20} + \cdots\right). \quad (13)$$

The series may be used for practical computation, provided that y is not too small compared with 20, since the first few terms will then give a good approximation. For example, when $x = 10$, $y = 10$,

$$U(10,10) = \frac{100}{\pi}\left(e^{-\pi/2} - \frac{1}{3}e^{-3\pi/2} + \frac{1}{5}e^{-5\pi/2} - \cdots\right)$$
$$= \frac{100}{\pi}(0.2079 - 0.0030 + 0.0001) = 6.53. \quad (14)$$

Let us next consider the steady-state temperatures for a long rectangle *ABCD* as determined by a different set of boundary conditions. We again take the prescribed temperatures as 0° for *AD*, *DC*, and *BC*. But along *AB* let the temperature be any given function of the distance from *A*, $f(x)$. And let us now assume that $AB = L$ cm. Then

$$U(0,y) = 0, \quad U(L,y) = 0, \quad U(x, +\infty) = 0, \quad U(x,0) = f(x). \quad (15)$$

In place of Eq. (7) we now have

$$U(x,y) = \sum_{n=1}^{\infty} B_n e^{-n\pi y/L} \sin \frac{n\pi x}{L}, \qquad (16)$$

which satisfies Eq. (2) and the first three boundary conditions of Eq. (15). It will also satisfy the last boundary condition if we replace the B_n in Eq. (16) by the b_n of Eq. (9). Except for certain simple forms of $f(x)$ it is necessary to determine these b_n from Eq. (10) by calculations like those made in Secs. 18 and 19.

When $f(x) = Ax + B$ for $0 < x < L$, we may use Eq. (11) to find the desired Fourier sine series as we did in forming Eq. (12).

When $f(x)$ is a single sine term whose frequency equals $n\pi/L$ for some integral value of n, the desired Fourier sine series consists of this one term. For example, suppose that in Eq. (15) $L = 14$, and $f(x) = 5 \sin (3\pi x/7)$. Since $3\pi/7 = 6\pi/14 = n\pi/L$ for $n = 6$, $b_6 = 5$, and all the other coefficients b_n, $n \neq 6$, are zero. Hence the final solution in this case is

$$U(x,y) = 5e^{-3\pi y/7} \sin \frac{3\pi x}{7} \qquad (17)$$

A similar procedure may be used if $f(x)$ is given as a finite sum of sine terms, and the frequency of each term is an integral multiple of π/L. Thus suppose that in Eq. (15) $L = 14$ and

$$f(x) = 8 \sin \pi x - 3 \sin \frac{\pi x}{2}. \qquad (18)$$

Since $L = 14$, we may write $\pi = 14\pi/L$, and $\pi/2 = 7\pi/L$. Thus in this case all the b_n are zero except $b_{14} = 8$ and $b_7 = -3$. And it follows directly from Eq. (18) that the final solution is

$$U(x,y) = 8e^{-\pi y} \sin \pi x - 3e^{-\pi y/2} \sin \frac{\pi x}{2}. \qquad (19)$$

EXERCISE XX

A long rectangular plate has its surfaces insulated and the two long sides, as well as one of the short sides, maintained at 0°C.

Find an expression for the steady-state temperature $U(x,y)$ if

1. The other short side, $y = 0$, is kept at 50° and is 30 cm. long.

2. $U(x,0) = 4x$, and the short side is 6 cm. long.

3. $U(x,0) = 2x - 4$, and the short side is 4 cm. long.

4. $U(x,0) = 100 \sin \dfrac{\pi x}{40}$, and the short side is 40 cm. long.

5. $U(x,0) = 4 \sin \dfrac{\pi x}{3} - 6 \sin \dfrac{\pi x}{5}$ and the short side is 30 cm. long.

6. $U(x,0) = 10, \ 0 < x < 4; \ U(x,0) = 0, \ 4 < x < 8$ and the short side is 8 cm. long.

7. $U(x,0) = c$, and the short side is L cm. long.

8. $U(x,0) = cx$, and the short side is L cm. long.

9. $U(x,0) = c(2x - L)$ and the short side is L cm. long.

10. Verify that Eq. (4) is the only form of those in Eqs. (63) of Sec. 30 for which some choice of constants would make $Y(y) = 0$ for $y = +\infty$, and $X(x) = 0$ for two different values of x, as 0 and L.

11. Let $Z = e^{\pi(-y+ix)/L}$ and $S(Z) = \sum\limits_{n=1}^{\infty} B_n Z^n$. Show that Eq. (16) is equivalent to $U(x,y) = \text{Im } S(Z)$, where Im means imaginary component, as in Sec. 12.

12. In the series which defines $S(Z)$ in Prob. 11, replace the B_n by the values which gave the solution of Prob. 8. And use the Maclaurin's series $\ln (1 + Z) = Z - \dfrac{Z^2}{2} + \dfrac{Z^3}{3} - \dfrac{Z^4}{4} + \cdots$ to show that $S(Z) = \dfrac{2cL}{\pi} \ln (1 + Z)$. Then deduce from Prob. 11 that

$$U(x,y) = \frac{2cL}{\pi} \tan^{-1} \left(\frac{e^{-\pi y/L} \sin \dfrac{\pi x}{L}}{1 + e^{-\pi y/L} \cos \dfrac{\pi x}{L}} \right),$$

the solution in closed form of Prob. 8, where $U(x,0) = cx$.

13. Verify directly that the closed form for $U(x,y)$ in Prob. 12 satisfies all the boundary conditions given in Prob. 8.

14. In the series which defines $S(Z)$ in Prob. 11, replace the B_n by the values which gave the solution of Prob. 7. And use the Maclaurin's series $\frac{1}{2} \ln \frac{1+Z}{1-Z} = Z + \frac{Z^3}{3} + \frac{Z^5}{5} + \cdots$ to show that $S(Z) = \frac{2c}{\pi} \ln \frac{1+Z}{1-Z}$. Then deduce from Prob. 11 that

$$U(x,y) = \frac{2c}{\pi} \tan^{-1}\left(\frac{\sin \dfrac{\pi x}{L}}{\sinh \dfrac{\pi y}{L}}\right),$$

the solution in closed form of Prob. 7, where $U(x,0) = c$.

15. Verify directly that the closed form for $U(x,y)$ in Prob. 14 satisfies all the boundary conditions given in Prob. 7.

16. With the notation of Prob. 11, show that we may write the solution

$$U(x,y) = \operatorname{Im} S(Z) = \frac{1}{2i} S[e^{-i\pi(x+iy)/L}] - \frac{1}{2i} S[e^{i\pi(x-iy)/L}].$$

It follows directly from this and Prob. 9 of Exercise XV that $\operatorname{Im} S(Z)$, and in particular the closed forms of Probs. 12 and 14 satisfy Eq. (2).

17. A rectangular plate is bounded by the lines $x = 0$, $x = L$, $y = 0$, $y = M$. Its surfaces are insulated, and the temperatures along the four edges are given by $U(0,y) = 0$, $U(L,y) = 0$, $U(x,M) = 0$, $U(x,0) = f(x)$. Find particular solutions of Eq. (2) which satisfy the first three boundary conditions by suitably restricting the constants in Eq. (4). And show that a series of such particular solutions

$$U(x,y) = \sum_{n=1}^{\infty} B_n \sin \frac{n\pi x}{L} \sinh \frac{n\pi(y - M)}{L}$$

will satisfy $U(x,0) = f(x)$, and hence solve the boundary value problem, if

$$B_n = -\frac{b_n}{\sinh \dfrac{n\pi M}{L}}$$

where the b_n are the coefficients of Eq. (9) determined from Eq. (10).

18. If the temperatures along the edges of the plate of Prob. 17 are given by $U(0,y) = G(y)$, $U(L,y) = g(y)$, $U(x,M) = F(x)$, $U(x,0) = f(x)$, show that the steady-state temperature $U(x,y)$ may be found by adding together four solutions of Eq. (2)

$$U(x,y) = U_1(x,y) + U_2(x,y) + U_3(x,y) + U_4(x,y),$$

determined by the respective boundary conditions:

$$U_1(0,y) = G(y), \quad U_1(L,y) = 0, \quad U_1(x,M) = 0, \quad U_1(x,0) = 0;$$
$$U_2(0,y) = 0, \quad U_2(L,y) = g(y), \quad U_2(x,M) = 0, \quad U_2(x,0) = 0;$$
$$U_3(0,y) = 0, \quad U_3(L,y) = 0, \quad U_3(x,M) = F(x), \quad U_3(x,0) = 0;$$
$$U_4(0,y) = 0, \quad U_4(L,y) = 0, \quad U_4(x,M) = 0, \quad U_4(x,0) = f(x).$$

A method of finding U_4 is outlined in Prob. 17. And with slight modifications this method may be used to find U_1, U_2, and U_3.

19. In Prob. 17 let $U(x,0) = c$, so that $f(x) = c$. Show that

$$U(x,y) = \frac{4c}{\pi} \sum_{n \text{ odd}} \frac{1}{n} \frac{\sin \dfrac{n\pi x}{L} \sinh \dfrac{n\pi(M - y)}{L}}{\sinh \dfrac{n\pi M}{r}},$$

where n odd means that $n = 1, 3, 5, \cdots$.

20. Deduce the solution of Prob. 7 from Prob. 19 by letting M tend to plus infinity.

40. Temperatures in a Circular Plate

We shall next find the steady-state temperature distribution of a circular plate whose faces are insulated and whose circumference is kept at prescribed temperatures. In particular, let one diameter of the circle be AB, and let the radius $OA = 25$ cm. Let the

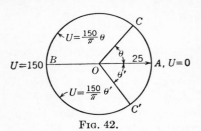

FIG. 42.

temperature be $0°$ at A and $150°$ at B, and increase linearly along the circumference between those points. Thus in Fig. 42 at C on the upper semicircle $U = 150\theta/\pi$, and at C' on the lower semicircle

$$U = 150\theta'/\pi.$$

If we use polar coordinates, $\theta' = -\theta$, and the boundary conditions are

$$U(25,\theta) = \frac{150\theta}{\pi}, \qquad \text{if } 0 < \theta < \pi,$$

$$= -\frac{150\theta}{\pi}, \qquad \text{if } -\pi < \theta < 0. \tag{20}$$

Since U must satisfy Laplace's equation, $U(r,\theta)$ is a solution of

$$\frac{\partial^2 U}{\partial r^2} + \frac{1}{r^2}\frac{\partial^2 U}{\partial \theta^2} + \frac{1}{r}\frac{\partial U}{\partial r} = 0, \tag{21}$$

which is Eq. (2) in polar coordinates by Eq. (86) of Sec. 32.

From Prob. 14 of Exercise XVI, it follows that Eq. (21) admits

$$U = (c_1 r^k + c_2 r^{-k})(c_3 \sin k\theta + c_4 \cos k\theta) \tag{22}$$

as a particular solution of special form.

From the nature of polar coordinates, $U(r,\theta)$ will be periodic of period 2π. Hence we make the particular solutions, Eq. (22), of period 2π by taking $k = n$ where n is zero or a positive integer. And since r^{-n} is infinite for $r = 0$, we take $c_2 = 0$. Also we write A_n for the product $c_1 c_4$ and B_n for the product $c_1 c_3$ which goes with a particular n. Then

$$A_0 \text{ and } A_n r^n \cos n\theta + B_n r^n \sin n\theta, \qquad n = 1,2,3, \cdots \tag{23}$$

is a set of particular solutions of period 2π, and we write

$$U(r,\theta) = A_0 + \sum_{n=1}^{\infty} (A_n r^n \cos n\theta + B_n r^n \sin n\theta). \quad (24)$$

This will satisfy the boundary condition, Eq. (20), if

$$U(25,\theta) = A_0 + \sum_{n+1}^{\infty} (A_n 25^n \cos n\theta + B_n 25^n \sin n\theta). \quad (25)$$

It follows from the discussion of Fourier series based on Eq. (47) of Sec. 18 and Eq. (55) of Sec. 19 that

$$f(x) = a + \sum_{n=1}^{\infty} (a_n \cos n\omega x + b_n \sin n\omega x), \quad \text{for } -L < x < L \quad (26)$$

for any piecewise regular function $f(x)$, if

$$a = \frac{1}{2L} \int_{-L}^{L} f(x)dx, \qquad a_n = \frac{1}{L} \int_{-L}^{L} f(x) \cos n\omega x\, dx,$$

$$b_n = \frac{1}{L} \int_{-L}^{L} f(x) \sin n\omega x\, dx, \qquad \omega = \frac{\pi}{L} \quad \text{or} \quad L = \frac{\pi}{\omega}. \quad (27)$$

A comparison of Eq. (25) with Eq. (26) shows that $A_0 = a$, $A_n 25^n = a_n$, $B_n 25^n = b_n$, the coefficients in the expansion of $U(25,\theta)$ in a Fourier series with frequency $1 = \omega$ and half-period $L = \pi$. The values of a, a_n, b_n could be found from Eqs. (27) and (20) with $f(x) = U(25,x)$.

Since $U(25,\theta)$ is an even function, the b_n and hence the B_n will all be zero. Also a and the a_n may be found from Eq. (56) of Sec. 19. In fact, since the graph of $U(25,\theta)$ against θ differs from Fig. 32 only by a change in the vertical scale, the coefficients may be obtained from those of Eq. (60) of Sec. 19 by multiplication by $150/\pi$. Hence

$$A_0 = a = 75, \quad A_n = 25^{-n}a_n = -\frac{600}{\pi^2 n^2} 25^{-n}, \quad \text{if } n \text{ is odd.} \quad (28)$$

Thus the solution of our problem in series form is

$$U(r,\theta) = 75 - \frac{600}{\pi^2} \left(\frac{r}{25} \cos \theta + \frac{r^3}{3^2 \cdot 25^3} \cos 3\theta \right.$$
$$\left. + \frac{r^5}{5^2 \cdot 25^5} \cos 5\theta + \cdots \right). \quad (29)$$

Let us next consider the steady-state temperature for a circular plate as determined by a different boundary condition. We now assume that the radius of the plate is R cm. And on the circumference let the prescribed temperature be any given function of the polar angle θ, so that $U(R,\theta) = f(\theta)$. Then Eq. (24) still applies, but in place of Eq. (25) we now have

$$f(\theta) = A_0 + \sum_{n=1}^{\infty} (A_n R^n \cos n\theta + B_n R^n \sin n\theta). \quad (30)$$

Comparing with Eq. (26), with $x = \theta, \omega = 1, L = \pi$, we find that

$$A_0 = a, \qquad A_n = R^{-n} a_n, \qquad B_n = R^{-n} b_n. \quad (31)$$

The Fourier coefficients a, a_n, b_n must be determined from Eq. (27) with $\omega = 1, L = \pi$, unless $f(\theta)$ has one of the special properties mentioned in Sec. 19 which permit the use of the simpler formulas there derived. Once a, a_n, b_n are known, we may find A_0, A_n, B_n from Eq. (31). Substitution of these values in Eq. (24) then leads to the solution of the problem.

EXERCISE XXI

Find $U(r,\theta)$, the steady-state temperature distribution of a circular plate of radius R whose surfaces are insulated, if

1. $R = 9$ and $U(9,\theta) = 1$, if $0 < \theta < \pi$, and $= 0$, if $-\pi < \theta < 0$.
2. $R = 20$ and $U(20,\theta) = 80 \sin \theta + 800 \sin 2\theta$.
3. $R = 1$ and $U(1,\theta) = 2\theta, \qquad 0 < \theta < 2\pi$.
4. $R = 10$ and $U(10,\theta) = 3,000 \cos (3\theta - 25°)$.

5. A plate in the form of a circular sector is bounded by the lines $\theta = 0, \theta = \alpha, r = R$. Its surfaces are insulated, and the temperatures along the boundary are $U(r,0) = 0, U(r,\alpha) = 0$,

$U(R,\theta) = f(\theta)$. By restricting the constants in Eq. (22), deduce the particular solution that satisfies the first two conditions, $C_n r^{\pi n/\alpha} \sin \dfrac{\pi n \theta}{\alpha}$.

6. Using a series of the particular solutions of Prob. 5, find $U(r,\theta)$ if $\alpha = \pi/3$ and $f(\theta) = 100$.

7. A plate in the form of a ring is bounded by the lines $r = 2$, $r = 4$. Its surfaces are insulated, and the temperatures along the boundary are $U(2,\theta) = 10 \sin \theta + 6 \cos \theta$,

$$U(4,\theta) = 17 \sin \theta + 15 \cos \theta.$$

Using a series of particular solutions of the appropriate form here $(C_n r^n + D_n r^{-n}) \cos n\theta + (E_n r^n + F_n r^{-n}) \sin n\theta$, find the steady-state temperature in the ring, $U(r,\theta)$.

8. Let $U(r,\theta)$ be the steady-state temperature distribution of a circular plate of radius R whose surfaces are insulated. If $U(R,\theta) = f(\theta)$, show that the solution may be written as

$$U(r,\theta) = \frac{1}{\pi} \int_{-\pi}^{\pi} \left[\frac{1}{2} + \sum_{n=1}^{\infty} \left(\frac{r}{R}\right)^n \cos n(\theta - t) \right] f(t)\,dt.$$

9. If Re means real component as in Sec. 12, show that $\left(\dfrac{r}{R}\right)^n \cos n(\theta - t) = \mathrm{Re}\left(\dfrac{z}{Z}\right)^n$, if $z = re^{i\theta}$, $Z = Re^{it}$. Hence the bracket in Prob. 8 is the real component of the geometric series $\dfrac{1}{2} + \sum\limits_{n=1}^{\infty} \left(\dfrac{z}{Z}\right)^n = \dfrac{Z + z}{Z - z}$. Use this fact to reduce the solution of Prob. 8 to the form

$$U(r,\theta) = \frac{1}{2} \int_{-\pi}^{\pi} \frac{R^2 - r^2}{R^2 - 2Rr \cos(t - \theta) + r^2} f(t)\,dt.$$

This expression for the solution of Laplace's equation, Eq. (21), in terms of prescribed values on the boundary of a circular region is known as *Poisson's integral*.

10. Use Prob. 9 to show that if $U(R,\theta) = c$ for $0 < \theta < \pi$ and

$= 0$ for $-\pi < \theta < 0$, the solution in closed form is

$$U(r,\theta) = \frac{c}{2} + \frac{c}{\pi} \tan^{-1}\left[\frac{2rR \sin \theta}{R^2 - r^2}\right].$$

11. Use Prob. 9 to show that if $U(R,\theta) = c$ for $0 < \theta < \pi$ and $= -c$ for $-\pi < \theta < 0$, the solution in closed form is

$$U(r,\theta) = \frac{2c}{\pi} \tan^{-1}\left[\frac{2rR \sin \theta}{R^2 - r^2}\right]$$

12. Use Prob. 10 to solve Prob. 1 in closed form, and show that this is equivalent to the series found in Prob. 1. HINT: Take imaginary components of the Maclaurin's series in $z = re^{i\theta}$,

$$\frac{1}{2} \ln \frac{R + z}{R - z} = \frac{z}{R} + \frac{z^3}{3R^3} + \frac{z^5}{5R^5} + \cdots$$

to deduce that

$$\tan^{-1}\left[\frac{2rR \sin \theta}{R^2 - r^2}\right] = \frac{r}{R} \sin \theta + \frac{r^3}{3R^3} \sin 3\theta + \frac{r^5}{5R^5} \sin 5\theta \cdots$$

41. Cooling of a Rod

Consider the changing temperatures of a thin uniform rod, AB in Fig. 43, whose sides are insulated. Let $U(x,t)$ denote the

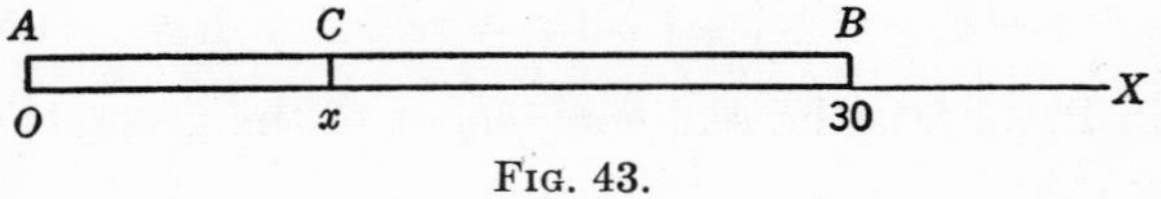

FIG. 43.

temperature of the cross section C for which $AC = x$ at time t. It was shown in Eq. (5) of Sec. 26, that

$$\frac{\partial U}{\partial t} = a^2 \frac{\partial^2 U}{\partial x^2}. \tag{32}$$

In particular let AB be 30 cm. long, of material for which the thermal diffusivity $a^2 = 2$ cm.^{2}/sec. Suppose that originally all points of the rod were at $15°$ but that at time $t = 0$ the ends of the rod A and B had their temperatures suddenly changed to $0°$

and kept at this temperature. We wish to find $U(x,t)$ for any later time $t > 0$. The initial and boundary conditions are

$$U(x,0) = 15, \qquad U(0,t) = 0, \qquad U(30,t) = 0. \qquad (33)$$

Thus our boundary value problem is to find the solution of Eq. (32) which also satisfies the conditions (33).

It follows from Prob. 1 of Exercise XVI that Eq. (32) admits

$$U = (c_3 \sin bx + c_4 \cos bx)e^{-a^2b^2t} \qquad (34)$$

as a particular solution of the form $X(x) \cdot T(t)$. The second condition of Eq. (33) will be satisfied if $c_4 = 0$. And the third condition will be satisfied if

$$\sin 30b = 0, \quad 30b = n\pi, \quad \text{or} \quad b = \frac{n\pi}{30} \text{ and } a^2b^2 = \frac{n^2\pi^2}{450}, \qquad (35)$$

where n is any positive integer. We write B_n for the constant c_3 which goes with a particular n, and have

$$B_n \sin \frac{n\pi x}{30} e^{-n^2\pi^2 t/450}, \qquad n = 1,2,3, \cdots \qquad (36)$$

as a set of terms each of which satisfies Eq. (32) and the last two conditions of Eq. (33). Hence we put

$$U(x,t) = \sum_{n=1}^{\infty} B_n \sin \frac{n\pi x}{30} e^{-n^2\pi^2 t/450}. \qquad (37)$$

The remaining initial condition of Eq. (33) will be satisfied if

$$15 = U(x,0) = \sum_{n=1}^{\infty} B_n \sin \frac{n\pi x}{30}, \qquad \text{for } 0 < x < 30. \qquad (38)$$

A comparison of this with Eq. (9) shows that the B_n are the coefficients b_n of the expansion of 15 in a Fourier sine series with frequency $\pi/30 = \pi/L = \omega$ and half-period $L = 30$. The values of b_n could be found from Eq. (10) with $f(x) = 15$. But it is simpler to put $A = 0$, $B = 15$, $L = 30$ in Eq. (11) and so find that $p = 60$, $q = 0$, and

$$15 = \frac{60}{\pi} \left(\sin \frac{\pi x}{30} + \frac{1}{3} \sin \frac{3\pi x}{30} + \frac{1}{5} \sin \frac{5\pi x}{30} + \cdots \right),$$

$$\text{for } 0 < x < 30. \quad (39)$$

We must now replace the B_n in Eq. (37) by the values obtained when we identify Eq. (39) with Eq. (38). The result is

$$U(x,t) = \frac{60}{\pi} \left(\sin \frac{\pi x}{30} e^{-\pi^2 t/450} + \frac{1}{3} \sin \frac{3\pi x}{30} e^{-\pi^2 t/50} + \cdots \right). \quad (40)$$

For large values of t this series converges very rapidly owing to the exponential terms. In fact, if t exceeds 20, the first two terms give a result correct to within one part in ten thousand.

The process used above requires modification if the ends of the rod are suddenly changed to fixed temperatures different from zero. We illustrate the revised procedure by solving the following problem.

Suppose that the rod of Fig. 43 has end A kept at 30° and end B kept at 120° until temperatures indistinguishable from the steady state are reached. We again assume $AB = 30$ cm. and $a^2 = 2$ cm.²/sec. At some later time, let us suddenly lower the temperature of A to 15° and that of B to 45°, and from then on maintain these temperatures. We wish to find $U(x,t)$ for $t > 0$, where t is measured from the sudden change.

We must make use of the steady-state solution of Eq. (32). Since this is independent of t, it will be a solution of

$$\frac{d^2 U}{dx^2} = 0, \quad \text{or} \quad U = c_1 x + c_2. \quad (41)$$

We first find constants c_1 and c_2 such that this takes on the original end values, 30 at A, $x = 0$, and 120 at B, $x = 30$. Hence

$$30 = c_2, \; 120 = 30c_1 + c_2 \quad \text{and} \quad c_2 = 30, \; c_1 = 3. \quad (42)$$

This shows that $3x + 30$ was the temperature before the sudden change and, for our problem, the initial condition is

$$U(x,0) = 3x + 30. \quad (43)$$

The temperatures for our problem will approach the steady-state solution for the changed end values, 15 at A, $x = 0$, and 45 at B, $x = 30$. The values of c_1 and c_2 which make the U of Eq. (41) take on these values are found from

$$15 = c_2, \quad 45 = 30c_1 + c_2 \qquad \text{to be} \qquad c_2 = 15, \; c_1 = 1. \quad (44)$$

This shows that the steady-state solution

$$U_S = x + 15 \qquad (45)$$

satisfies the changed boundary conditions for our problem

$$U(0,t) = 15, \qquad U(30,t) = 45. \qquad (46)$$

Mathematically considered, our problem is to find a solution of Eq. (32) that satisfies the initial condition (43) and the boundary conditions (46). We transform this to a problem with end values zero by putting

$$U = U_S + U_T = x + 15 + U_T. \qquad (47)$$

This makes the new function U_T satisfy the relation

$$U_T = U - U_S = U - x - 15. \qquad (48)$$

Since U and U_S are each solutions of Eq. (32), their difference U_T is also a solution. It follows from the way in which U_S was determined, and may be verified from Eqs. (48) and (46) that

$$U_T(0,t) = 0, \qquad U_T(30,t) = 0. \qquad (49)$$

Also from Eqs. (48) and (43) we may deduce that

$$U_T(x,0) = U(x,0) - x - 15 = 2x + 15. \qquad (50)$$

The problem of finding $U_T(x,t)$, a solution of Eq. (32) which satisfies the initial condition (50) and the boundary conditions (49), is similar in type to the first problem solved in this section. To solve it, we begin with the relation similar to Eq. (37),

$$U_T(x,t) = \sum_{n=1}^{\infty} B_n \sin \frac{n\pi x}{30} \, e^{-n^2\pi^2 t/450}. \qquad (51)$$

This satisfies the differential equation (32) and the end conditions (49). The initial condition (50) will also be satisfied if

$$2x + 15 = U_T(x,0) = \sum_{n=1}^{\infty} B_n \sin \frac{n\pi x}{30}. \tag{52}$$

The coefficients of this Fourier sine series of frequency $\pi/30$ and half-period $L = 30$ may be found by putting $A = 2$, $B = 15$, $L = 30$ in Eq. (11). This makes $p = 180$, $q = 120$, so that

$$B_n = \frac{180}{\pi n} \qquad \text{for } odd\ n = 1,3,5, \cdots$$

and

$$B_n = \frac{120}{\pi n} \qquad \text{for } even\ n = 2,4,6, \cdots. \tag{53}$$

On substituting these values in Eq. (51) we obtain the transient part of the solution, U_T. And from this and Eq. (47) we find that

$$U(x,t) = x + 15 + \frac{1}{\pi} \left(180 \sin \frac{\pi x}{30}\, e^{-\pi^2 t/450} - 60 \sin \frac{2\pi x}{30}\, e^{-2\pi^2 t/225} \right.$$
$$\left. + 60 \sin \frac{3\pi x}{30}\, e^{-\pi^2 t/50} - \cdots \right). \tag{54}$$

Let us outline our methods of solution in more general terms. First suppose that originally the temperature was some given function of the distance, $g(x)$, and that at time $t = 0$ the ends of the rod A and B had their temperatures suddenly changed to $0°$ and kept at this temperature. We now assume that $AB = L$ cm. and write a^2 for the thermal diffusivity. The boundary conditions now are

$$U(x,0) = g(x), \qquad U(0,t) = 0, \qquad U(L,t) = 0. \tag{55}$$

And in place of Eq. (37) in this case we have

$$U(x,t) = \sum_{n=1}^{\infty} B_n \sin \frac{n\pi x}{L}\, e^{-a^2 n^2 \pi^2 t/L^2}, \tag{56}$$

which satisfies Eq. (32) and the last two boundary conditions of
Eq. (55).   It will also satisfy the last boundary condition if we
replace the B_n in Eq. (56) by the b_n of Eq. (9) with $f(x) = g(x)$.
We determine these b_n from Eq. (10) or one of the alternatives to
it mentioned in Sec. 39.

Next consider the same rod of length L with initial temperature
$g(x)$, but assume that at time $t = 0$ the end A had its temperature changed to $r°$ and that the end B had its temperature $s°$,
and both ends kept at the new temperatures.   Here the boundary
conditions are

$$U(x,0) = g(x), \qquad U(0,t) = r, \qquad U(L,t) = s. \tag{57}$$

We transform this to a problem involving U_T by writing

$$U = U_S + U_T = \frac{s - r}{L} x + r + U_T, \tag{58}$$

in which we have replaced U_S by an expression like that in Eq.
(41) with constants such that the end conditions of Eq. (57) are
satisfied.   The boundary conditions for U_T in this case are

$$U_T(x,0) = g(x) - \frac{s - r}{L} x - r, \; U_T(0,y) = 0, \; U_T(L,t) = 0. \tag{59}$$

The determination of $U_T(x,t)$ from these conditions and Eq. (32)
is similar in type to the problem of finding $U(x,t)$ from Eqs. (55)
and (32).   Thus we may find U_T from a series like that in Eq.
(56),

$$U_T(x,t) = \sum_{n=1}^{\infty} B_n \sin \frac{n\pi x}{L} e^{-a^2 n^2 \pi^2 t / L^2}. \tag{60}$$

This will satisfy the first condition of Eq. (59) if we replace the
B_n in Eq. (60) by the b_n of Eq. (9) with $f(x) = g(x) - \dfrac{s - r}{L} x - r$.
We determine these b_n from Eq. (10) or one of the alternatives to
it mentioned in Sec. 39.   We may then insert the values of B_n in

$$U(x,t) = \frac{s - r}{L} x + r + \sum_{n=1}^{\infty} B_n \sin \frac{n\pi x}{L} e^{-a^2 n^2 \pi^2 t / L^2}, \tag{61}$$

obtained from Eqs. (58) and (60), to give the solution of the problem with boundary conditions (57).

EXERCISE XXII

The ends A and B of a rod 50 cm. long have their temperatures kept at 0° and 100°, respectively, until the temperatures are indistinguishable from those for the steady state. At some time after this, there is a sudden change. Find the temperature of any point in the rod, $U(x,t)$, as a function of x cm., the distance from A, and t sec., the time elapsed after the sudden change, if the new temperatures maintained at A and B are

1. 0° at A, 0° at B.   **2.** 100° at A, 100° at B.
3. 0° at A, 50° at B.   **4.** 50° at A, 0° at B.
5. 25° at A, 75° at B.   **6.** 50° at A, 150° at B.

7. In Prob. 1 compute the temperature at the mid-point 2 min. after the sudden change if the rod is made of silver for which $a^2 = 1.74$.

8. A rod 80 cm. long has one half its length at 0°, and the other half at 50°. If the sides are suddenly insulated, the temperature of the hot end reduced to 0°, and from then on the two ends are kept at 0°, find the temperature of the rod $U(x,t)$ as a function of the distance from the end originally at 0° and the time after the sudden change.

9. In Prob. 8 compute the temperature for a point 20 cm. from the end originally at 0°, 1 hr. after the sudden change if the rod is made of wrought iron for which $a^2 = 0.173$.

If the rod is made of glass for which $a^2 = 0.00571$, compute the temperature at a point 5 cm. from A, 3 hr. after the sudden change

10. For the rod of Prob. 2.   **11.** For the rod of Prob. 6.

In Prob. 5 compute the temperature at a point 12.5 cm. from A, 5 min. after the sudden change if

12. The rod is made of silver for which $a^2 = 1.74$.
13. The rod is made of wrought iron for which $a^2 = 0.173$.
14. The rod is made of glass for which $a^2 = 0.00571$.

15. Evaluate the result of Prob. 5 for $x = 25$. Note that

$U(25,t)$ does not depend on t or a^2 in this case. This shows that at the mid-point of the rod of Prob. 5 the temperature does not change with the time and is also independent of the kind of homogeneous material out of which the rod is made.

16. The ends of a rod 60 cm. long are insulated so that $\frac{\partial U}{\partial x} = 0$ at $x = 0$ and $\frac{\partial U}{\partial x} = 0$ at $x = 60$. Show that for $n = 0, 1, 2, 3, \cdots, A_n \cos \frac{n\pi x}{60} e^{-a^2 n^2 \pi^2 t/3,600}$ is a particular solution of Eq. (32) satisfying the end conditions.

17. Suppose that the rod of Prob. 16 had its end points kept at $0°$ and $180°$ until the steady state was approximated and that the ends were then suddenly insulated at $t = 0$. Derive the proper initial condition $U(x,0) = 3x$ and, using a series of particular solutions of the type found in Prob. 16, find $U(x,t)$. Take $a^2 = 2$.

18. A rod AB is 60 cm. long, of material for which $a^2 = 2$. Originally all of its points were at $0°$. From $t = 0$ on, heat was supplied to the rod through the end A at a constant rate of $120KA$ cal./sec. By Sec. 26, $-KA \frac{\partial U}{\partial x} = 120KA$, so that $\frac{\partial U}{\partial x} = -120$ at $x = 0$ for $t > 0$. And at $t = 0$ the end B was suddenly insulated, so that $\frac{\partial U}{\partial x} = 0$ at $x = 60$ for $t > 0$. Show that $A(x^2 + 2a^2t) + Bx$ is a particular solution of Eq. (32), and that it will satisfy the end conditions if $A = 1$, $B = -120$. Now put $U(x,t) = x^2 - 120x + 4t + U_1(x,t)$ and find $U_1(x,t)$ by the method of Prob. 17.

19. A rod AB is 20 cm. long. The end A is kept at $0°$ so that $U(0,t) = 0$. The end B is insulated so that $\frac{\partial U}{\partial x} = 0$ at $x = 20$. Show that for $n = 1, 3, 5, \cdots$, any odd integer,

$$B_n \sin \frac{n\pi x}{40} e^{-a^2 n^2 \pi^2 t/1,600}$$

is a particular solution of Eq. (32) satisfying the end conditions.

20. Suppose that just before the end conditions of Prob. 19

were imposed the temperature distribution was $U(x,0) = 5x$. Using a series of particular solutions of the type found in Prob. 19, find $U(x,t)$.   The coefficients in the expansion of $5x$ in an odd-harmonic sine series of period 80, valid for $0 < x < 20$ can be found from integrals taken over this interval.   This follows from an argument like that at the end of Sec. 19, based on consideration of an odd, odd-harmonic function of period 80 equal to $5x$ for $0 < x < 20$.

21. A rod 40 cm. long has its mid-point raised to 100° while the ends are at 0° until each half approximates the steady state. The source of heat is then removed from the mid-point and this is insulated.   Find the temperature $U(x,t)$.

22. From physical considerations, deduce that the solution of Prob. 21 is symmetrical about the mid-point and gives the solution of Prob. 20 when x is restricted to values between 0 and 20.

23. The equation for the flow of heat in a rod with radiating surfaces is $\dfrac{\partial U}{\partial t} = a^2 \dfrac{\partial^2 U}{\partial x^2} - b^2(U - U_0)$.   Show that if $U_0 = 0$, for any value of k, $e^{-(a^2k^2+b^2)t}\,(A \cos kx + B \sin kx)$ is a particular solution.

24. Find the temperature $U(x,t)$ of the radiating rod of Prob. 23 if $U_0 = 0$, $U(0,t) = 0$, $U(10,t) = 0$, $U(x,0) = x$.   HINT: Use a sum of particular solutions with $A = 0$, $k = n\pi/10$.   Take $a^2 = 2$, $b^2 = 5$.

25. Show that $U = U_0 + e^{-b^2t}V$ will be a solution of the equation of Prob. 23 if $V(x,t)$ is a solution of Eq. (32).   Use this to check Prob. 24.

26. The *Fourier integral* of Sec. 22 may be used to combine particular solutions of Eq. (32).   With $b = u$, $c_3 = \cos uv$, $c_4 = \sin uv$ the particular solution in Eq. (34) becomes

$$\cos u(x - v)e^{-a^2u^2t}.$$

Equation (111) of Sec. 22 suggests that we form the expression

$$U(x,t) = \frac{1}{\pi} \int_0^\infty du \int_{-\infty}^\infty f(v)e^{-a^2u^2t} \cos u(x - v)dv.$$

If $f(x)$ is such that differentiation inside the double infinite integral is legitimate, show that this will be a solution of Eq. (32). Also show that if $t = 0$, the expression is equivalent to the right member of Eq. (111) of Sec. 22, and thus reduces to $f(x)$.

Thus for suitable $f(x)$ defined for $-\infty < x < \infty$, the equation just written gives the solution of the boundary value problem made up of Eq. (32) and $U(x,0) = f(x)$ for $-\infty < x < \infty$.

27. By using contour integration in the complex plane, and the fact that $\int_0^\infty e^{-x^2} dx = \frac{1}{2}\sqrt{\pi}$, it may be shown that the definite integral $\int_0^\infty e^{-k^2u^2} \cos bu\, du = \frac{1}{2a}\sqrt{\pi}e^{-b^2/4k^2}$. Invert the order of integration in Prob. 26, and use the result just stated to evaluate the inner integral. By introducing a new variable $w = \dfrac{v - x}{2a\sqrt{t}}$, reduce the result to the form

$$U(x,t) = \frac{1}{\sqrt{\pi}} \int_{-\infty}^\infty f(x + 2aw\sqrt{t})e^{-w^2}\, dw.$$

28. By differentiating under the integral sign, and using integration by parts, show that the expression in Prob. 27 satisfies Eq. (32). Also show that it makes $U(x,0) = f(x)$ for

$$-\infty < x < \infty.$$

The operations used are legitimate for some $f(x)$, like that of Prob. 29, for which the Fourier integral used in Prob. 26 diverges.

29. An infinite rod has its initial temperature $U(x,0) = f(x)$, where $f(x) = r$ if $x < 0$ and $f(x) = s$ if $x > 0$. Use Probs. 28 and 27 to find $U(x,t)$ for $t > 0$. And show that

$$U(x,t) = \frac{r}{\sqrt{\pi}} \int_{-\infty}^{-\frac{x}{2a\sqrt{t}}} e^{-w^2}\, dw + \frac{s}{\sqrt{\pi}} \int_{-\frac{x}{2a\sqrt{}}}^\infty e^{-w^2}\, dw \text{ for } t > 0.$$

30. The *error function* is defined by erf $x = \dfrac{2}{\sqrt{\pi}} \int_0^x e^{-w^2}\, dw$. As stated in Prob. 27, erf $\infty = 1$. Show that the result of Prob.

29 may be written in the form

$$U(x,t) = \frac{r+s}{2} + \frac{(s-r)}{2} \operatorname{erf}\left(\frac{x}{2a\sqrt{t}}\right) \qquad \text{if } x > 0$$

and

$$U(x,t) = \frac{r+s}{2} + \frac{(r-s)}{2} \operatorname{erf}\left(\frac{x}{2a\sqrt{t}}\right) \qquad \text{if } x < 0.$$

31. A semiinfinite rod has its initial temperature $U(x,0) = c$, and $U(0,t) = 0$ for $t > 0$. Find $U(x,t)$ for $x > 0$, $t > 0$. HINT: Put $s = c$, $r = -c$ in Prob. 30 to get $U(x,t) = c \operatorname{erf}\left(\frac{x}{2a\sqrt{t}}\right)$.

32. A very long rod has $a^2 = 0.04$. Assume that the rod is on the x axis, and that at $t = 0$ the temperature was $20°$ for $x < 0$ and $100°$ for $x > 0$. Use Prob. 30 and tables of erf x to compute U at a point 1.2 m. to the right of the origin after 100 hr., or $U(120, 360,000)$.

42. The Long Transmission Line

In Eq. (96) of Sec. 33 we showed that the equations governing the propagation of potential $e(x,t)$ and current $i(x,t)$ along an

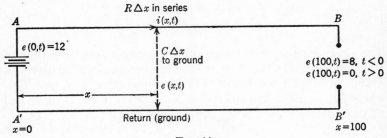

Fig. 44.

electrical cable having a series resistance of R ohms per mile and a shunt capacitance of C farads per mile are the *telegraph equations*

$$-\frac{\partial e}{\partial x} = Ri, \qquad -\frac{\partial i}{\partial x} = C\frac{\partial e}{\partial t}, \qquad \frac{\partial^2 e}{\partial x^2} = RC\frac{\partial e}{\partial t}. \qquad (62)$$

The third relation has the same form as Eq. (32). When boundary conditions for e are known, this equation may be solved by the methods given in Sec. 41. And after e has been found, we may obtain the value of i from the first relation of Eq. (62).

As an example, let us consider a line AB 100 miles long for which $R = 0.1$ ohms per mile and $C = 2$ microfarads per mile. Then $C = 2 \times 10^{-6}$ farad per mile, and in Eq. (62) the coefficient $RC = 2 \times 10^{-7}$. Suppose that originally the line was under steady-state conditions, with potential 12 volts at A, $x = 0$, and 8 volts at B, $x = 100$. At some instant, taken as $t = 0$ in Fig. 44, the terminal B is suddenly grounded, reducing its potential to 0 volts. But the potential at A is kept at 12 volts. We wish to find the potential $e(x,t)$ and the current $i(x,t)$ at any point of the line $0 < x < 100$, and at any time subsequent to the grounding, $t > 0$.

The steady-state solution of

$$\frac{\partial^2 e}{\partial x^2} = RC\,\frac{\partial e}{\partial t}, \qquad \text{or} \qquad \frac{\partial e}{\partial t} = \frac{1}{RC}\,\frac{\partial^2 e}{\partial x^2}, \tag{63}$$

will be independent of t and hence a solution of

$$\frac{d^2 e}{dx^2} = 0, \qquad \text{or} \qquad e = c_1 x + c_2. \tag{64}$$

This will take on the original end values if

$$12 = c_2,\ 8 = 100c_1 + c_2 \qquad \text{and} \qquad c_2 = 12,\ c_1 = -0.04. \tag{65}$$

This shows that the emf just before the sudden change was

$$e(x,0) = -0.04x + 12. \tag{66}$$

After the sudden change, as t increases, the emf will approach the steady-state solution for the changed end values

$$e(0,t) = 12, \qquad e(100,t) = 0. \tag{67}$$

The e of Eq. (64) will take on these values if

$$12 = c_2,\ 0 = 100c_1 + c_2 \qquad \text{and} \qquad c_2 = 12,\ c_1 = -0.12. \tag{68}$$

This shows that the steady-state solution of Eq. (63)

$$e_S = -0.12x + 12 \qquad (69)$$

satisfies the boundary conditions on e for our problem, Eq. (67).

For the potential $e(x,t)$, our boundary value problem is to find a solution of Eq. (63) that satisfies the initial condition Eq. (66) and the boundary conditions, Eqs. (67). We transform this to a problem with end values zero as we did in Eq. (47). Here we set

$$e = e_S + e_T = -0.12x + 12 + e_T. \qquad (70)$$

This makes the transient effect e_T satisfy the relation

$$e_T = e + 0.12x - 12. \qquad (71)$$

As the difference of two solutions of Eq. (63), e_T is also a solution. From the way we found e_S, or from Eqs. (71) and (67), we see that

$$e_T(0,t) = 0, \qquad e_T(100,t) = 0. \qquad (72)$$

And from Eqs. (71) and (66) we may deduce the initial condition

$$e_T(x,0) = e(x,0) + 0.12x - 12 = 0.08x \qquad (73)$$

To obtain a series for e_T, we set $a^2 = 1/RC$ and $L = 100$ in the right member of Eq. (60). We also write ϵ for the exponential base to avoid confusion with e for emf. This leads to

$$e_T(x,t) = \sum_{n=1}^{\infty} B_n \sin \frac{n\pi x}{100} \, \epsilon^{-n^2\pi^2 t/10^4 RC}, \qquad (74)$$

which satisfies Eq. (63) and the boundary conditions (72). It will also satisfy the remaining initial condition (73) if

$$0.08x = e_T(x,0) + \sum_{n=1}^{\infty} B_n \sin \frac{n\pi x}{100}, \qquad \text{for } 0 < x < 100. \qquad (75)$$

This requires the B_n to be the coefficients b_n of the expansion of $0.08x$ in a Fourier sine series with frequency $\pi/100 = \pi/L$ and half-period $L = 100$. The values of b_n could be found from Eq. (10) with $f(x) = 0.08x$. But it is simpler to put $A = 0.08$, $B = 0$,

$L = 100$ in Eq. (11) and thus find that $p = 16$, $q = 16$, and

$$B_n = b_n = (-1)^{n+1} \frac{16}{\pi n}. \tag{76}$$

Now put these values in Eq. (74), with $RC = 2 \times 10^{-7}$, and substitute the series in Eq. (70). This gives the solution for e,

$$e(x,t) = -0.12x + 12 - \frac{16}{\pi} \sum_{n=1}^{\infty} (-1)^n \frac{1}{n} \sin \frac{n\pi x}{100} \epsilon^{-500n^2\pi^2 t}. \tag{77}$$

The current i may be found from the first relation of Eq. (62), written in the form

$$i = -\frac{1}{R} \frac{\partial e}{\partial x}. \tag{78}$$

We find $\dfrac{\partial e}{\partial x}$ from Eq. (77), and put the result in Eq. (78) with $R = 0.1$. This gives the solution for i,

$$i(x,t) = 1.2 + 1.6 \sum_{n=1}^{\infty} (-1)^n \cos \frac{n\pi x}{100} \epsilon^{-500n^2\pi^2 t}. \tag{79}$$

The presence of the exponential terms in Eqs. (77) and (79) makes both series converge rapidly for $t > 0$, unless t is very small. For $t = 0$ and $0 < x < 100$, the series in Eq. (77) equals the initial values given by Eq. (66), and these values are approached by $e(x,t)$ as $t \to 0$. But for $t = 0$ and $0 < x < 100$, the series in Eq. (79) oscillates, and no values are approached by $i(x,t)$ as $t \to 0$. This indetermination of $i(x,0)$ is due to the discontinuity of our boundary conditions. For $t = 0$ and $x = 100$ the series in Eq. (79) does diverge to plus infinity, showing that $i(100,t)$ is very large for very small values of t.

Let us outline the method of solution in more general terms. Suppose that originally for a line AB, S miles long, the potential was some given function of the distance, $g(x)$, and that at time $t = 0$ the terminal A had its potential changed to r volts and that the terminal B had its potential changed to s volts, and that both terminals were maintained at the new voltages. Here the boundary conditions are

$$e(x,0) = g(x), \qquad e(0,t) = r, \qquad e(S,t) = s. \qquad (80)$$

We transform this to a problem involving e_T by writing

$$e = e_S + e_T = \frac{s - r}{S} x + r + e_T, \qquad (81)$$

in which we have replaced e_S by an expression like that in Eq. (64) with constants such that the end conditions of Eq. (80) are satisfied. The boundary conditions for e_T then become

$$e_T(x,0) = g(x) - \frac{s - r}{S} x - r, \quad e_T(0,t) = 0, \quad e_T(S,t) = 0. \qquad (82)$$

We may find e_T from a series like that in Eq. (74),

$$e_T(x,t) = \sum_{n=1}^{\infty} B_n \sin \frac{n\pi x}{S} \, \epsilon^{-n^2\pi^2 t/RCS^2}, \qquad (83)$$

which satisfies Eq. (63) and the last two boundary conditions of Eq. (82). It will also satisfy the first condition of Eq. (82) if we replace the B_n in Eq. (83) by the coefficients b_n of the expansion of

$f(x) = g(x) - \dfrac{s - r}{S} x - r$ in a Fourier sine series of half-period S.

We determine these b_n from Eq. (10) or one of the alternatives to it mentioned in Sec. 39. We may then insert the values of B_n in

$$e(x,t) = \frac{s - r}{S} x + r + \sum_{n=1}^{\infty} B_n \cos \frac{n\pi x}{S} \, \epsilon^{-n^2\pi^2 t/RCS^2}. \qquad (84)$$

and in the relation obtained from it and Eq. (78)

$$i(x,t) = \frac{r - s}{RS} - \frac{\pi}{RS} \sum_{n=1}^{\infty} nB_n \cos \frac{n\pi x}{S} \, \epsilon^{-n^2\pi^2 t/RCS^2}. \qquad (85)$$

Equations (84) and (85) then give the solution of Eqs. (62) and the boundary conditions (80).

EXERCISE XXIII

The length of an ocean cable is $3,142 = 1,000\pi$ miles. The series resistance is 3 ohms per mile, the shunt capacitance is $\frac{1}{3}$ microfarad per mile or $\frac{1}{3} \times 10^{-6}$ farad per mile. Assuming that Eqs. (62) apply, find $e(x,t)$ and $i(x,t)$ where x miles is the distance from one end and t sec. is the time after both ends were suddenly grounded if initially the potential was

1. $e(x,0) = E \sin \dfrac{x}{500}$.   **2.** $e(x,0) = E_1 \sin \dfrac{x}{1,000} + E_{10} \sin \dfrac{x}{100}$.

3. $e(x,0) = E$.   **4.** $e(x,0) = \dfrac{Ex}{1,000\pi}$.

A telegraph cable is S miles long. Assuming that Eqs. (62) apply, find $e(x,t)$ and $i(x,t)$ t sec. after

5. The ends are grounded, if initially $e(x,0) = Ex/S$, the steady-state condition due to one end being grounded and the other at the constant potential E.

6. The ends are grounded, if initially $e(x,0) = E$, a constant potential.

7. The end $x = 0$ is grounded and the end $x = S$ is suddenly connected to a constant potential E, if initially $e(x,0) = 0$.

8. For the cable of Prob. 7, show that the current at the receiving end, $x = 0$, is given by

$$i(0,t) = -\frac{E}{RS}\left[1 - 2(\epsilon^{-\pi^2 t/S^2 RC} - \epsilon^{-4\pi^2 t/S^2 RC} + \epsilon^{-9\pi^2 t/S^2 RC} - \cdots)\right].$$

9. Jacobi's theta function $\theta(z,q)$ is defined by

$$\theta(z,q) = 1 + 2\sum_{n=1}^{\infty} (-1)^n q^{n^2} \cos 2nz$$

Some authors use θ_4 or θ_0 in place of θ. Show that in Prob. 8

$$i(0,t) = -\frac{E}{RS}\,\theta(0,\epsilon^{-\pi^2 t/S^2 RC}).$$

10. It is shown in the theory of theta functions, or from the Poisson sum formula in the theory of Fourier series and integrals that

$$\theta(0,\epsilon^{-u}) = 1 + 2 \sum_{n=1}^{\infty} (-1)^n \epsilon^{-n^2 u} = 2 \sqrt{\frac{\pi}{u}} \sum_{n=1}^{\infty} \epsilon^{-(2n-1)^2 \pi^2 / 4u}.$$

Verify that the two sides are equal for $u = 1$. This transformation is useful in computing $i(0,t)$ of Probs. 8 and 9 for t near 0.

Use the data given in connection with Probs. 1 to 4, and the result of Prob. 8 combined with the equations in Probs. 9 and 10 where useful, to show that when a signal is sent the current received is

11. Approximately 90 per cent of its maximum value after 3 sec.
12. Approximately 73 per cent of its maximum at the end of 2 sec.
13. Approximately 30 per cent of its maximum at the end of 1 sec.
14. Less than 0.0004 of its maximum after $\frac{1}{4}$ sec.

15. Use the defining equation for $\theta(z,q)$ in Prob. 9 to show that for the cable of Prob. 7 the current at any point x after time t may be written

$$i(x,t) = -\frac{E}{RS} \theta\left(\frac{\pi x}{2S}, \epsilon^{-\pi^2 t / S^2 R C}\right).$$

Graphs, brief tables, and references to literature on theta functions are given in Jahnke-Emde's *Tables of Functions*. But it is necessary to be familiar with the meaning of several parameters and to make considerable preliminary computations in order to obtain a particular numerical value of $\theta(z,q)$ from most of the existing tables.

43. The Vibrating String

The wave equation in one dimension,

$$\frac{\partial^2 u}{\partial t^2} = v^2 \frac{\partial^2 u}{\partial x^2} \tag{86}$$

was introduced as Eq. (81) of Sec. 31, where we showed that its general solution represented traveling waves. Equation (86) is fundamental in the study of wave motion. As the discussion of Secs. 31, 33, and 36 indicates, problems involving mechanical vibrations, sound waves, electromagnetic waves, or the propagation of electricity along a lossless transmission line all lead to an equation of this form.

For definiteness, in this section we shall investigate problems suggested by the small vibrations of a tightly stretched string, such as that in a violin or other stringed musical instrument. Then as in Eq. (81) of Sec. 31 u is the small transverse displacement of a point originally at distance x along the string and $v^2 = gT/D$, where T is the tension, D the weight per unit length, and g the acceleration of gravity. Thus v has the units of velocity, or of x/t.

In particular let us consider the string AB of length 100 units, and measure x from A as in Fig. 45. Denote the displacement by

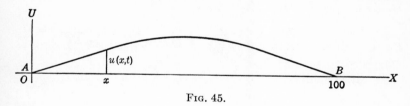

FIG. 45.

$u(x,t)$ and the transverse velocity by $u_t(x,t) = \dfrac{\partial u}{\partial t}$. Then, if the ends are fixed,

$$u(0,t) = 0, \qquad u(100,t) = 0. \tag{87}$$

We assume that the initial displacement and velocity are given by

$$u(x,0) = 12 \sin \frac{\pi x}{50}, \qquad u_t(x,0) = 5 \sin \frac{\pi x}{25}. \tag{88}$$

We wish to determine the subsequent motion, that is, the solution

$u(x,t)$ for $t > 0$ of Eq. (86) which satisfies the boundary conditions (87) and the initial conditions (88).

It follows from Prob. 5 of Exercise XVII that Eq. (86) admits

$$u = (c_1 \sin kx + c_2 \cos kx)(c_3 \sin kvt + c_4 \cos vt) \qquad (89)$$

as a particular solution of the form $X(x) \cdot T(t)$. The first condition (87) will be satisfied if $c_2 = 0$, and the second will be satisfied if

$$\sin 100k = 0, \qquad 100k = n\pi, \qquad \text{or} \qquad k = \frac{n\pi}{100}, \qquad (90)$$

where n is any positive integer. Let us write C_n for the product $c_1 c_4$ which goes with a particular n, and D_n for the product $c_1 c_3$ which goes with a particular n. Then we have

$$\left(C_n \cos \frac{n\pi vt}{100} + D_n \sin \frac{n\pi vt}{100} \right) \sin \frac{n\pi x}{100}, \qquad n = 1, 2, 3, \cdots \quad (91)$$

as a set of terms each of which satisfies Eq. (86) and the boundary conditions of Eq. (87). Hence we put

$$u(x,t) = \sum_{n=1}^{\infty} \left(C_n \cos \frac{n\pi vt}{100} + D_n \sin \frac{n\pi vt}{100} \right) \sin \frac{n\pi x}{100}. \qquad (92)$$

The initial conditions (88) will be satisfied, provided that

$$u(x,0) = 12 \sin \frac{\pi x}{50} = \sum_{n=1}^{\infty} C_n \sin \frac{n\pi x}{100}, \qquad (93)$$

and

$$u_t(x,0) = 5 \sin \frac{\pi x}{25} = \sum_{n=1}^{\infty} \frac{n\pi v}{100} D_n \sin \frac{n\pi x}{100}. \qquad (94)$$

This suggests that we expand the given values of $u(x,0)$ and $u_t(x,0)$ in Fourier sine series of frequency $\pi/100$, and half-period 100. In this case we may use the procedure which led to Eqs. (17) and (19). We observe that $\pi/50 = 2\pi/100$ and

$$\frac{\pi}{25} = \frac{4\pi}{100},$$

each an integral multiple of the desired frequency $\pi/100$. Hence Eq. (93) will be satisfied if $C_2 = 12$, and $C_n = 0$ if $n \neq 2$. And Eq. (94) will hold if

$$5 = \frac{4\pi v}{100} D_4, \quad \text{or} \quad D_4 = \frac{125}{\pi v} \quad \text{and} \quad D_n = 0, \quad \text{if } n \neq 4.$$

On putting the values of C_n and D_n just found in Eq. (92), we have

$$u(x,t) = 12 \cos \frac{\pi v t}{50} \sin \frac{\pi x}{50} + \frac{125}{\pi v} \sin \frac{\pi v t}{25} \sin \frac{\pi x}{25} \qquad (95)$$

as the solution of our problem.

Let us outline the method of solution in more general terms. Suppose that the string is S units long and that the ends are fixed so that

$$u(0,t) = 0, \qquad u(S,t) = 0. \qquad (96)$$

And let the initial displacement and velocity be given by

$$u(x,0) = f(x), \qquad u_t(x,0) = g(x). \qquad (97)$$

Our problem is to determine the subsequent motion, that is, to find the solution $u(x,t)$ for $t > 0$ of Eq. (86) which satisfies the boundary conditions, Eqs. (96), and the initial conditions, Eqs. (97).

In place of Eq. (92) in this case we now have

$$u(x,t) = \sum_{n=1}^{\infty} \left(C_n \cos \frac{n\pi v t}{S} + D_n \sin \frac{n\pi v t}{S} \right) \sin \frac{n\pi x}{S}, \qquad (98)$$

which satisfies Eqs. (86) and (96). It will also satisfy Eq. (97) if

$$u(x,0) = f(x) = \sum_{n=1}^{\infty} C_n \sin \frac{n\pi x}{S} \qquad (99)$$

and

$$u_t(x,0) = g(x) = \sum_{n=1}^{\infty} \frac{n\pi v}{S} D_n \sin \frac{n\pi x}{S}. \qquad (100)$$

Equation (99) shows that the C_n are the b_n of Eq. (9) with $L = S$. These may be determined from Eq. (10) with $L = S$ or one of the alternatives to it mentioned in Sec. 37.   And from Eq. (100) we have

$$b_n = \frac{n\pi v}{S} D_n \qquad \text{and} \qquad D_n = \frac{S}{n\pi v} b_n, \qquad (101)$$

where here the b_n are those of Eq. (9) with $f(x) = g(x)$ and $L = S$. These coefficients of the expansion of $g(x)$ in a Fourier sine series of half-period S are also found by one of the methods of Sec. 37.

After calculating the C_n and D_n, substitution of their values in Eq. (98) leads to the solution of Eq. (86) which satisfies the conditions of Eqs. (96) and (97).

EXERCISE XXIV

Find the displacement $u(x,t)$ of a tightly stretched string of length S units vibrating between fixed end points if the initial velocity was zero and the initial displacement $u(x,0)$ was

1. $2 \sin \dfrac{\pi x}{S}.$ **2.** $p \sin^3 \dfrac{\pi x}{S}.$ **3.** $pSx - px^2.$

4. $p \sin \dfrac{k\pi x}{S}$, where k is some particular positive integer.

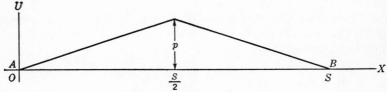

Fig. 46. $u(x,0)$ for the plucked string.

5. $\dfrac{2px}{S}$, if $0 < x < \dfrac{S}{2}$, and $2p - \dfrac{2px}{S}$, if $\dfrac{S}{2} < x < S$.   This displacement, Fig. 46, approximates that for a *plucked* musical string.

Find the displacement $u(x,t)$ of a tightly stretched string of length S units vibrating between fixed end points if the string was initially in the equilibrium position, $u(x,0) = 0$, and the initial velocity $\dfrac{\partial u}{\partial t}$ at $t = 0$ or $u_t(x,0)$ was

6. $5 \sin \dfrac{3\pi x}{S}.$ **7.** $q \sin^3 \dfrac{\pi x}{S}.$ **8.** $qSx - qx^2.$

9. $q \sin \dfrac{k\pi x}{S}$, where k is some particular positive integer.

10. 0, if $0 < x < \dfrac{S - w}{2}$; q, if $\dfrac{S - w}{2} < x < \dfrac{S + w}{2}$;

$$0, \text{ if } \frac{S + w}{2} < x < S.$$

This condition approximates that for a *hammered* musical string.

11. Find the displacement $u(x,t)$ of a tightly stretched string of length S units vibrating between fixed end points if initially the displacement $u(x,0) = 3 \sin \dfrac{2\pi x}{S}$ and the velocity

$$u_t(x,0) = 4 \sin \frac{5\pi x}{S}.$$

12. Let $f(x)$ be defined for $0 < x < S$, and $F(x)$ be an odd function of period $2S$ which equals $f(x)$ on the interval $0,S$. Thus $F(x) = f(x)$, $0 < x < S$; $F(-x) = F(x)$; $F(x + 2S) = F(x)$. Show that if Eq. (99) holds, for $0 < x < S$, then its right member equals $F(x)$ for all values of x. Replace x by $x + vt$ and then by $x - vt$ and deduce that

$$F(x + vt) + F(x - vt) = \sum_{n=1}^{\infty} C_n \left[\sin \frac{n\pi(x + vt)}{S} \right.$$

$$\left. + \sin \frac{n\pi(x - vt)}{S} \right]$$

$$= \sum_{n=1}^{\infty} 2C_n \cos \frac{n\pi vt}{S} \sin \frac{n\pi x}{S}.$$

13. Using Prob. 12, show that for any one of Probs. 1 to 5 the solution may be written in the form

$$u(x,t) = \tfrac{1}{2}[F(x + vt) + F(x - vt)],$$

where $f(x) = u(x,0)$ as given for $0 < x < S$, and $F(x)$ is obtained from $f(x)$ as described in Prob. 12.

14. By reasoning like that used for the general solution of Eq. (81) in Sec. 31, show that the position of the string in Prob. 13 at any time t can be found by moving the curve $u = \tfrac{1}{2}F(x)$ to the right a distance vt and moving an identical curve to the left a distance vt, and then adding the ordinates of the two curves in the interval $0,S$.

15. Apply Probs. 13 and 14 to the plucked string of Prob. 5.

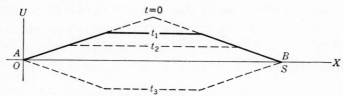

Fig. 47. $u(x,t)$ for the plucked string.

Hence show that, as in Fig. 47, the general position is an isosceles trapezoid.

16. Let $g(x)$ be defined for $0 < x < S$, and $G(x)$ be an odd function of period $2S$ which equals $g(x)$ on the interval $0,S$. Thus $G(x) = g(x),\, 0 < x < S;\, G(-x) = G(x);\, G(x + 2S) = G(x)$. Show that if Eq. (100) holds, for $0 < x < S$, then its right member equals $G(x)$ for all values of x. Replace x by z, and integrate with respect to z from $x - vt$ to $x + vt$ to show that

$$\int_{x-vt}^{x+vt} G(z)dz = \sum_{n=1}^{\infty} vD_n \left[\cos \frac{n\pi(x + vt)}{S} - \cos \frac{n\pi(x - vt)}{S} \right]$$

$$= \sum_{n=1}^{\infty} 2vD_n \sin \frac{n\pi vt}{S} \sin \frac{n\pi x}{S}.$$

17. Using Prob. 16, show that for any one of Probs. 6 to 10 the solution may be written in the form

$$u(x,t) = \frac{1}{2v} \int_{x-vt}^{x+vt} G(z)dz,$$

where $g(x) = u_t(x,0)$ as given for $0 < x < S$, and $G(x)$ is obtained from $g(x)$ as described in Prob. 16.

18. Let $F(x)$ be related to the $f(x)$ of Eq. (99) as in Probs. 12 and 13 and let $G(x)$ be related to the $g(x)$ of Eq. (100) as in Probs. 16 and 17. Show that the solution of Eq. (86) satisfying the conditions (96) and (97) found from Eq. (98) is equivalent to

$$u(x,t) = \frac{1}{2} [F(x + vt) + F(x - vt)] + \frac{1}{2v} \int_{x-vt}^{x+vt} G(z)dz.$$

19. Apply Prob. 17 to the hammered string of Prob. 10, at its mid-point $x = S/2$. In particular, show that $u\left(\frac{S}{2},t\right) = qt$ if $0 < t < \frac{w}{2v}$ and $u\left(\frac{S}{2},t\right) = \frac{qw}{2v}$ if $\frac{w}{2v} < t < \frac{3S}{2v} - \frac{w}{2v}$.

44. The Lossless Transmission Line

In Eq. (97) of Sec. 33 we showed that the equations governing the propagation of potential $e(x,t)$ and current $i(x,t)$ along a lossless transmission line having a series inductance of L henrys per mile and a shunt capacitance of C farads per mile are the *radio equations*

$$-\frac{\partial e}{\partial x} = L \frac{\partial i}{\partial t}, \qquad -\frac{\partial i}{\partial x} = C \frac{\partial e}{\partial t}, \qquad \frac{\partial^2 e}{\partial x^2} = LC \frac{\partial^2 e}{\partial t^2}. \quad (102)$$

The third relation is equivalent to

$$\frac{\partial^2 e}{\partial t^2} = v^2 \frac{\partial^2 e}{\partial x^2}, \qquad \text{if } v = \frac{1}{\sqrt{LC}}. \quad (103)$$

This has the same form as Eq. (86). When boundary conditions for e are known, Eq. (103) may be solved by the method of Sec.

41. And after e has been found, the first two relations of Eq. (102) determine i to within an additive constant of integration.

As an example, let us consider a line AB 100 miles long for which $L = 2 \times 10^{-4}$ henry per mile and $C = 2$ microfarads per mile. Suppose that the initial potential was given by

$$e(x,0) = E \sin \frac{\pi x}{100}, \qquad (104)$$

and that the initial current was constant

$$i(x,0) = I_0. \qquad (105)$$

And as indicated in Fig. 48, suppose that at the instant taken as

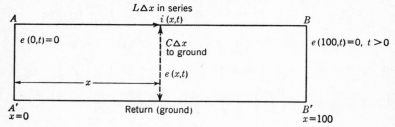

FIG. 48.

$t = 0$ the two ends of the line A and B were suddenly grounded. Then

$$e(0,t) = 0, \qquad e(100,t) = 0. \qquad (106)$$

We wish to find the potential $e(x,t)$ and the current $i(x,t)$ at any point of the line $0 < x < 100$, and at any time after the grounding, $t > 0$.

We assume that the initial state was the result of a physical situation. Then Eqs. (102) hold, and from the second relation

$$e_t(x,0) = \frac{\partial e}{\partial t}\Big|_{t=0} = -\frac{1}{C}\frac{\partial i}{\partial x}\Big|_{t=0} = -\frac{1}{C}\frac{\partial i(x,0)}{\partial x}. \qquad (107)$$

But from Eq. (105), the last derivative is $\dfrac{\partial I_0}{\partial x} = 0$ so that

$$e_t(x,0) = 0. \qquad (108)$$

Our boundary value problem for the potential is to determine the solution $e(x,t)$ for $t > 0$ of Eq. (103) which satisfies the boundary conditions (106) and the initial conditions (104) and (108). The similarity of Eqs. (103) and (106) to Eqs. (86) and (87) leads us to examine particular solutions of the form (91). If $D_n = 0$ these will also satisfy the condition (108). Thus we write

$$e(x,t) = \sum_{n=1}^{\infty} C_n \cos \frac{n\pi vt}{100} \sin \frac{n\pi x}{100}. \tag{109}$$

This satisfies Eqs. (103), (106), and (108). It will also satisfy the remaining condition (104), provided that

$$e(x,0) = E \sin \frac{\pi x}{100} = \sum_{n=1}^{\infty} C_n \sin \frac{n\pi x}{100}. \tag{110}$$

Since the given sine term has the same frequency as the series, $\pi/100$, we take $C_1 = E$ and the remaining $C_n = 0$, $n \neq 1$. Hence (109) becomes

$$e(x,t) = E \cos \frac{\pi vt}{100} \sin \frac{\pi x}{100}. \tag{111}$$

To find $i(x,t)$ we use Eq. (102). The first relation gives:

$$\frac{\partial i}{\partial t} = -\frac{1}{L} \frac{\partial e}{\partial x} = -\frac{E\pi}{100L} \cos \frac{\pi vt}{100} \cos \frac{\pi x}{100}. \tag{112}$$

The result of integrating both sides with respect to t is

$$i(x,t) = -\frac{E}{vL} \sin \frac{\pi vt}{100} \cos \frac{\pi x}{100} + f(x). \tag{113}$$

Here $f(x)$ is an arbitrary function of x, since x was kept constant during the integration. Now substitute the value of $\dfrac{\partial i}{\partial x}$ as obtained from Eq. (113) and the value of $\dfrac{\partial e}{\partial t}$ as obtained from

Eq. (111) in the second relation of Eq. (102).   By observing that
the definition of v in Eq. (103) implies that $v^2 = 1/(LC)$ or
$Cv = 1/(vL)$, one may reduce the relation to $f'(x) = 0$ which
shows that $f(x)$ must be a constant.   And Eq. (105) shows that
the constant must be I_0.
Hence

$$i(x,t) = -\frac{E}{vL} \sin \frac{\pi vt}{100} \cos \frac{\pi x}{100} + I_0. \tag{114}$$

Finally we recall that $L = 2 \times 10^{-4}$ and $C = 2 \times 10^{-6}$, so that
$v = 1/\sqrt{LC} = 5 \times 10^4$, $v/100 = 500$, $vL = 10$.   Hence   Eqs.
(111) and (114) give

$$e(x,t) = E \cos 500\pi t \sin \frac{\pi x}{100},$$

$$i(x,t) = -\frac{E}{10} \sin 500\pi t \cos \frac{\pi x}{100}, \tag{115}$$

as the solution of our problem.

Let us outline the method of solution for a more general case.
Suppose that originally for a line AB, S miles long, the potential
was a given function of the distance $f(x)$, and the current was
another such function $g(x)$.   And assume that at time $t = 0$ the
terminal A had its potential changed to r volts and that the
terminal B had its potential changed to s volts and that both
terminals were maintained at the new voltages.   Here the
boundary conditions are

$$e(x,0) = f(x), \quad i(x,0) = g(x), \quad e(0,t) = r, \quad e(S,t) = s. \tag{116}$$

As in Eq. (81) we transform this to a problem involving e_T by
writing

$$e = e_s + e_T = \frac{s - r}{S} x + r + e_T. \tag{117}$$

The boundary conditions for e_T then become

$$e_T(x,0) = f(x) - \frac{s - r}{S} x - r, \quad e_T(0,t) = 0, \quad e_T(S,t) = 0, \tag{118}$$

obtained directly from Eqs. (116) and (117), together with

$$e_{T,t}(x,0) = \left.\frac{\partial e_T}{\partial t}\right|_{t=0} = e_t(x,0) = -\frac{1}{C}g'(x), \qquad (119)$$

obtained from Eqs. (117) and (107) and from $i(x,0) = g(x)$. We may find e_T from a series like that in Eq. (98),

$$e_T(x,t) = \sum_{n=1}^{\infty}\left(C_n \cos\frac{n\pi vt}{S} + D_n \sin\frac{n\pi vt}{S}\right)\sin\frac{n\pi x}{S}. \qquad (120)$$

This satisfies the end conditions in Eq. (118). Equations similar to Eqs. (99) and (100) show that the C_n must be the coefficients of the expansion of $f(x) - \dfrac{s-r}{S}x - r$ in a Fourier sine series of half-period S to satisfy the first condition of Eq. (118) and that the D_n must be found from Eq. (101) from b_n, the coefficients of the expansion of $-\dfrac{1}{C}g'(x)$ in a Fourier sine series of half-period S to satisfy the condition of Eq. (119). The values so found may be inserted in

$$e(x,t) = \frac{s-r}{S}x - r$$
$$+ \sum_{n=1}^{\infty}\left(C_n \cos\frac{n\pi vt}{S} + D_n \sin\frac{n\pi vt}{S}\right)\sin\frac{n\pi x}{S} \qquad (121)$$

to give the solution for $e(x,t)$.

Use of the first two relations of Eqs. (102) in a manner similar to that which leads from Eqs. (111) to (114) shows that the $i(x,t)$ which corresponds to the $e(x,t)$ of Eq. (121) is given by

$$i(x,t) = -\frac{1}{L}\frac{s-r}{S}t + a$$
$$- \frac{1}{vL}\sum_{n=1}^{\infty}\left(C_n \sin\frac{n\pi vt}{S} - D_n \cos\frac{n\pi vt}{S}\right)\cos\frac{n\pi x}{S}, \qquad (122)$$

where

$$v = \frac{1}{\sqrt{LC}} \quad \text{and} \quad a = \frac{1}{S} \int_0^S g(x)dx, \qquad (123)$$

so that a is the constant term in the expansion of $g(x)$ in a Fourier cosine series of half-period S.

EXERCISE XXV

A transmission line is S miles long, and it is lossless so that Eqs. (102) apply. Initially $i(x,0) = I_0$ so that $e_t(x,0) = 0$. Find $e(x,t)$ and $i(x,t)$ t sec. after both ends were suddenly grounded if initially the potential was

1. $e(x,0) = E \sin \dfrac{\pi x}{S}.$ **2.** $e(x,0) = E_2 \sin \dfrac{2\pi x}{S} + E_5 \sin \dfrac{5\pi x}{S}.$

3. $e(x,0) = E.$ **4.** $e(x,0) = \dfrac{Ex}{S}.$

5. A lossless transmission line of length S is initially uncharged, so that $i(x,0) = 0$, $e(x,0) = 0$, $e_t(x,0) = 0$. At $t = 0$ the end $x = S$ is suddenly connected with a constant potential E while the other end is grounded. Thus $e(S,t) = E$, $e(0,t) = 0$. Use Eq. (102) and find $e(x,t)$ and $i(x,t)$ for $t > 0$.

6. A lossless transmission line is S miles long. The end $x = 0$ is grounded so that $e(0,t) = 0$. The other end is left open, so that $i(S,t) = 0$ and $e_x(S,t) = -Li_t(S,t) = 0$. Show that for $n = 1, 3, 5, \cdots$ any odd integer, $B_n \sin \dfrac{n\pi x}{2S} \cos \dfrac{n\pi vt}{2S}$ is a particular solution of Eq. (103) satisfying the end condition.

7. Suppose that just before the end conditions of Prob. 6 were imposed, the line had $e(x,0) = Ex/S$. Find $e(x,t)$ by using a series of particular solutions of Prob. 6 and an expansion in an odd-harmonic sine series similar to that used in Prob. 20 of Exercise XXII.

8. A lossless transmission line of length S is initially uncharged, so that $i(x,0) = 0$, $e(x,0) = 0$, $e_t(x,0) = 0$. At $t = 0$, the end $x = 0$ is suddenly connected with a constant potential E, while the other end $x = S$ is left open as in Prob. 6, so that $i(S,t) = 0$, $e_x(S,t) = 0$. Find $e(x,t)$ and hence $i(x,t)$. HINT: Put $e(x,t) = E + e_t(x,t)$, and determine $e_T(x,t)$ by the method used in Prob. 7.

9. Show that for any one of Probs. 1 to 4 the solution for the potential may be written in the form

$$e(x,t) = \tfrac{1}{2}[F(x + vt) + F(x - vt)],$$

where $f(x) = e(x,0)$ as given for $0 < x < S$, and $F(x)$ is related to $f(x)$ as in Probs. 12 and 13 of Exercise XXIV.

10. If the emf for a line of length S satisfies Eq. (103) and the conditions $e(x,0) = 0$, $e_t(x,0) = g(x)$, $e(0,t) = 0$, $e(S,t) = 0$ show that the potential may be written in the form

$$e(x,t) = \frac{1}{2v} \int_{x-vt}^{x+vt} G(z)dz$$

where $G(x)$ is related to $g(x)$ as in Probs. 16 and 17 of Exercise XXIV.

A line is 50 miles long, has series resistance $R = 0.12$ ohms per mile, series inductance $L = 2 \times 10^{-3}$ henry per mile, conductance to ground $G = \frac{4}{3} \times 10^{-8}$ mho per mile, and shunt capacitance to ground $C = 1.2 \times 10^{-8}$ farad per mile. Hence Eqs. (92), (93) and (94) of Sec. 33 must be used. For this line

11. Show that $i = I_0 \epsilon^{0.00004x}$, $e = 3{,}000 I_0 \epsilon^{0.00004x}$ are possible steady-state values.

12. Show that if $e(0,t) = 0$ and $e(50,t) = 0$, then Eq. (93) of Sec. 33 admits $C_n \sin \dfrac{n\pi x}{50} \epsilon^{-30.3t} \left(\dfrac{30.3}{\beta_n} \sin \beta_n t + \cos \beta_n t \right)$ as particular solutions satisfying the end conditions if

$$\beta_n = \sqrt{\frac{n^2\pi^2}{6} - 851}$$

and n is a positive integer.

13. If the initial values $i(x,0)$ and $e(x,0)$ are those given in Prob. 11 so that $e_t(x,0) = 0$, and the ends are suddenly grounded, find the emf $e(x,t)$ by using a series of the particular solutions found in Prob. 12.

14. If the line is initially uncharged $e(x,0) = 0$, $i(x,0) = 0$, $e_t(x,0) = 0$, $i_t(s,0) = 0$. Find $e(x,t)$ if at $t = 0$ the end $x = 50$ has a constant potential E suddenly impressed on it and the other end is suddenly grounded. Note that the steady-state solution for the permanent end conditions has the form $c_1\epsilon^{\sqrt{RG}x} + c_2\epsilon^{-\sqrt{RG}x}$, and with constants chosen to take on the proper end values is

$$e_S = E\, \frac{\epsilon^{0.00004x} - \epsilon^{-0.00004x}}{\epsilon^{0.002} - \epsilon^{-0.002}} = \frac{E \sinh 0.00004x}{\sinh 0.002}$$

Put $e = e_S + e_T$, and find e_T by the method of Prob. 13.

45. Hollow Wave Guides

The discussion of Maxwell's equations in Secs. 34 and 36 showed that in a homogeneous isotropic nonconducting medium free of electric charge, such as the space inside a copper pipe, an electromagnetic field may be mathematically characterized by the electric field intensity vector **E,** with scalar components E_x, E_y, E_z and the magnetic field intensity vector **H,** with scalar components H_x, H_y, H_z. There are four fundamental vector relations which **E** and **H** must satisfy.

We shall restate here in terms of the components those equations implied by Maxwell's laws which are useful in studying the fields inside hollow wave guides. It follows from Eq. (117) of Sec. 36 that each of the six scalar components E_x, E_y, E_z, H_x, H_y, H_z satisfies a *wave equation*

$$\nabla^2 u = \frac{\partial^2 u}{\partial x^2} + \frac{\partial^2 u}{\partial y^2} + \frac{\partial^2 u}{\partial z^2} = \frac{1}{c^2} \frac{\partial^2 u}{\partial t^2}. \tag{124}$$

The *continuity equation* for E,

$$\frac{\partial E_x}{\partial x} + \frac{\partial E_y}{\partial y} + \frac{\partial E_z}{\partial z} = 0, \tag{125}$$

follows from Eq. (114) of Sec. 36 and Eq. (103) of Sec. 34. And the time derivatives of the components of magnitic field intensity are related to the electric field intensity by the first relation of Eq. (114) of Sec. 36, or Eq. (101) of Sec. 34, namely,

$$-\mu_0 \frac{\partial H_x}{\partial t} = \frac{\partial E_z}{\partial y} - \frac{\partial E_y}{\partial z},$$

$$-\mu_0 \frac{\partial H_y}{\partial t} = \frac{\partial E_x}{\partial z} - \frac{\partial E_z}{\partial x}, \tag{126}$$

$$-\mu_0 \frac{\partial H_z}{\partial t} = \frac{\partial E_y}{\partial x} - \frac{\partial E_x}{\partial y}.$$

Consider a hollow conducting tube of constant rectangular cross section, Fig. 49. Let the sides of the rectangle be a and b

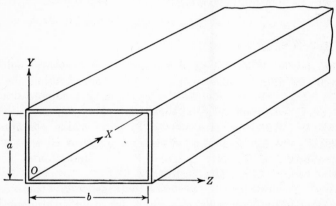

Fig. 49. Hollow wave guide. At the bounding faces **E** is parallel to OY for $y = 0$ and $y = a$, **E** is parallel to OZ for $z = 0$ and $z = b$.

units in length parallel, respectively, to the y and z axes, and let the x axis coincide with one longitudinal edge of the tube. Thus the plane faces of the tube lie in the planes $y = 0$, $y = a$, $z = 0$, and $z = b$.

We assume that the tube is a perfect conductor. Hence the components of **E** tangent to the surface of the tube must be zero. That is, in our case,

$$E_x = 0 \quad \text{and} \quad E_y = 0 \quad \text{if } z = 0 \text{ or if } z = b$$
$$E_x = 0 \quad \text{and} \quad E_z = 0 \quad \text{if } y = 0 \text{ or if } y = a. \tag{127}$$

The discussion in connection with Eqs. (81) and (82) of Sec. 31 showed that $f(x - vt)$ corresponded to wave motion in the positive x direction. The same will be true of any function of $(\omega t - \beta x)$ since

$$\omega t - \beta x = -\beta(x - vt) \text{ if } v = \frac{\omega}{\beta}. \qquad (128)$$

In order to restrict our problem, we assume that the wave form is sinusoidal. Then each component of **E** and **H** will have the form

$$u = U(y,z)[c_1 \cos (\omega t - \beta x) + c_2 \sin (\omega t - \beta x)]. \qquad (129)$$

This will be solution of Eq. (124), provided that

$$\frac{\partial^2 U}{\partial y^2} + \frac{\partial^2 U}{\partial z^2} = -k^2 U, \qquad \text{where } k^2 = \frac{\omega^2}{c^2} - \beta^2. \qquad (130)$$

Since all the relations are linear, other wave forms could be built up by combining solutions of the type of Eq. (129) for different ω in finite sums, Fourier series, or Fourier integrals. Here we shall confine our attention to a single frequency. Then ω is given, subject to certain restrictions which we shall derive presently, and β or k is a constant chosen so as to satisfy the boundary conditions.

The restricted problem requires us to find three solutions of Eq. (130) which may be combined with pairs of constants in Eq. (129) to give values E_x, E_y, E_z, which satisfy the boundary conditions, Eq. (127), and Eq. (125). The boundary conditions (127) suggest the use of products of trigonometric functions, and the seeking of solutions of Eq. (130) of the form $Y(y) \cdot Z(z)$ as in Sec. 30. We begin by noting that

$$U(y,z) = \begin{Bmatrix} \sin \\ \cos \end{Bmatrix} ry \begin{Bmatrix} \sin \\ \cos \end{Bmatrix} sz \qquad (131)$$

will be a solution of Eq. (130) if $r^2 + s^2 = k^2$. To satisfy Eq. (127), we use $\sin ry$ in E_x and E_z with $r = m\pi/a$ and we use $\sin sz$ in E_x and E_y with $s = n\pi/b$. Here m and n are each zero or a positive integer. To make possible a cancellation of the derivatives in Eq. (125), use use $\cos ry$ in E_y and $\cos sz$ in E_z. This leads us to write

$$E_x = \sin \frac{m\pi y}{a} \sin \frac{n\pi z}{b} [A_x \cos (\omega t - \beta x) + B_x \sin (\omega t - \beta x)],$$

$$E_y = \cos \frac{m\pi y}{a} \sin \frac{n\pi z}{b} [A_y \cos (\omega t = \beta x) + B_y \sin (\omega t - \beta x)],$$

$$E_z = \sin \frac{m\pi y}{a} \cos \frac{n\pi z}{b} [A_z \cos (\omega t - \beta x)$$
$$+ B_z \sin (\omega t - \beta x)]. \quad (132)$$

For any values of the constant coefficients A_x, B_x, A_y, B_y, A_z, B_z these will satisfy the conditions (127) if

$$m,n = 0, 1, 2, 3, \cdots . \quad (133)$$

And E_x, E_y, E_z will each satisfy the wave equation, Eq. (124), if $r^2 + s^2 = k^2$, or from Eq. (130) if

$$\pi^2 \left(\frac{m^2}{a^2} + \frac{n^2}{b^2}\right) = k^2 = \frac{\omega^2}{c^2} - \beta^2. \quad \text{Hence}$$

$$\beta^2 = \frac{\omega^2}{c^2} - \pi^2 \left(\frac{m^2}{a^2} + \frac{n^2}{b^2}\right). \quad (134)$$

To make β real, the last right member in Eq. (134) must be positive or zero. This requires that for any pair m,n

$$\omega^2 \geqq \pi^2 c^2 \left(\frac{m^2}{a^2} + \frac{n^2}{b^2}\right) \quad \text{and}$$

$$\beta = \frac{\omega}{c} \sqrt{1 - \frac{\pi^2 c^2}{\omega^2} \left(\frac{m^2}{a^2} + \frac{n^2}{b^2}\right)}. \quad (135)$$

Since $m = 0$, $n = 0$ would make all three components in Eq. (132) equal to zero, for a nonzero solution the smallest value of ω results when we take $m = 0$, $n = 1$ or $n = 0$, $m = 1$. Thus if

$$b > a, m = 0, n = 1, \beta = 0 \quad \text{and} \quad \omega = \frac{\pi c}{b} \quad (136)$$

is the least possible value of the frequency ω.

The condition (125) will be satisfied if

$$-A_x - \frac{m\pi}{a} B_y - \frac{n\pi}{b} B_z = 0$$

$$B_x - \frac{m\pi}{a} A_y - \frac{n\pi}{b} A_z = 0. \qquad (137)$$

These may be solved for two of the constants, for example, A_z and B_z, in terms of the remaining four. Some particular cases are worked out in more detail in the problems of Exercise XXVI. These problems also illustrate the use of Eq. (126) to determine **H**.

As we indicated in Prob. 15 of Exercise XIX, when the wave guide is a round pipe, or hollow tube of circular cross section, it is convenient to use polar coordinates in the plane of cross section and the particular solutions for a given frequency involve Bessel functions.

46. References

Additional illustrations of the use of series of particular solutions to solve boundary value problems will be found in many of the books on heat, vibrations, sound, and electricity such as those already referred to in Secs. 14 and 37.

An elementary, but more complete, treatment which deduces the continuity of some of our solutions from Abel's theorem will be found in the first two texts mentioned in Sec. 25.

One method of justifying the validity and uniqueness of the series solutions of boundary value problems rests on the theory of integral equations. This will be found in such comprehensive works as Frank and von Mises, *Differential- und Integralgleich- ungen der Mechanik und Physik*, or Courant-Hilbert, *Methoden der mathematischen Physik*.

EXERCISE XXVI

1. Let $A_x = 0$, $A_y = 0$, $B_x = 0$. Show that Eq. (137) implies that $A_z = 0$ when $n \neq 0$ and that it also determines the ratio of B_y to B_z. This leads to a particular solution which may be written

$$E_x = 0,$$

$$E_y = -B \frac{\omega\mu_0}{k^2} \frac{n\pi}{b} \cos \frac{m\pi y}{a} \sin \frac{n\pi z}{b} \sin (\omega t - \beta x),$$

$$E_z = B \frac{\omega\mu_0}{k^2} \frac{m\pi}{a} \sin \frac{m\pi y}{a} \cos \frac{n\pi z}{b} \sin (\omega t - \beta x).$$

Since **E** has no component in the axial or x direction, this is known as a *transverse electric* wave, or $TE_{m,n}$ wave.

2. If **E** is known, Eq. (126) determines H_x, H_y, H_z to within an additive arbitrary function of x, y, z for each component. These three functions must all be zero to make the components of **H** have the form of u in Eq. (129), as we assumed. Use these facts to show that for the $TE_{m,n}$ wave of Prob. 1, the magnetic field intensity vector **H** has components

$$H_x = -B \cos \frac{m\pi y}{a} \cos \frac{n\pi z}{b} \cos (\omega t - \beta x),$$

$$H_y = B \frac{\beta}{k^2} \frac{m\pi}{a} \sin \frac{m\pi y}{b} \cos \frac{n\pi z}{b} \sin (\omega t - \beta x),$$

$$H_z = B \frac{\beta}{k^2} \frac{n\pi}{b} \cos \frac{m\pi y}{a} \sin \frac{n\pi z}{b} \sin (\omega t - \beta x).$$

3. For the $TE_{m,n}$ wave let $\omega_{m,n}$ denote the *cutoff angular frequency* or smallest value of ω which leads to a real β. Show that

$$\omega_{m,n} = \pi c \sqrt{\frac{m^2}{a^2} + \frac{n^2}{b^2}}.$$

If $\omega < \omega_{m,n}$ $\beta^2 < 0$. Hence β is imaginary and the field is rapidly attenuated in the x direction. Since c has the order of magnitude of 10^8, and a, b are comparable with unity, only ultra-high frequencies $\omega > \omega_{m,n}$ can be propagated by wave guides of reasonable size.

4. Let $A_x = A$, $A_y = 0$, $B_x = 0$, and assume that

$$\frac{E_y}{E_z} = \frac{m}{n}, \; n \neq 0.$$

From Eqs. (132) and (137) deduce that in this case

$$E_x = A \sin \frac{m\pi y}{a} \sin \frac{n\pi z}{b} \cos (\omega t - \beta x),$$

$$E_y = A \frac{\beta}{k^2} \frac{m\pi}{a} \cos \frac{m\pi y}{a} \sin \frac{nz}{b} \sin (\omega t - \beta x),$$

$$E_z = A \frac{\beta}{k^2} \frac{n\pi}{b} \sin \frac{m\pi y}{a} \cos \frac{nz}{b} \sin (\omega t - \beta x).$$

5. Use the procedure of Prob. 2 to show that the components of **H** which correspond to the vector **E** given in Prob. 4 are

$$H_x = 0,$$

$$H_y = -A \frac{K_0 \omega}{k^2} \frac{n\pi}{b} \sin \frac{m\pi y}{a} \cos \frac{n\pi z}{b} \sin (\omega t - \beta x),$$

$$H_z = A \frac{K_0 \omega}{k^2} \frac{m\pi}{a} \cos \frac{m\pi y}{a} \sin \frac{n\pi z}{b} \sin (\omega t - \beta x).$$

To reduce the coefficients to this form, note that by Eq. (116) of Sec. 36, $1/c^2 = \mu_0 k_0$, and hence from Eq. (134)

$$1 + \frac{\beta^2}{k^2} = \frac{\omega^2}{c^2 k^2} = \frac{\mu_0 K_0 \omega^2}{k^2}.$$

The condition $E_y/E_z = m/n$ in Prob. 4 was motivated by the desire to make $H_x = 0$. Since **H** has no component in the axial or x direction, the wave of Probs. 4 and 5 is known as a *transverse magnetic* wave, or $TM_{m,n}$.

6. Show that a more general solution with $E_x = 0$ equivalent to the form of Eq. (132) satisfying Eq. (137) than that of Prob. 1 results if we replace $(\omega t - \beta x)$ by $(\omega t - \beta x + \phi_1)$ in E_y, E_z as written in Prob. 1. The vector $\mathbf{H_1}$ which corresponds to this $\mathbf{E_1}$ is found by making the same substitution in H_x, H_y, H_z as written in Prob. 2.

7. Show that a more general solution $\mathbf{E_2}$, $\mathbf{H_2}$ with $H_x = 0$ than that of Probs. 4 and 5 where **E** and **H** are related by Eq. (126) and **E** is of the form (132) and satisfies Eq. (137) may be found by replacing $(\omega t - \beta x)$ by $(\omega t - \beta x + \phi_2)$ in the six components as written in Probs. 4 and 5.

8. For the vectors of Probs. 6 and 7 show that $\mathbf{H} = \mathbf{H}_1 + \mathbf{H}_2$ is related to $\mathbf{E} = \mathbf{E}_1 + \mathbf{E}_2$ by Eq. (126). Also show that $\mathbf{E} = \mathbf{E}_1 + \mathbf{E}_2$ is of the form of Eq. (132) and satisfies Eq. (137). As it involves four constants: A, B, ϕ_1, ϕ_2, it is the most general solution to be obtained from Eqs. (132) and (137).

9. For the electromagnetic fields of Probs. 1 and 2 or 6 show that

$$E_x = 0, \qquad E_y = -\mu_0 \frac{\omega}{\beta} H_z, \qquad E_z = \mu_0 \frac{\omega}{\beta} H_y.$$

10. For the electromagnetic fields of Probs. 4 and 5 or 7 show that

$$H_x = 0, \qquad H_y = -K_0 \frac{\omega}{\beta} E_z, \qquad H_z = K_0 \frac{\omega}{\beta} E_y.$$

11. From Probs. 9 and 10 deduce that for each type of electromagnetic field there considered

$$E_x H_x + E_y H_y + E_z H_z = \mathbf{E} \cdot \mathbf{H} = 0,$$

so that the vectors $\mathbf{E}$ and $\mathbf{H}$ are perpendicular.

CHAPTER 5

LAPLACE TRANSFORMS. TRANSIENTS

In Chaps. 1 and 3 we discussed a number of physical phenomena which were governed by a system of ordinary or partial linear differential equations. In many applications we seek the solution of such a linear system which satisfies certain initial conditions, or which takes on given values of the functions and their derivatives at time $t = 0$. For example, in studying the stability of a mechanical system it is helpful to know the response to a sudden jar, or to a periodic forcing term. And for an electric network we may wish to study the transient currents in a particular element when an electromotive force of given type is suddenly impressed on the input terminals.

For a simple system of one or two ordinary differential equations, each linear with constant coefficients, elementary methods could be applied. That is, we would first find the general solution in terms of arbitrary constants and then determine what value of the constants would fit the initial conditions. But for complicated systems the calculation of the solutions is greatly facilitated by using some form of *operational calculus*, or set of rules of procedure for translating the physical problem into a simplified system of equations from which we may directly calculate the solution which fits the initial conditions. Operational methods were initiated by an electrical engineer, Heaviside, and used by him to obtain a number of correct solutions of involved problems in electric circuit theory. Although some of Heaviside's original derivations were incomplete, it was later found possible to give sound proofs of his rules based on any one of several known mathematical theories, such as complex contour integration, integral equations, or the Laplace transformation.

198

Since the approach through Laplace transforms has proved to be the simplest and most comprehensive, we shall adopt it here. And we shall present the modern form of the operational calculus, differing in one minor point from Heaviside's form, which naturally follows from a consideration of the Laplace transform.

We first recall the definition of a Laplace transform and some of its properties which were given in Sec. 24, and derive some further properties. We then show how the transform converts a system of ordinary differential equations to an algebraic system and use this fact to solve certain electric and mechanical networks. Finally we show how the transform converts a system of partial differential equations to a system of ordinary differential equations and illustrate this procedure by some problems on the lossless long line.

47. The Laplace Transformation

Let t be a real variable, and $f(t)$ be any function given on the semiinfinite interval $0, +\infty$ and hence defined for all positive values of t. In many applications t is the time, and it is convenient to consider $f(t) = 0$ for $t < 0$. Then $F(p)$, the *Laplace transform* of $f(t)$, is defined by the equation

$$F(p) = \int_0^\infty e^{-pt} f(t) dt. \tag{1}$$

The new function $F(p)$ determined from $f(t)$ by the Laplace transformation does not involve the variable t, since the integration is between fixed limits. But it does involve the new variable p which was introduced in the exponential factor. Thus to each given function of t, Eq. (1) relates a transformed function of p. This relation may be expressed by writing

$$F(p) = \text{Lap } f(t) \qquad \text{or} \qquad F = \text{Lap } f. \tag{2}$$

When seeking the $f(t)$ which gave rise to $F(p)$, we may write

$$f(t) = \text{Lap}^{-1} F(p) \qquad \text{or} \qquad f = \text{Lap}^{-1} F. \tag{3}$$

In Eq. (2), Lap is read "the Laplace transform of." And in Eq. (3), Lap^{-1} is read "the inverse Laplace transform of."

Frequently the use of a small letter for the function of t and the corresponding capital for the transformed function of p is enough to indicate the relationship.   Thus in Eq. (123) of Sec. 24, we defined $G = \text{Lap } g$, and discussed some of the properties of the relation in connection with Fourier transforms.   We pointed out that if g did not increase too rapidly for large positive values of t, or x in Eq. (117) of Sec. 24, and the real part of p exceeded some fixed positive value, the a of Eq. (121) of Sec. 24, then the integral defining the Laplace transform necessarily converged.   And the discussion of Eq. (125) of Sec. 24, which held for $g = \text{Lap}^{-1} G$, showed that if g is made up of regular pieces it is uniquely determined by G inside any regular piece.

In this chapter all functions $f(t)$ of which we take the transforms will be piecewise regular, and will either be bounded or will increase less rapidly in numerical value than e^{at} for some positive a.   And all the functions $F(p)$ whose inverse transforms we seek will admit of such functions $\text{Lap}^{-1} F(p)$ satisfying the conditions imposed on $f(t)$.

In applying Eq. (1), we shall think of p as real, positive, and sufficiently large so that the integral on the right converges. We illustrate this process for some simple functions.

Suppose that $f(t) = 1$ for $t > 0$.   When we take $f(t) = 0$ for $t < 0$, this function is known as the *unit step*.   We find from Eq. (1) that

$$\text{Lap } 1 = \int_0^\infty 1 \cdot e^{-pt}\, dt = -\frac{1}{p} e^{-pt}\Big|_0^\infty$$

$$= \frac{1}{p}. \tag{4}$$

Let us next put $f(t) = e^{ct}$ in Eq. (1).   We find

$$\text{Lap } e^{ct} = \int_0^\infty e^{ct} e^{-pt}\, dt = -\frac{1}{p-c} e^{-(p-c)t}\Big|_0^\infty$$

$$= \frac{1}{p-c}. \tag{5}$$

Here we must take $p > c$ to make the integral finite at $t = +\infty$. The operation of forming the transform is linear in character.

In particular, it follows directly from our definition that

$$\text{Lap } [c_1 f(t)] = c_1 \text{ Lap } f(t) = c_1 F(p), \tag{6}$$

$$\text{Lap } [f(t) + g(t)] = \text{Lap } f(t) + \text{Lap } g(t) = F(p) + G(p), \tag{7}$$

$$\text{Lap } [c_1 f(t) + c_2 g(t)] = c_1 F(p) + c_2 G(p). \tag{8}$$

We may use these relations to find the transforms of $\cosh kt$ and $\sinh kt$. From Eq. (35) of Sec. 4, we have

$$\cosh kt = \tfrac{1}{2}(e^{kt} + e^{-kt}), \qquad \sinh kt = \tfrac{1}{2}(e^{kt} - e^{-kt}). \tag{9}$$

By putting $c = k$, and $c = -k$ in Eq. (5), and using Eqs. (6) and (7), we find

$$\text{Lap } \cosh kt = \frac{1}{2} \left(\text{Lap } e^{kt} + \text{Lap } e^{-kt} \right) = \frac{1}{2} \left(\frac{1}{p-k} + \frac{1}{p+k} \right)$$

$$= \frac{p}{p^2 - k^2}. \tag{10}$$

$$\text{Lap } \sinh kt = \frac{1}{2} \left(\text{Lap } e^{kt} - \text{Lap } e^{-kt} \right) = \frac{1}{2} \left(\frac{1}{p-k} - \frac{1}{p+k} \right)$$

$$= \frac{k}{p^2 - k^2}. \tag{11}$$

Since p and t are real, it also follows from the definition that if i is the imaginary unit and if u, v, U, V are real, then

$$\text{Lap } (u + iv) = U + iV \qquad \text{implies that} \qquad \text{Lap } u = U$$
$$\text{and Lap } v = V. \tag{12}$$

Or, using the notation of Sec. 12, when f and F are complex functions of the real variables t and p, we have

$$\text{Lap } (\text{Re } f) = \text{Re } F \qquad \text{and} \qquad \text{Lap } (\text{Im } f) = \text{Im } F. \tag{13}$$

If we put $c = -a + ki$ in Eq. (5), the result may be written

$$\text{Lap } e^{-at+ikt} = \frac{1}{p+a-ki} = \frac{p+a+ki}{(p+a)^2 + k^2}. \tag{14}$$

But, from Eq. (28) of Sec. 4,

$$e^{-at+ikt} = e^{-at} \cos kt + ie^{-at} \sin kt. \tag{15}$$

It follows from the last four equations that

$$\text{Lap } e^{-at} \cos kt = \frac{p + a}{(p + a)^2 + k^2}. \tag{16}$$

$$\text{Lap } e^{-at} \sin kt = \frac{k}{(p + a)^2 + k^2}. \tag{17}$$

48. Transforms of Derivatives

Suppose that we know $F(p)$, the transform of $f(t)$ and wish to find the transform of $f'(t)$, the derivative of $f(t)$. We assume that $f'(t)$ is piecewise regular, and that $f(t)$ is the integral of $f'(t)$ and hence continuous for all positive values of t. From the defining equation, Eq. (1), we have

$$\text{Lap } f'(t) = \int_0^\infty f'(t)e^{-pt}\, dt. \tag{18}$$

Integrating by parts, with $u = e^{-pt}$ and $dv = f'(t)dt$, $v = f(t)$, we find

$$\text{Lap } f'(t) = f(t)e^{-pt}\big|_0^\infty + p \int_0^\infty f(t)e^{-pt}\, dt$$
$$= -f(0+) + p \text{ Lap } f(t). \tag{19}$$

Here $f(0+)$ means the limit of $f(t)$ as t approaches zero through positive values.

As an illustration, let $f(t) = e^{ct}$. Then by Eqs. (19) and (5)

$$\text{Lap } ce^{ct} = -1 + p\,\frac{1}{p - c} = c\,\frac{1}{p - c}. \tag{20}$$

This is in agreement with Eqs. (5) and (6).

We may derive relations similar to Eq. (19) for higher derivatives, whenever the highest derivative considered is piecewise regular, and all lower derivatives are continuous for positive values of t. Thus for the second derivative, $f''(t)$, we first replace $f(t)$ by $f'(t)$ in Eq. (19) and so find

$$\text{Lap } f''(t) = -f'(0+) + p \text{ Lap } f'(t), \tag{21}$$

and then replace Lap $f'(t)$ in the right member by its value from Eq. (19). The result is

$$\text{Lap } f''(t) = -f'(0+) - pf(0+) + p^2 \text{ Lap } f(t). \tag{22}$$

Let us next obtain the transform of the integral

$$g(t) = \int_{t_0}^t f(t)dt = \int_{t_0}^t f(u)du. \tag{23}$$

We note that this makes $g'(t) = f(t)$. Then from Eq. (19), with f replaced by g throughout, we find

$$\text{Lap } f(t) = -g(0+) + p \text{ Lap } g(t). \tag{24}$$

Consequently,

$$\text{Lap } g(t) = \frac{\text{Lap } f(t) + g(0+)}{p} \tag{25}$$

In view of Eq. (23), this may be written

$$\text{Lap } \int_{t_0}^t f(u)du = \frac{\text{Lap } f(t) + \int_{t_0}^0 f(u)du}{p} \tag{26}$$

As an application of this formula, consider the charge on a condenser which was discharged at time t_0,

$$q = \int_{t_0}^t i \, dt. \tag{27}$$

If q_0 denotes the charge at $t = 0$, or integral from t_0 to 0, from Eq. (26) we have

$$\text{Lap } q = \frac{\text{Lap } i + q_0}{p} \quad \text{or} \quad Q = \frac{I + q_0}{p} \tag{28}$$

49. Zero Initial Values

The relations of the preceding section take a simpler form if we assume that the initial value of the function, $f(0+)$, and of the first derivative $f'(0+)$ are each zero. In that case Eqs. (19) and (22) become

$$\text{Lap } f'(t) = p \text{ Lap } f(t), \quad \text{for } f(0+) = 0, \tag{29}$$

$$\text{Lap } f''(t) = p^2 \text{ Lap } f(t), \quad \text{for } f'(0+) = 0, f(0+) = 0. \tag{30}$$

Again, if we take $t_0 = 0$ in Eq. (26), it becomes

$$\text{Lap } \int_0^t f(u)du = \frac{1}{p} \text{ Lap } f(t). \tag{31}$$

The conditions $f(0+) = 0$, $f'(0+) = 0$ are met in mechanical systems if we start at rest, and choose the coordinate systems so that the initial displacements are zero. And in electrical systems dead for $t < 0$, all the condensers are discharged and the impressed emfs are zero for $t = 0$, so that if a current is determined by an nth-order differential equation, the initial value of the current and of each of its first $(n - 1)$ derivatives will be zero.

For such cases Eqs. (29) and (30) and the similar ones for higher derivatives show that in forming all the derivatives up to the nth we may consider differentiation of the function as corresponding to multiplication of the transform by p. And Eq. (31) shows that integration of the function with lower limit zero corresponds to division of the transform by p. Thus for the case of zero initial values the complicated operations of differentiation and integration are transformed into mere multiplication and division by p.

We shall apply Eq. (31) to find the transforms of the integral powers of t. Using Eq. (4), we find successively:

$$t = \int_0^t 1 \, dt, \qquad \text{Lap } t = \frac{1}{p} \text{ Lap } 1 = \frac{1}{p^2}. \tag{32}$$

$$t^2 = 2 \int_0^t t \, dt, \qquad \text{Lap } t^2 = 2 \frac{1}{p} \text{ Lap } t = \frac{2}{p^3}. \tag{33}$$

$$t^n = n \int_0^t t^{n-1} \, dt, \qquad \text{Lap } t^n = n \frac{1}{p} \text{ Lap } t^{n-1} = \frac{n!}{p^{n+1}}. \tag{34}$$

Here $n! = 1 \cdot 2 \cdot 3 \cdots n$. If $n = 0$, $0! = 1$, $t^0 = 1$, and Eq. (34) reduces to Eq. (4).

50. Substitution and Translation Properties

Let us replace p by $p + a$ in the defining equation, Eq. (1). We thus find

$$\begin{aligned}
F(p + a) &= \int_0^\infty e^{-(p+a)t} f(t) dt \\
&= \int_0^\infty e^{-pt} [e^{-at} f(t)] dt \\
&= \text{Lap } e^{-at} f(t).
\end{aligned} \tag{35}$$

This proves that *multiplying the function by e^{-at} corresponds to substituting $p + a$ for p in its Laplace transform.*

As an application of this substitution property, we may deduce from Eq. (32) that since

$$\frac{1}{p^2} = \text{Lap } t, \qquad \frac{1}{(p + a)^2} = \text{Lap } te^{-at}. \qquad (36)$$

Let b be any positive number. Then if $f(t) = 0$ for $t < 0$, and the graph of $f(t)$ is translated or shifted b units to the right, the translated graph represents the function defined by

$$g(t) = 0 \qquad \text{for } t < b, \qquad g(t) = f(t - b) \qquad \text{for } t > b. \qquad (37)$$

For example, Fig. 50 represents $f(t) = 0$ for $t < 0$ and $f(t) = t$

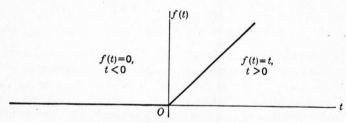

Fig. 50.   Graph of a particular $f(t)$.

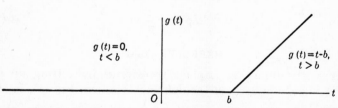

Fig. 51.   Graph of $g(t) = f(t - b)$ is obtained by translating graph of $f(t)$ b units to the right.

for $t > 0$. And Fig. 51 represents $g(t) = 0$ for $t < b$, and $g(t) = t - b$ for $t > b$.

For the $g(t)$ of Eq. (37), we may use Eq. (1) to find

$$G(p) = \text{Lap } g(t).$$

We have

$$G(p) = \int_0^\infty e^{-pt}g(t)dt = \int_0^b e^{-pt}g(t)dt + \int_b^\infty e^{-pt}g(t)dt$$
$$= \int_0^b e^{-pt}0\,dt + \int_b^\infty e^{-pt}f(t-b)dt$$
$$= \int_b^\infty e^{-pu}f(u-b)du. \quad (38)$$

Here we have used the values of $g(t)$ for the intervals $0,b$ and b,∞ as given in Eq. (37), noted that the integral from 0 to b is zero and we have replaced the variable of integration t by u.

Now make the substitution $u = t + b$ which implies that

$$du = dt, \qquad t = u - b \qquad (39)$$

and $t = 0$ when $u = b$, $t = \infty$ when $u = \infty$. Thus from Eq. (38),

$$G(p) = \int_b^\infty e^{-pu}f(u-b)du = \int_0^\infty e^{-pt-pb}f(t)dt$$
$$= e^{-pb}\int_0^\infty e^{-pt}f(t)dt = e^{-pb}F(p). \quad (40)$$

This proves that for a function 0 for $t < 0$, *translating the function b units to the right corresponds to multiplying its transform by e^{-bp}.* More specifically, if $g(t)$ is the translated function given by Eq. (37), then Lap $g(t) = e^{-bp}$ Lap $f(t)$.

As an illustration of this translation property, we may deduce from Eq. (32) that for the $g(t)$ of Fig. 51, the Laplace transform is

$$e^{-bp}\text{ Lap } t = \frac{1}{p^2}e^{-bp}. \quad (41)$$

EXERCISE XXVII

Verify the following Laplace transforms by setting up and evaluating the integral of the defining equation, Eq. (1), in each case.

1. Lap $4 = \dfrac{4}{p}$.

2. Lap $4e^{-2t} = \dfrac{4}{p+2}$.

3. Lap $4t = \dfrac{4}{p^2}$.

4. Lap $(2 - 2e^{-2t}) = \dfrac{4}{p(p+2)}$.

5. Lap $3te^{-2t} = \dfrac{3}{(p+2)^2}$.

6. Lap $(3 - 6t)e^{-2t} = \dfrac{3p}{(p+2)^2}$.

Use Eq. (8) to deduce the result of

7. Prob. 4 from Probs. 1 and 2.
8. Prob. 6 from Probs. 2 and 4.

Use the methods or results of Sec. 46 to verify that

9. Lap 2 sinh $3t = \dfrac{6}{p^2 - 9}$.   **10.** Lap 2 cosh $3t = \dfrac{2p}{p^2 - 9}$.

11. Lap $(\cosh 3t - 1) = \dfrac{9}{p(p^2 - 9)}$.   **12.** Lap 3 sin $2t = \dfrac{6}{p^2 + 4}$.

13. Lap 3 cos $2t = \dfrac{3p}{p^2 + 4}$.   **14.** Lap $(\cos 2t - 1) = \dfrac{-4}{p(p^2 + 4)}$.

15. By evaluating each of its terms, check Eq. (22) when $f(t) = e^{2t}$.

16. Use Probs. 9 and 10 to check Eq. (19) when
$$f(t) = 2 \cosh 3t.$$

17. Use Probs. 12 and 13 to check Eq. (19) when
$$f(t) = 3 \cos 2t.$$

18. Check Eq. (26) when $f(t) = 2e^{-t}$ and $t_0 = 1$.

Show that Eq. (29) may be used to deduce the result of

19. Prob. 1 from that of Prob. 3.
20. Prob. 2 from that of Prob. 4.
21. Prob. 6 from that of Prob. 5.

Show that Eqs. (31) and (6) may be used to deduce the result of

22. Prob. 9 from that of Prob. 10.
23. Prob. 11 from that of Prob. 9.
24. Prob. 12 from that of Prob. 13.
25. Prob. 14 from that of Prob. 12.

26. Show that Lap $(1 - 2t) = \dfrac{p - 2}{p^2}$.

27. Show that the Laplace transform of the polynomial
$a + bt + ct^2 + dt^3$ is $\dfrac{ap^3 + bp^2 + 2cp + 6d}{p^4}$.

From the substitution property, Eq. (35), and the result of

28. Prob. 12 deduce that Lap $3e^{-t} \sin 2t = \dfrac{6}{(p+1)^2 + 4}$.

29. Prob. 13 deduce that Lap $3e^{-t} \cos 2t = \dfrac{3p+3}{(p+1)^2 + 4}$.

30. Prob. 26 deduce that Lap $(1 - 2t)e^{-2t} = \dfrac{p}{(p+2)^2}$.

31. Use Eqs. (17) and (6) to check Prob. 28.
32. Use Eqs. (16) and (6) to check Prob. 29.
33. Use Prob. 5 and Eqs. (29) and (6) to check Prob. 30.

From the translation property, Eqs. (37) and (40), show that

34. If $f(t) = 0$ for $t < 3$ and $f(t) = 5$ for $t > 3$, then
Lap $f(t) = \dfrac{5}{p} e^{-3p}$.

35. If $f(t) = 0$ for $t < 2\pi$ and $f(t) = \sin t$ for $t > 2\pi$, then
Lap $f(t) = \dfrac{e^{-2\pi p}}{p^2 + 1}$.

36. If $f(t) = 0$ for $t < \pi$ and $f(t) = \sin t$ for $t > \pi$, then
Lap $f(t) = \dfrac{-e^{-\pi p}}{p^2 + 1}$.

37. If $f(t) = 0$ for $t < \pi/2$ and $f(t) = \sin t$ for $t > \pi/2$, then
Lap $f(t) = \dfrac{pe^{-\pi p/2}}{p^2 + 1}$.

51. Differential Equations

Many problems involving differential equations may be solved by means of Laplace transforms. To illustrate the method we consider the following problem:

Find the solution of the differential equation

$$\frac{dy}{dt} = 4 \qquad \text{for } t > 0, \tag{42}$$

which has $y = 5$ when $t = 0$.

If $y = f(t)$, $f(0+) = 5$. Hence if we call the transform of our function $F(p)$, by Eq. (19) we have

$$\text{Lap} \frac{dy}{dt} = \text{Lap} f'(t) = -f(0+) + p \text{ Lap } f(t)$$
$$= -5 + pF(p). \tag{43}$$

The transform of the right member of Eq. (42) is found from Eqs. (6) and (4) to be

$$\text{Lap } 4 = \text{Lap } 4 \cdot 1 = 4 \text{ Lap } 1 = 4\frac{1}{p} = \frac{4}{p}. \tag{44}$$

If we take the Laplace transforms of both sides of Eq. (42), in view of Eqs. (43) and (44) we find that

$$-5 + pF(p) = \frac{4}{p}. \tag{45}$$

This may be solved for $F(p)$ to give

$$F(p) = \frac{4}{p^2} + \frac{5}{p}. \tag{46}$$

By Eq. (32), $\text{Lap}^{-1} \frac{1}{p^2} = t$. And by Eq. (4), $\text{Lap}^{-1} \frac{1}{p} = 1$. Hence by Eq. (8),

$$f(t) = \text{Lap}^{-1} \left(\frac{4}{p^2} + \frac{5}{p} \right) = 4 \text{ Lap}^{-1} \frac{1}{p^2} + 5 \text{ Lap}^{-1} \frac{1}{p}$$
$$= 4t + 5. \tag{47}$$

This is the solution of our problem. It is a solution because our steps are reversible. And it is the only solution because for $t > 0$, it consists of one regular piece, and inside a regular piece the inverse Laplace transform is uniquely determined.

We have introduced $f(t)$ and $F(p)$ to conform to our earlier notation. Since the variable here was y, it would be more natural to use Y for $Y(p)$, the transform of $y(t)$. With this notation we would write in place of Eqs. (45), (46), and (47)

$$-5 + pY = \frac{4}{p}, \qquad Y = \frac{4}{p^2} + \frac{5}{p}, \qquad y = 4t + 5. \tag{48}$$

Let us consider the Laplace transform method of solving a single linear differential equation with constant coefficients.   If the right member is a linear combination of the simple functions whose transforms were found in Secs. 47 and 49, the transform of that member may be found by applying these results and combining them by using Eqs. (6), (7), and (8).   The transform of the left member may be found by using these same equations to combine the results of Sec. 48, or for a dead system those of Sec. 49. The transformed equation may contain polynomial or rational functions of p, but will involve Lap $f(t) = F(p)$, or Lap $y = Y$ to the first power only.   Hence it is easy to solve for Y as a function of p.   If the function of t which has this as its transform can be found, it will be the solution of our given equation and initial values.

The final step of the above procedure, as well as the evaluation of the transform of the right member, is facilitated by consulting a table of some common functions, their transforms, and the effect on the transforms of certain operations on functions.   The table given in the next section, and repeated at the end of the book, is adequate for all the problems of this chapter.

52. Table of Transforms

For easy reference, we collect several of our results in tabular form.   Most of these were established in Secs. 47 to 50.   For the derivations of the rest, see Probs. 38, 39, 40, and 46 of Exercise XXVIII.

We note that items 1 to 13 involve general functions and express a correspondence between operations on the function and other operations on the transform.   Specifically, to find the transforms of derivatives in the general case we use items 2, 3, and 4, while for derivatives in problems on systems dead initially we use items 7, 8, and 9.   And to transform integrals we use items 5, 6, and 10. Item 1 expresses the linearity property by which the problem of finding the transform, or inverse transform, of a linear combination of terms is reduced to the corresponding problem for the individual terms.   Item 11, the substitution property, item 12,

TABLE OF LAPLACE TRANSFORMS

	Function $f(t) = \text{Lap}^{-1} F(p)$	Transform $\text{Lap } f(t) = F(p)$
1	$c_1 f(t) + c_2 g(t)$	$c_1 F(p) + c_2 G(p)$
2	$f'(t)$	$-f(0+) + pF(p)$
3	$f''(t)$	$-f'(0+) - pf(0+) + p^2 F(p)$
4	$f^{(n)}(t)$	$-f^{(n-1)}(0+) - pf^{(n-2)}(0+) -$ $\cdots - p^{n-1}f(0+) + p^n F(p)$
5	$\int_{t_0}^{t} f(u)du$	$\dfrac{1}{p} F(p) + \dfrac{1}{p} \int_{t_0}^{0} f(u)du$
6	$\int_{0}^{t} f(u)du$	$\dfrac{1}{p} F(p)$
7	$f'(t)$, when $f(0+) = 0$	$pF(p)$
8	$f''(t)$, when $f(0+) = 0, f'(0+) = 0$	$p^2 F(p)$
9	$f^{(n)}(t)$ when $f(0+) = \cdots = f^{(n-1)}(0+) = 0$	$p^n F(p)$
10	$q = \int_{t_0}^{t} i \, dt$	$\dfrac{I + q_0}{p}$
11	$e^{-at}f(t)$	$F(p + a)$
12	$g(t) = 0$ for $t < b$ $g(t) = f(t - b)$ for $t > b$	$G(p) = e^{-bp}F(p)$
13	$h(t) = \int_{0}^{t} f(u)g(t - u)du$ $= \int_{0}^{t} f(t - u)g(u)du$	$H(p) = F(p)G(p)$
14	1	$\dfrac{1}{p}$

TABLE OF LAPLACE TRANSFORMS.—(*Continued*)

	Function $f(t) = \text{Lap}^{-1} F(p)$	Transform $\text{Lap } f(t) = F(p)$
15	e^{-at}	$\dfrac{1}{p + a}$
16	t	$\dfrac{1}{p^2}$
17	$\dfrac{t^2}{2}$	$\dfrac{1}{p^3}$
18	$\dfrac{t^n}{n!}$	$\dfrac{1}{p^{n+1}}$
19	$\sin kt$	$\dfrac{k}{p^2 + k^2}$
20	$\cos kt$	$\dfrac{p}{p^2 + k^2}$
21	$\sinh kt$	$\dfrac{k}{p^2 - k^2}$
22	$\cosh kt$	$\dfrac{p}{p^2 - k^2}$
23	te^{-at}	$\dfrac{1}{(p + a)^2}$
24	$\dfrac{t^n}{n!} e^{-at}$	$\dfrac{1}{(p + a)^{n+1}}$
25	$e^{-at} \sin kt$	$\dfrac{k}{(p + a)^2 + k^2}$
26	$e^{-at} \cos kt$	$\dfrac{p + a}{(p + a)^2 + k^2}$

the translation property, and item 13, the convolution property, are all used for finding either direct or inverse transforms for terms of the appropriate form.

The last portion of the table, items 14 to 26, gives the transforms of particular functions. We may either find a given function of t in the first column and obtain its transform from the second column, or find a given function of p in the second column and obtain its inverse transform from the first column.

The use of the Table of Laplace Transforms first to introduce transforms of given functions of t and later on to find a desired solution from its transform function of p is roughly analogous to the use of a table of logarithms to facilitate numerical computations.

EXERCISE XXVIII

Find the Laplace transform of each of the following given functions of t by using the Table of Laplace Transforms.

1. 5. **2.** $5t$. **3.** $(4 - 2t)$.
4. $5e^{-t}$. **5.** $2te^{-3t}$. **6.** $(2 - 6t)e^{-3t}$.
7. $4 \sinh 5t$. **8.** $4 \cosh 5t$. **9.** $\cosh 4t - 1$.
10. $5 \sin 3t$. **11.** $5 \cos 3t$. **12.** $\cos 5t - 1$.
13. $t^3 - 2t^4$. **14.** $e^{-2t} \sin t$. **15.** $e^{-3t} \cos 2t$.

16. $f(t) = 0$ for $t < 4$ and $f(t) = 6$ for $t > 4$.
17. $f(t) = 0$ for $t < 4$ and $f(t) = 2t - 8$ for $t > 4$.
18. $f(t) = 0$ for $t < 4$ and $f(t) = 2t$ for $t > 4$.
19. $f(t) = 0$ for $t < 2$ and $f(t) = e^{2-t}$ for $t > 2$.
20. $f(t) = 0$ for $t < 2$ and $f(t) = e^{-t}$ for $t > 2$.
21. $f(t) = 0$ for $t < \pi$ and $f(t) = \sin t$ for $t > \pi$.

For each of the following given functions of p, use the table to find the inverse Laplace transform, that is, the function of t which has the given function as its Laplace transform.

22. $\dfrac{3}{p}$. **23.** $\dfrac{7}{p^2}$. **24.** $\dfrac{2 + 6p}{p^3}$.

25. $\dfrac{4}{p+5}$.

26. $\dfrac{2}{(p+3)^2}$.

27. $\dfrac{6}{p^2+3p} = \dfrac{2}{p} - \dfrac{2}{p+3}$.

28. $\dfrac{4}{p^2+4}$.

29. $\dfrac{4p}{p^2+4}$.

30. $\dfrac{2p}{(p+3)^2} = \dfrac{2}{p+3} - \dfrac{6}{(p+3)^2}$.

31. $\dfrac{4}{p^2-4}$.

32. $\dfrac{4p}{p^2-4}$.

33. $\dfrac{2}{p(p^2+1)} = \dfrac{2}{p} - \dfrac{2p}{p^2+1}$.

34. $\dfrac{e^{-\pi p}}{p^2+1}$.

35. $\dfrac{6}{(p+2)^2+9}$.

36. $\dfrac{6p}{(p+2)^2+9}$.

37. Deduce item 4 of the table for $n = 3$ from items 2 and 3, or Eqs. (21) and (22).

38. Prove item 4 for n any positive integer by mathematical induction.

39. Prove item 9 for n any positive integer by mathematical induction.

40. Deduce the properties of the convolution expressed in item 13 from the results of Probs. 15, 16, and 17 of Exercise XI by making suitable changes in the notation.

Use item 11 of the table to deduce

41. Item 15 from item 1. **42.** Item 23 from item 16.
43. Item 24 from item 18. **44.** Item 25 from item 19.
45. Item 26 from item 20.

46. Using item 6 and mathematical induction, prove item 18.
47. Show that if $g(t) = 1$, item 13 is equivalent to item 6.

Verify that item 13 gives a correct result when

48. $f(t) = t$, $g(t) = t$.   **49.** $f(t) = e^{-2t}$, $g(t) = e^{-2t}$.

Verify the following statements, which lead up to the relations of Probs. 54 and 55 involving $pF(p) = p$ Lap $f(t)$

50. For any small positive number b, and large positive number B

$p \int_b^B e^{-pt} dt = e^{-pb} - e^{-pB}$.   Hence if $|g(t)| < M$ for

$$b < t < B,$$

$\left| p \int_b^B e^{-pt} g(t) dt \right| < M(e^{-pb} - e^{-pB})$ which approaches zero when $p \to +\infty$. It also approaches zero when $p \to 0$, even when $b = 0$.

51. If $|g(t)| < e^{at}$ for $t > B$,

$$\left| p \int_B^\infty e^{-pt} g(t) dt \right| < p \int_B^\infty e^{(a-p)t} dt$$

or for $p > a$, $\dfrac{p}{p-a} e^{(a-p)B}$ which approaches zero when $p \to +\infty$.

52. $p \int_0^\infty e^{-pt} dt = 1$.   Hence $f(0+) = p \int_0^\infty e^{-pt} f(0+) dt$.   Also since pe^{-pt} is positive, $p \int_0^b e^{-pt} dt < 1$, and

$$\left| p \int_0^b e^{-pt} [f(t) - f(0+)] dt \right| < m$$

if $|f(t) - f(0+)| < m$ for $0 < t < b$.

53. Also from the equations of Prob. 52,

$$f(+\infty) = p \int_0^\infty e^{-pt} f(+\infty) dt.$$

And $p \int_B^\infty e^{-pt} < 1$, and $\left| p \int_B^\infty e^{-pt} [f(t) - f(+\infty)] dt \right| < m$ if $|f(t) - f(+\infty)| < m$ for $t > B$.

54. If as t approaches zero through positive values, $f(t) \to f(0+)$, then $\lim\limits_{p \to \infty} pF(p) = f(0+)$. This is the *initial value* theorem.

Prove it by the following steps:

$pF(p) - f(0+) = p \int_0^\infty e^{-pt} [f(t) - f(0+)] dt$, by Prob. 52.   Next write the integral from 0 to ∞ as the sum of three integrals, I from 0 to b, II from b to B, and III from B to ∞.   With

$$g(t) = f(t) - f(0+),$$

by Prob. 50, II $\to$ 0 and by Prob. 51, III $\to$ 0 when $p = +\infty$. Hence $|\text{II}| < m$ and $|\text{III}| < m$ for $p > p_1$. And by Prob. 52, $|\text{I}| < m$ if b is so small that $|f(t) - f(0+)| < m$ for $0 < t < b$. Since we may choose m arbitrarily small, and then find a suitable b, it follows that $|pF(p) - f(0+)| < 3m$ for $p > p_1$. Hence $pF(p) - f(0+) \to 0$, and $pF(p) \to f(0+)$ when $p \to \infty$.

55. If as t becomes positively infinite, $f(t) \to f(\infty +)$, a finite limit, then $\lim_{p \to 0} pF(p) = f(+\infty)$. This is the *final value theorem.*

Prove it by the following steps:

$pF(p) - f(+\infty) = p \int_0^\infty e^{-pt}[f(t) - f(+\infty)]dt$, by Prob. 53. Next write the integral from 0 to ∞ as the sum of two integrals, I from 0 to B, and II from B to ∞. With $g(t) = f(t) - f(\infty +)$, I $\to$ 0 by the last statement of Prob. 50 when $p \to 0$. Hence $|\text{I}| < m$ for $p < p_1$. And by Prob. 53, $|\text{II}| < m$ if B is so large that $|f(t) - f(+\infty)| < m$ for $t > b$. Since we may choose m arbitrarily small, and then find a suitable B, it follows that

$$|pF(p) - f(+\infty)| < 2m$$

for $p < p_1$. Hence $pF(p) - f(+\infty) \to 0$, and $pF(p) \to f(+\infty)$ when $p \to 0$.

56. Verify that for items 14, 15, 20, 22, and 26, $f(0+) = 1$, and $\lim_{p \to \infty} pF(p)$ also $= 1$, in accord with the initial value theorem of Prob. 54.

57. Verify that for items 16, 19, 21, 23 and 25, $f(0+) = 0$, $f(t) \to 0$ like t, while $\lim_{p \to \infty} pF(p) \to 0$, with $pF(p) \to 0$ like $1/p$.

58. Verify that for items 18 and 24, $f(0+) \to 0$, $f(t) \to 0$ like t^n, while $\lim_{p \to \infty} pF(p) = 0$, with $pF(p) \to 0$ like $1/p^n$.

59. Verify that $f(+\infty)$ and $\lim_{p \to 0} pF(p)$ are each 1 for item 14, and each zero for item 15 with $a > 0$, items 16, 17, 18, and 23, 24, 25, and 26, with $a > 0$. This is in accord with the final value theorem of Prob. 55.

60. Prove that Lap $f(at) = \frac{1}{a} F\left(\frac{p}{a}\right)$, by making a change of variable $at = u$.

61. Show that $\text{Lap}^{-1} F(bp) = \frac{1}{b} f\left(\frac{t}{b}\right)$ by using Prob. 60 with $a = \frac{1}{b}$.

62. Assuming items 15, 23, and 24 given for $a = 1$, use Prob. 60 to deduce these items for any a.

63. Assuming items 19 and 20 given for $k = 1$, use Prob. 60 to deduce these items for any k.

64. In Prob. 55 we assumed that $\lim_{t \to +\infty} f(t)$ was finite. Show that the final value theorem does not necessarily hold when $\lim_{t \to +\infty} f(t) = +\infty$ by considering items 15 with $a > 0$ and items 21 and 22.

53. General Initial Conditions

The particular solution of a differential equation may be prescribed by fixing the initial values of the unknown function and certain of its derivatives, the disposable initial values for the equation or system which gave rise to it. These values are all zero for any system which was dead initially. In most of the following paragraphs we assume this condition to hold. This will enable us to use the simplified relations of Sec. 49, or items 6 to 9 of the table. For such systems an additional merit of the transform method is that we can obtain the solution without bothering to figure our separately how many initial values must be assigned as zero.

But in this section we consider some applications of the transform method to systems not dead originally but having general initial conditions. In such cases, when finding the transforms of derivatives, we must use Eqs. (19) and (22), or items 2, 3, and 4 of the Table of Laplace Transforms.

As an illustration, suppose that we wish to find the solution of the differential equation

$$\frac{d^2x}{dt^2} + 4\frac{dx}{dt} + 13x = 0 \tag{49}$$

which satisfies the initial conditions

$$x = 3, \qquad \frac{dx}{dt} = 6 \qquad \text{for } t = 0. \tag{50}$$

We apply items 2 and 3 with x, X, dx/dt, d^2x/dt^2 in place of f, F, f', f'', respectively. And we set $f(0+) = x(0+) = 3$ and $f'(0+) = x(0+) = 6$ in accordance with Eq. (50). Thus we obtain

$$\text{Lap } \frac{dx}{dt} = -3 + pX, \tag{51}$$

$$\text{Lap } \frac{d^2x}{dt^2} = -6 - 3p + p^2X. \tag{52}$$

Hence for Eq. (49) the transformed equation is

$$-6 - 3p + p^2X + 4(-3 + pX) + 13X = 0.$$

or

$$(p^2 + 4p + 13)X = 3p + 18.$$

It follows that

$$X = \frac{3p + 18}{p^2 + 4p + 13}. \tag{53}$$

The denominator is $(p + 2)^2 + 9$. Hence we write the numerator as $3(p + 2) + 12$ and

$$X = 3\frac{p + 2}{(p + 2)^2 + 3^2} + 4\frac{3}{(p - 2)^2 + 3^2}. \tag{54}$$

Finally, from items 1, 26, and 25 of the table, we have as the solution

$$x = 3e^{-2t} \cos 3t + 4e^{-2t} \sin 3t. \tag{55}$$

As a second example, consider a condenser of capacity C initially carrying a charge q_0 and discharging through a resistance

R. Here the differential equation for the charge q is

$$R\frac{dq}{dt} + \frac{q}{C} = 0, \tag{56}$$

and $q = q_0$ when $t = 0$.

To find q, we may apply item 2 of the table with q, Q, dq/dt in place of f, F, f', respectively. And we set $f(0+) = q(0+) = q_0$. Thus

$$\text{Lap } \frac{dq}{dt} = -q_0 + pQ. \tag{57}$$

Hence for Eq. (56) the transformed equation is

$$R(-q_0 + pQ) + \frac{Q}{C} = 0, \qquad \text{or} \qquad (RCp + 1)Q = RCq_0.$$

It follows that

$$Q = \frac{RCq_0}{RCp + 1} = q_0 \frac{1}{p + \dfrac{1}{RC}}. \tag{58}$$

Hence from items 1 and 15 of the table we obtain the value of q as

$$q = q_0 \epsilon^{-t/RC}. \tag{59}$$

Since the current $i = dq/dt$, i is given by

$$i = -\frac{q_0}{RC} \epsilon^{-t/RC}. \tag{60}$$

We might have used the fact that $i = dq/dt$ to write

$$Ri + \frac{q}{C} = 0 \qquad \text{or} \qquad Ri + \frac{1}{C}\int_{t_0}^{t} i\, dt = 0 \tag{61}$$

in place of Eq. (56). With I as the transform of i, and the given initial value q_0 we could apply item 10 of the table to either of these and thus obtain as the transformed equation

$$RI + \frac{1}{C}\left(\frac{I + q_0}{p}\right), \qquad \text{or} \qquad (RCp + 1)I = -q_0. \tag{62}$$

It follows that

$$I = \frac{-q_0}{RCp + 1} = -\frac{q_0}{RC} \frac{1}{p + \dfrac{1}{RC}}. \tag{63}$$

Hence from items 1 and 15 of the table we obtain the value of i as

$$i = -\frac{q_0}{RC} \epsilon^{-t/RC}. \tag{64}$$

If the value of i alone is desired, this alternative procedure based on Eq. (61) is preferable to the method used to obtain Eq. (60).

54. Partial Fractions

For problems involving a forcing function, or nonzero right-hand member, the Laplace transform of the solution is usually too complicated to be found directly in our short table. But it may often be decomposed into simpler parts each of a type found in the table by the method of partial fractions, which we shall now discuss.

As our first example, let us find the solution of the equation

$$\frac{d^2x}{dt^2} - 3\frac{dx}{dt} + 2x = 1 \tag{65}$$

which satisfies the initial conditions $x = 0$ and $dx/dt = 0$ when $t = 0$. As this system is initially dead, we may apply items 7 and 8 of the table with x, X, dx/dt, d^2x/dt^2 in place of f, F, f', f'' to obtain

$$\text{Lap}\frac{dx}{dt} = pX \qquad \text{and} \qquad \text{Lap}\frac{d^2x}{dt^2} = p^2X \tag{66}$$

And by item 14, Lap $1 = 1/p$. Hence the result of taking the Laplace transform of each member of Eq. (65) is

$$p^2X - 3pX + 2X = \frac{1}{p}, \qquad \text{or} \qquad (p^2 - 3p + 2)X = \frac{1}{p}. \tag{67}$$

It follows that

$$X = \frac{1}{p(p^2 - 3p + 2)} = \frac{1}{p(p - 1)(p - 2)}. \qquad (68)$$

The fraction just written is proper, that is, its denominator is of higher degree than the numerator. And the denominator is the product of distinct first-degree factors. Hence there exist constants A, B, and C such that

$$\frac{1}{p(p - 1)(p - 2)} = \frac{A}{p} + \frac{B}{p - 1} + \frac{C}{p - 2}. \qquad (69)$$

The three constants A, B, C could be evaluated by clearing of fractions, equating coefficients of corresponding powers of p, and solving the set of three linear equations that result. But there are two simpler methods.

To derive these, consider the general relation

$$\frac{N(p)}{D(p)} = \frac{A_1}{p - r_1} + \frac{M(p)}{E_1(p)}. \qquad (70)$$

Here A_1 is a constant, $N(p)$, $M(p)$, $D(p)$, $E_1(p)$ are all polynomials, and r_1 is a simple root of $D(p) = 0$, so that

$$D(p) = (p - r_1)E_1(p), \qquad D(r_1) = 0, \qquad E_1(r_1) \neq 0. \quad (71)$$

Let us multiply both sides of Eq. (70) by $p - r_1$, and then let $p \to r_1$. The first term on the right is A_1, and the other term contains the factor $p - r_1$, and thus approaches 0 when $p \to r_1$. Thus

$$A_1 = \lim_{p \to r_1} (p - r_1) \frac{N(p)}{D(p)} = N(r_1) \lim_{p \to r_1} \frac{p - r_1}{D(p)}. \qquad (72)$$

If we use the first relation of Eq. (71), and cancel the factor $(p - r_1)$, we see that the last limit in Eq. (72) is $1/E_1(r_1)$. Hence

$$A_1 = \frac{N(r_1)}{E_1(r_1)} = \frac{N(p)}{E_1(p)}\bigg|_{p = r_1}. \qquad (73)$$

This leads to the first rule: In Eq. (70), A_1 *may be found by deleting* *the factor $p - r_1$ from the denominator $D(p)$ and then evaluating the left member for $p = r_1$.*

Or we may apply l'Hospital's rule to the last limit in Eq. (72) and thus obtain $1/D'(r_1)$.   Hence we have our second rule:

$$A_1 = \frac{N(r_1)}{D'(r_1)} = \frac{N(p)}{dD/dp}\Big|_{p=r_1} \tag{74}$$

On applying the first rule to Eq. (69) we find that

$$A = \frac{1}{(p-1)(p-2)}\Big|_{p=0} = \frac{1}{2}, \quad B = \frac{1}{p(p-2)}\Big|_{p=1} = -1,$$

$$C = \frac{1}{p(p-1)}\Big|_{p=2} = \frac{1}{2}. \tag{75}$$

To apply the second rule, Eq. (74), we note that

$$D(p) = p(p-1)(p-2) = p^3 - 3p^2 + 2p,$$

so that

$$D'(p) = \frac{dD}{dp} = 3p^2 - 6p + 2.$$

Hence the right member of Eq. (74) for this case becomes

$$\frac{N(p)}{D'(p)} = \frac{1}{3p^2 - 6p + 2} \tag{76}$$

Evaluating this for each of the roots 0, 1, 2 we find that

$$A = \frac{N(0)}{D'(0)} = \frac{1}{2} \quad B = \frac{N(1)}{D'(1)} = -1, \quad C = \frac{N(2)}{D'(2)} = \frac{1}{2}. \tag{77}$$

Equations (77) and (75) check, and either process shows that from Eqs. (68) and (69),

$$X = \frac{1}{2}\frac{1}{p} - \frac{1}{p-1} + \frac{1}{2}\frac{1}{p-2}. \tag{78}$$

Finally, from items 1, 14, and 15 of the table we find the solution

$$x = \frac{1}{2} - e^t + \frac{1}{2}e^{2t}. \tag{79}$$

Our two rules determine all the constants only when the factors in the denominator of the expression to be expanded are linear and nonrepeated. In case a factor is repeated k times we must assume k terms in the partial fraction expansion, corresponding to the successive powers of the repeated factor. For example,

$$\frac{1}{(p-1)^2(p-2)} = \frac{A}{p-2} + \frac{B}{p-1} + \frac{C}{(p-1)^2}. \tag{80}$$

Here the first rule may be used to find A as

$$A = \frac{1}{(p-1)^2}\bigg|_{p=2} = 1. \tag{81}$$

And on multiplying both sides of Eq. (80) by $(p-1)^2$ and letting $p \to 1$, we find C as

$$C = \frac{1}{p-2}\bigg|_{p=1} = -1. \tag{82}$$

Since A and C are known, we may find B in this case by putting $A = 1, C = -1$, and p any particular value distinct from 1 and 2, for example, $p = 0$. Using these values in Eq. (80), we find

$$-\tfrac{1}{2} = -\tfrac{1}{2} - B - 1 \qquad \text{so that} \qquad B = -1. \tag{83}$$

For two double factors or one triple factor there would be two constants not found from our modified rule. In such a case we would use two particular values of p, to obtain two simultaneous equations for the two unknown constants.

The reader may easily verify that the relation

$$\frac{1}{(p-1)^2(p-2)} = \frac{1}{p-2} + \frac{-1}{p-1} + \frac{-1}{(p-1)^2} \tag{84}$$

which results from combining Eqs. (80), (81), (82), and (83) is a correct identity by adding the fractions on the right.

To illustrate the modifications of our methods necessary when quadratic factors arise, we shall find the solution of the equation

$$\frac{d^2x}{dt^2} + 2\frac{dx}{dt} + 5x = 10 \tag{85}$$

which satisfies the initial conditions $x = 0$ and $dx/dt = 0$ when $t = 0$. From items 1 and 14, Lap $10 = 10/p$. Using this and Eq. (66) to take the Laplace transform of Eq. (85), we obtain

$$p^2X + 2pX + 5X = \frac{10}{p}, \quad \text{or} \quad (p^2 + 2p + 5)X = \frac{10}{p}. \quad (86)$$

It follows that

$$X = \frac{10}{p(p^2 + 2p + 5)} \quad (87)$$

In this case constants A, B, and C exist such that

$$\frac{10}{p(p^2 + 2p + 5)} = \frac{A}{p} + \frac{Bp + C}{p^2 + 2p + 5}. \quad (88)$$

Note that for a quadratic factor in the denominator of a simple fraction, we must assume a first-degree numerator.

Since zero is a simple root, the first rule may be used to find A as

$$A = \frac{10}{p^2 + 2p + 5}\bigg|_{p=0} = 2. \quad (89)$$

To evaluate B and C, we multiply Eq. (88) by $p^2 + 2p + 5$ and let $p \to -1 + 2i$, one root of $p^2 + 2p + 5 = 0$. This leads to

$$\frac{10}{-1 + 2i} = B(-1 + 2i) + C. \quad (90)$$

By the procedure of Eq. (6) of Sec. 1, we have

$$\frac{10}{-1 + 2i} = \frac{10}{-1 + 2i} \frac{-1 - 2i}{-1 - 2i} = \frac{10}{5}(-1 - 2i) = -2 - 4i \quad (91)$$

so that

$$-2 - 4i = (-B + C) + 2Bi. \quad (92)$$

Equating real and imaginary parts separately, we have

$$-2 = -B + C, \qquad -4 = 2B, \qquad \text{so that} \qquad B = -2$$
$$\text{and } C = B - 2 = -4. \quad (93)$$

From Eqs. (87) and (88) and the values given in Eqs. (89) and (93) we find

$$X = \frac{2}{p} + \frac{-2p - 4}{p^2 + 2p + 5}.$$ (94)

When, as here, there is only one quadratic factor, the numerator may be found by subtraction. Thus, after finding $A = 2$ in Eq. (89), we might have deduced from Eq. (88) that

$$\begin{aligned}
\frac{Bp + C}{p^2 + 2p + 5} &= \frac{10}{p(p^2 + 2p + 5)} - \frac{2}{p} \\
&= \frac{-2p^2 - 4p}{p(p^2 + 2p + 5)} \\
&= \frac{-2p - 4}{p^2 + 2p + 5}.
\end{aligned}$$ (95)

This shows that $B = -2$ and $C = -4$ as in Eq. (93) and therefore gives Eq. (94).

To take the inverse transform, we rewrite Eq. (94) in the form

$$X = 2\frac{1}{p} - 2\frac{p + 1}{(p + 1)^2 + 2^2} - \frac{2}{(p + 1)^2 + 2^2}.$$ (96)

We now apply items 1, 14, 26, and 25 of the Table of Laplace Transforms to deduce that

$$x = 2 - 2e^{-t} \cos 2t - e^{-t} \sin 2t.$$ (97)

This is the desired solution of Eq. (85).

It is possible to replace quadratic factors by products of first-degree factors involving complex roots. As this is sometimes desirable when there are several complex roots in the denominator, we shall illustrate the method as applied to Eq. (87). Since the roots of $p^2 + 2p + 5 = 0$ are $-1 \pm 2i$, we have

$$\begin{aligned}
\frac{10}{p(p^2 + 2p + 5)} &= \frac{10}{p(p + 1 + 2i)(p + 1 - 2i)} \\
&= \frac{A}{p} + \frac{D}{p + 1 - 2i} + \frac{\bar{D}}{p + 1 + 2i} \\
&= \frac{A}{p} + 2 \operatorname{Re} \frac{D}{p + 1 - 2i}.
\end{aligned}$$ (98)

Since the left side is real, the two fractions with complex factors will be conjugate. Thus D and $\bar{D}$ will be conjugate complex numbers. Once the complex roots are known, it is only necessary to use one of each pair, and to take twice the real part of the corresponding fraction as in the last expression of Eq. (98).

We find $A = 2$ as in Eq. (89). And we may also use the first rule to find D, since the complex factors are not repeated. Thus

$$D = \frac{10}{p(p + 1 + 2i)}\bigg|_{p = -1+2i} = \frac{10}{(-1 + 2i)4i}$$
$$= \frac{1}{2i}(-1 - 2i). \tag{99}$$

The last reduction is similar to Eq. (91). We have left the i in the denominator, because for any complex number $z = a + bi$,

$$\text{Re}\,\frac{z}{i} = \text{Re}\,(b - ai) = b = \text{Im}\,z, \qquad \text{and} \qquad 2\,\text{Re}\,\frac{z}{2i} = \text{Im}\,z. \tag{100}$$

From Eqs. (87), (98), (89), (99), and (100) we may conclude that

$$X = 2\,\frac{1}{p} + \text{Im}\,(-1 - 2i)\frac{1}{p + 1 - 2i}. \tag{101}$$

We now apply items 1, 14, and 15 of the Table of Laplace Transforms to deduce that

$$x = 2 + \text{Im}\,(-1 - 2i)e^{-(1-2i)t}. \tag{102}$$

But by Sec. 2,
$$e^{-(1-2i)t} = e^{-t}e^{2it} = e^{-t}(\cos 2t + i \sin 2t),$$
and
$$(-1 - 2i)(\cos 2t + i \sin 2t) = \cdots + i(-2 \cos 2t - \sin 2t),$$
so that
$$\text{Im}\,(-1 - 2i)e^{-(1-2i)t} = e^{-t}(-2 \cos 2t - \sin 2t). \tag{103}$$

Equations (102) and (103) show that

$$x = 2 - 2e^{-t} \cos 2t - e^{-t} \sin 2t. \tag{104}$$

This checks the result found in Eq. (97).

By the procedure of Sec. 6, for the factor in Eq. (102), we have $-1 - 2i = re^{i\theta}$, where $r = \sqrt{5} = 2.2361$ and

$$\theta = \tan^{-1} \frac{-2}{-1} = -2.0345.$$

This shows that

$$(-1 - 2i)e^{-(1-2i)t} = re^{-t}e^{i(2t-\theta)}. \tag{105}$$

We may combine these facts with Eq. (102) to deduce that

$$x = 2 + 2.2361e^{-t} \sin(2t - 2.0345). \tag{106}$$

This alternative form is often preferable to that of Eq. (104).

As a further example, let us find the solution of the equation

$$\frac{d^2x}{dt^2} + a^2x = \sin kt, \qquad k \neq a \tag{107}$$

which satisfies the initial conditions $x = 0$ and $dx/dt = 0$ when $t = 0$. Using item 19 and Eq. (66) to take the Laplace transform we obtain

$$p^2X + a^2X = \frac{k}{p^2 + k^2}, \qquad \text{or} \qquad (p^2 + a^2)X = \frac{k}{p^2 + k^2}. \tag{108}$$

It follows that

$$X = \frac{k}{(p^2 + a^2)(p^2 + k^2)}. \tag{109}$$

We first treat these real quadratic factors as in Eq. (88) and write

$$\frac{k}{(p^2 + a^2)(p^2 + k^2)} = \frac{Ap + B}{p^2 + a^2} + \frac{Cp + D}{p^2 + k^2} \tag{110}$$

To evaluate A and B, multiply Eq. (110) by $p^2 + a^2$ and let $p = ai$, one root of $p^2 + a^2 = 0$. Thus

$$\frac{k}{-a^2 + k^2} = Aai + B. \tag{111}$$

Equating real and imaginary parts separately gives

$$B = \frac{k}{k^2 - a^2}, \qquad A = 0. \tag{112}$$

To evaluate C and D, multiply Eq. (110) by $p^2 + k^2$ and let $p = ki$, one root of $p^2 + k^2 = 0$. Thus

$$\frac{k}{-k^2 + a^2} = Cki + D. \tag{113}$$

Equating real and imaginary parts separately gives

$$D = \frac{k}{a^2 - k^2}, \quad C = 0. \tag{114}$$

From Eqs. (109) and (110) and the values given in Eqs. (112) and (114) we find

$$X = \frac{k}{k^2 - a^2}\left(\frac{1}{p^2 + a^2} - \frac{1}{p^2 + k^2}\right)$$
$$= \frac{k}{k^2 - a^2}\left(\frac{1}{a}\frac{a}{p^2 + a^2} - \frac{1}{k}\frac{k}{p^2 + k^2}\right). \tag{115}$$

We now apply 1 and 19 of the Table of Laplace Transforms to deduce the solution

$$x = \frac{1}{a(k^2 - a^2)}(k \sin at - a \sin kt). \tag{116}$$

To treat Eq. (109) by the use of complex first-degree factors we note that the roots of the denominator are $\pm ai$, $\pm ki$. Hence, as in Eq. (98), we write here

$$X = \frac{k}{(p^2 + a^2)(p^2 + k^2)} = \frac{k}{(p + ai)(p - ai)(p + ki)(p - ki)}$$
$$= 2\,\mathrm{Re}\,\frac{E}{p - ai} + 2\,\mathrm{Re}\,\frac{F}{p - ki}. \tag{117}$$

By applying the first rule in each case we find that

$$E = \frac{k}{(p + ai)(p^2 + k^2)}\bigg|_{p=ai} = \frac{k}{2ai(k^2 - a^2)},$$
$$F = \frac{k}{(p^2 + a^2)(p + ki)}\bigg|_{p=ki} = \frac{1}{2i(a^2 - k^2)}. \tag{118}$$

From Eqs. (117), (118), and (100) we may conclude that

$$X = \text{Im} \frac{k}{a(k^2 - a^2)} \frac{1}{p - ai} + \text{Im} \frac{1}{a^2 - k^2} \frac{1}{p - ki}. \quad (119)$$

We now apply items 1 and 15 of the Table of Laplace transforms to deduce that

$$x = \text{Im} \frac{1}{a(k^2 - a^2)} (ke^{ait} - ae^{kit})$$

$$= \frac{1}{a(k^2 - a^2)} (k \sin at - a \sin kt). \quad (120)$$

This is in accord with the solution found in Eq. (116).

EXERCISE XXIX

1. Find the solution of $\dfrac{d^2x}{dt^2} + 4x = 0$ which has $x = 1$ and $\dfrac{dx}{dt} = 6$ when $t = 0$.

2. Find the solution of $\dfrac{d^2x}{dt^2} + 6 \dfrac{dx}{dt} + 10x = 0$ which has $x = 1$ and $\dfrac{dx}{dt} = 1$ when $t = 0$.

3. A condenser is discharged through an inductance, so that $L\dfrac{d^2q}{dt^2} + \dfrac{q}{c} = 0$. Find q and hence $i = \dfrac{dq}{dt}$, if $q = q_0$ and $i = 0$ when $t = 0$.

4. Check Prob. 3 by finding i directly as the appropriate solution of the equation $L \dfrac{di}{dt} + \dfrac{1}{C} \int_{t_0}^{t} i \, dt = 0$.

5. Find the solution of $\dfrac{d^2x}{dt^2} - 9x = 0$ which has $x = 5$ and $\dfrac{dx}{dt} = 3$ when $t = 0$.

6. Find the solution of $\dfrac{dx}{dt} + ax = 0$ which has $x = A$ when $t = 0$.

For each of the following equations, find the solution which has $x = A$ and $\dfrac{dx}{dt} = B$ when $t = 0$. Assume that $b \neq 0$.

7. $\dfrac{d^2x}{dt^2} + b^2x = 0.$ **8.** $\dfrac{d^2x}{dt^2} + 2a\,\dfrac{dx}{dt} + (a^2 + b^2)x = 0.$

9. $\dfrac{d^2x}{dt^2} - b^2x = 0.$ **10.** $\dfrac{d^2x}{dt^2} + 2a\,\dfrac{dx}{dt} + a^2x = 0.$

For each of the following functions of p, find the decomposition into partial fractions of simple type.

11. $\dfrac{2p + 3}{p^2 - 5p + 6}.$ **12.** $\dfrac{p + 2}{(p - 1)(p - 3)(p - 4)}.$

13. $\dfrac{ap + bk}{p^2 - k^2}.$ **14.** $\dfrac{p - 3}{p^3 + 3p^2 + 2p}.$

15. $\dfrac{p^2 + p - 4}{p^3 - p^2}.$ **16.** $\dfrac{cp + d}{(p - a)(p - b)}, \; a \neq b.$

17. $\dfrac{cp + d}{(p - a)^2}.$ **18.** $\dfrac{p}{(p^2 + 1)(p - 1)}.$

19. $\dfrac{4}{p^4 + p^2}.$ **20.** $\dfrac{25p^3}{(p^2 + 4)(p - 1)^2}.$

For each of the following equations, find the solution which has $x = 0$ and $\dfrac{dx}{dt} = 0$ when $t = 0$:

21. $\dfrac{d^2x}{dt^2} + 4x = 2.$ **22.** $\dfrac{d^2x}{dt^2} + 3\,\dfrac{dx}{dt} + 2x = e^{-t}.$

23. $\dfrac{d^2x}{dt^2} - x = \cosh 2t.$ **24.** $\dfrac{d^2x}{dt^2} + 4\,\dfrac{dx}{dt} + 4x = e^{-2t}.$

25. $\dfrac{d^2x}{dt^2} + x = \sin 2t.$ **26.** $\dfrac{d^2x}{dt^2} + 5\,\dfrac{dx}{dt} + 4x = e^{t}.$

27. $\dfrac{d^2x}{dt^2} + x = \sin t.$ HINT: Find the complex constants in

$$\frac{1}{(p^2 + 1)^2} = \frac{A}{(p - i)^2} + \frac{\bar{A}}{(p + i)^2} + \frac{B}{p - i} + \frac{\bar{B}}{p + i}$$

$$= -\frac{1}{2}\,\mathrm{Re}\,\frac{1}{(p - i)^2} + \frac{1}{2}\,\mathrm{Im}\,\frac{1}{p - i}.$$

Find the solution of the differential equation $\dfrac{dx}{dt} + x = 3$ which has

28. $x = 0$ at $t = 0$.   **29.** $x = 6$ at $t = 0$.

30. By using item 13 with $g(t) = e^{-at}$, show that the solution of the equation $\dfrac{dx}{dt} + ax = f(t)$ which has $x = A$ when $t = 0$ is given by

$$x = e^{-at} \left[\int_0^t e^{au} f(u)\,du + A \right].$$

31. By using the partial fraction decomposition of $\dfrac{1}{p^2 - a^2}$ and item 13, show that the solution of $\dfrac{d^2x}{dt^2} - a^2 x = f(t)$ which has $x = 0$ and $\dfrac{dx}{dt} = 0$ when $t = 0$ is given by

$$x = \frac{1}{2a}\, e^{at} \int_0^t e^{-au} f(u)\,du - \frac{1}{2a}\, e^{-at} \int_0^t e^{au} f(u)\,du.$$

32. Let $Q(p) = a_3 p^3 + a_2 p^2 + a_1 p + a_0$ be a third-degree polynominal whose roots are r_1, r_2, r_3 so that

$$Q(p) = a_3(p - r_1)(p - r_2)(p - r_3).$$

If M is a constant, and the four numbers m, r_1, r_2, r_3 are all different, use rule II, Eq. (74), to verify that

$$\frac{M}{(p - m)Q(p)} = \frac{M}{Q(m)} \frac{1}{p - m} - \sum_{k=1}^{3} \frac{M}{(m - r_k)Q'(r_k)} \frac{1}{p - r_k}.$$

33. Use the notation, assumptions, and result of Prob. 32 to show that the solution of the differential equation

$$a_3 \frac{d^3x}{dt^3} + a_2 \frac{d^2x}{dt^2} + a_1 \frac{dx}{dt} + a_0 = M e^{mt}$$

which has $x = 0$, $dx/dt = 0$, and $d^2x/dt^2 = 0$ when $t = 0$ is

$$x = \frac{M}{Q(m)} e^{mt} - \sum_{k=1}^{3} \frac{M}{(m - r_k)Q'(r_k)} e^{r_k t}.$$

This is a special case of the *Heaviside expansion*. A similar formula for an nth-order equation, with the summation running from 1 to n gives the solution whose derivatives vanish up to those of the $(n - 1)$st order, that is, for a system initially dead.

Use the Heaviside expansion of Prob. 33,

34. With $n = 2$ to check Prob. 22.

35. With $n = 1$ to check Prob. 28.

36. Let $Q(p) = a_3 p^3 + a_2 p^2 + a_1 p + a_0$ have three distinct roots r_1, r_2, r_3. Use rule II, Eq. (74), to verify that

$$\frac{1}{Q(p)} = \sum_{k=1}^{3} \frac{1}{Q'(r_k)} \frac{1}{p - r_k}.$$

37. Use item 13 with $g(t) = e^{r_k t}$ and the result of Prob. 36 to show that for a system initially dead the solution of the equation

$$a_3 \frac{d^3 x}{dt^3} + a_2 \frac{d^2 x}{dt^2} + a_1 \frac{dx}{dt} + a_0 = f(t)$$

is

$$x = \sum_{k=1}^{3} \frac{1}{Q'(r_k)} e^{r_k t} \int_0^t e^{-r_k u} f(u) du.$$

38. Provided that all the roots are distinct, the result of Prob. 37 holds when 3 is replaced by n. Use this fact with $n = 2$ to check Prob. 31.

55. Series Circuits

We shall next apply the Laplace transform method to problems on electric networks and mechanical systems. We begin with the simple series circuits described in Sec. 11.

As a first example, let it be required to find the current $i(t)$ in the circuit of Fig. 52, assumed dead at $t = 0$. From Eq. (132) of Sec. 11 with $L = 2$, $R = 10$, $e = 15$, we have as the differential equation

$$2 \frac{di}{dt} + 10i = 15. \tag{121}$$

As this system is initially dead, we may apply item 7 of the Table of Laplace Transforms with i, I, di/dt in place of f, F, f' to obtain

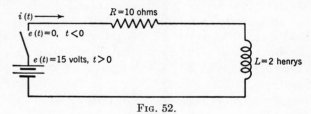

$i(t) \longrightarrow$ $R = 10$ ohms

$e(t) = 0, \quad t < 0$

$e(t) = 15$ volts, $t > 0$ $L = 2$ henrys

FIG. 52.

Lap $di/dt = pi$. And by items 1 and 14, Lap $15 = 15/p$. Hence the transformed equation is

$$2pI + 10I = \frac{15}{p}, \quad \text{or} \quad (2p + 10)I = \frac{15}{p}. \tag{122}$$

It follows that

$$I = \frac{15}{2} \frac{1}{p(p + 5)} = \frac{3}{2} \left(\frac{1}{p} - \frac{1}{p + 5} \right), \tag{123}$$

where the simple fractions are found as in Sec. 54.

From the last expression for I, using items 1, 14, and 15, we find

$$i = \frac{3}{2} (1 - \epsilon^{-5t}). \tag{124}$$

This is the resulting current. We note that $i = 0$ when $t = 0$, as it should for the solution of a first-order equation initially dead. And for $t = +\infty$, $i = \frac{3}{2}$, the current which would result if the inductance were short-circuited.

In practice it is not necessary to write down the differential equation (121), for the transformed equation (122) can be found from the following considerations. By Eq. (149) of Sec. 12 the impedance of our circuit for frequency ω is

$$Z(j\omega) = 2j\omega + 10. \tag{125}$$

In this equation we replace $j\omega$ by p throughout and obtain

$$Z(p) = 2p + 10, \tag{126}$$

the impedance function of p. Since we identify this p with the parameter in Eq. (1), we are chiefly concerned with the values of $Z(p)$ for positive real values of p.

Let $E(p)$ denote the transform of the source voltage $e(t)$, so that in the above problem where $e(t) = 15$, $E(p) = \text{Lap } 15 = 15/p$. Then in view of Eq. (126), Eq. (122) is equivalent to

$$Z(p)I(p) = E(p) \qquad \text{or} \qquad I(p) = \frac{E(p)}{Z(p)}. \tag{127}$$

This is the Laplace transform analogue of Ohm's law for direct currents, or of Eq. (166) of Sec. 12 for the complex representation of steady-state alternating currents.

For any simple circuit initially dead, $t_0 = 0$ in Eq. (132) of Sec. 11, and the differential equation is

$$L\frac{di}{dt} + Ri + \frac{1}{C}\int_0^t i\,dt = e(t). \tag{128}$$

Hence by items 7 and 10 of the Table of Laplace Transforms with $q_0 = 0$ and $i, I, di/dt$ in place of f, F, f' we may write as the transformed equation

$$LpI + RI + \frac{1}{C}\frac{I}{p} = E(p) \quad \text{or} \quad \left(Lp + R + \frac{1}{Cp}\right)I = E(p). \tag{129}$$

But by Eq. (149) of Sec. 12 the impedance for frequency ω is

$$Z(j\omega) = Lj\omega + R + \frac{1}{cj\omega}. \tag{130}$$

Hence the impedance function of p is

$$Z(p) = Lp + R + \frac{1}{Cp}. \tag{131}$$

A comparison of Eqs. (131) and (129) shows that the relation, Eq. (127), holds for any simple circuit.

For simple circuits and the more complicated networks treated in the next section, students to whom steady-state alternating-current theory is second nature will easily obtain the transfer impedance $Z(j\omega)$ appropriate to a given problem, and may then derive $Z(p)$ by replacing $j\omega$ by p as a final step. However, we may put p in place of $j\omega$ at any earlier stage. For example, we may pass directly from the circuit constants to Eq. (131) without using Eq. (130).

As a second example, let it be required to find the current $i(t)$

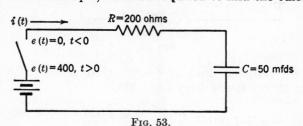

Fig. 53.

in the circuit of Fig. 53, assumed dead at $t = 0$. Here $R = 200$, $C = 50$ microfarads $= 50 \times 10^{-6}$ farad. Hence from Eq. (131)

$$Z(p) = 200 + \frac{10^6}{50p} = \frac{200(p + 100)}{p}. \tag{132}$$

And since $e(t) = 400$, $E(p) = \mathrm{Lap}\ 400 = 400/p$. Consequently, by Eq. (127),

$$I = \frac{E(p)}{Z(p)} = \frac{400}{p} \frac{p}{200(p + 100)} = \frac{2}{p + 100}. \tag{133}$$

Now by items 1 and 15 the inverse transform is found to be

$$i = 2\epsilon^{-100t}. \tag{134}$$

This is the resulting current. We note that $i = 2$ when $t = 0$.
This equals e/R or $400/200$, because the condenser, having zero
charge at time $t = 0$, does not impede the current. Since $L = 0$
here, Eq. (128) contains no first derivative. Hence the condition
that the circuit be dead imposes no condition on i at $t = 0$, but
merely makes $q = 0$ when $t = 0$, already effected by putting the
lower limit $t_0 = 0$ in Eq. (128). For $t = +\infty$, $i = 0$ since the
condenser can pass no direct current.

As a third example, let us find the current $i(t)$ in the circuit

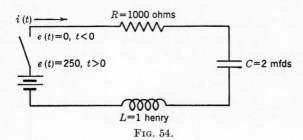

$L=1$ henry
FIG. 54.

of Fig. 54, assumed dead at $t = 0$. Here $L = 1$, $R = 1,000$,
$C = 2 \times 10^{-6}$. Hence from Eq. (131),

$$Z(p) = p + 1,000 + \frac{10^6}{2p} = \frac{p^2 + 1,000p + 500,000}{p}. \quad (135)$$

Since $e(t) = 250$, $E(p) = \text{Lap } 250 = 250/p$. Consequently, by
Eq. (127),

$$I = \frac{E(p)}{Z(p)} = \frac{250}{p} \frac{p}{p^2 + 1,000p + 500,000}$$
$$= \frac{1}{2} \frac{500}{(p + 500)^2 + 500^2}. \quad (136)$$

Finally by items 1 and 25 the inverse transform is found to be

$$i = \tfrac{1}{2} \, \epsilon^{-500t} \sin 500t \quad (137)$$

Thus the transient response of the circuit of Fig. 54 to a suddenly applied constant emf is an exponentially damped oscillating current.

56. Networks

It is possible to find i_2, the steady-state alternating-current response in, say, the second element of a network due to e_1 an applied alternating emf of frequency ω in, say, the first element of a network by means of a suitable transfer impedance $A_{12}(j\omega)$ having the property that

$$Z_{12}(j\omega) = \frac{\text{complex } e_1}{\text{complex } i_2} \text{ or } Z_{12}(j\omega) \, (\text{complex } i_2) = (\text{complex } e_1). \quad (138)$$

Such impedances may be found by the method outlined in Sec. 13 or in many cases more efficiently by other means developed in alternating-current network theory. If found as in Sec. 13, $Z_{12}(j\omega)$ results from algebraic operations on equations obtained from the differential equations by replacing d/dt by $j\omega$ and $\int dt$ by $1/(j\omega)$.

If we wished to find the complete transient response $i_2(t)$ to an emf $e_1(t)$ suddenly applied to a dead system, we could start with the same differential equations and take their transforms. To do this, we would replace $e_1(t)$ by $E(p)$, $i_1(t)$, $i_2(t)$, $\cdots$, $i_n(t)$ by $I_1(p)$, $I_2(p)$, $\cdots$, $I_n(p)$, d/dt by p and $\int dt$ by $1/p$. We would then eliminate all the I's except $I_2(p)$. Since this calculation differs from that of the preceding paragraph only in having p in place of $j\omega$, and e_1 and the i's changed to capital letters, the result would be

$$Z_{12}(p)I_2(p) = E_1(p). \quad (139)$$

Thus we may use any convenient means to find $Z_{12}(j\omega)$ for the steady-state alternating-current situation, form $Z_{12}(p)$ from it, and obtain $I_2(p)$ from Eq. (139).

We illustrate the general procedure for the two-mesh network of Fig. 55. If we call the element containing the terminals of the applied emf the first, and seek the resulting transient current in this same element, we shall be concerned with $E_1/I_1 = Z_{11}$ or simply Z, the *total impedance* or *driving point impedance* of this two-terminal network. To form Z, we consider Z_2 and Z_4 in series, and thus equivalent to $Z_2 + Z_4$. Then by the rule for

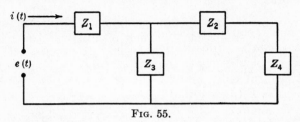

FIG. 55.

parallel impedances derived in Prob. 17 of Exercise V the impedances $(Z_2 + Z_4)$ and Z_3 in parallel combine to give

$$Z^* = \frac{(Z_2 + Z_4)Z_3}{(Z_2 + Z_4) + Z_3} \tag{140}$$

since this makes

$$\frac{1}{Z^*} = \frac{1}{Z_2 + Z_4} + \frac{1}{Z_3}.$$

Finally Z_1 and Z^* in series are equivalent to $Z_1 + Z^*$. Hence the total impedance is

$$Z = Z_1 + \frac{(Z_2 + Z_4)Z_3}{(Z_2 + Z_4) + Z_3} = \frac{(Z_2 + Z_4)(Z_1 + Z_3) + Z_1 Z_3}{Z_2 + Z_4 + Z_3}. \tag{141}$$

For use in a steady-state alternating-current calculation, as in Eq. (138), we would need $Z(j\omega)$. This could be found by writing the analogues of Eq. (130)

$$Z_1(j\omega) = L_1 j\omega + R_1 + \frac{1}{C_1 j\omega}, \tag{142}$$

and the similar expressions for Z_2, Z_3, Z_4 in terms of the appropriate lumped constants. Substitution of these in Eq. (141) gives $Z(j\omega)$.

To find the Laplace transform of a transient response, as in

Eq. (139), we need $Z(p)$. We make use of the analogues of Eq. (131)

$$Z_1(p) = L_1 p + R_1 + \frac{1}{C_1 p}, \qquad (143)$$

and the similar equations for Z_2, Z_3, Z_4 in terms of the appropriate lumped constants. Substitutions of these in Eq. (141) gives $Z(p)$. Since our problem involves the emf $e_1(t)$ and the current $i_1(t)$ in the first element only, we drop the subscripts 1, and in place of $Z_{11}(p)I_1(p) = E_1(p)$ write

$$Z(p)I(p) = E(p) \qquad \text{or} \qquad I(p) = \frac{E(p)}{Z(p)}. \qquad (144)$$

As a concrete example, let us find the transient current in the

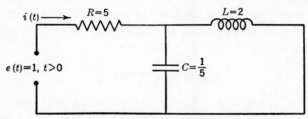

Fig. 56. Prototype network.

prototype network of Fig. 56, differing from an actual network by a scale factor, say 10^6. From Eq. (143) we have here

$$Z_1 = 5, \qquad Z_2 = 2p, \qquad Z_3 = \frac{5}{p}. \qquad (145)$$

Z_2 and Z_3 combine in parallel to give

$$Z^* = \frac{Z_2 Z_3}{Z_2 + Z_3} = \frac{2p \dfrac{5}{p}}{2p + \dfrac{5}{p}} = \frac{10p}{2p^2 + 5}. \qquad (146)$$

And this in series with $Z_1 = 5$ gives

$$Z = 5 + \frac{10p}{2p^2 + 5} = \frac{10p^2 + 10p + 25}{2p^2 + 5} \qquad (147)$$

Since $e(t) = 1$, by item 14, $E(p) = 1/p$. Hence from Eq. (144)

$$I = \frac{E}{Z} = \frac{1}{p} \frac{2p^2 + 5}{10p^2 + 10p + 25} = \frac{1}{10} \frac{2p^2 + 5}{p(p^2 + p + 2.5)}. \quad (148)$$

By the methods explained in Sec. 54, we may deduce that

$$\frac{2p^2 + 5}{p(p^2 + p + 2.5)} = \frac{2}{p} - \frac{2}{p^2 + p + 2.5} = 2\frac{1}{p}$$
$$- \frac{4}{3} \frac{1.5}{(p + 0.5)^2 + 1.5^2}$$

or

$$= 2\frac{1}{p} + 2 \operatorname{Im}\left(-\frac{2}{3}\right) \frac{1}{p + 0.5 + 1.5i}. \quad (149)$$

From items 1 and 14 for the first term and 25 or 15 for the second term, we may find the inverse transform of the last two expressions. Hence from either form, and Eq. (148), we find for $i(t) = \mathrm{Lap}^{-1} I$,

$$i = \tfrac{1}{5} - \tfrac{2}{15}\epsilon^{-0.5t} \sin 1.5t. \quad (150)$$

For the actual network with the resistance still 5 ohms, but inductance 2×10^{-6} henry and capacitance $\tfrac{1}{5} \times 10^{-6}$ farad, the response to an emf of 1 volt suddenly applied would be

$$i = \tfrac{1}{5} - \tfrac{2}{15}\epsilon^{-5\times10^5 t} \sin 1.5 \times 10^6 t. \quad (151)$$

This is obtained from Eq. (150) by multiplying the coefficients of t by 10^6.

EXERCISE XXX

Assume that the circuit of Fig. 57 is dead at time $t = 0$, and find the transient current response to a suddenly applied emf.

1. $e(t) = 3$, if $R = 2$, $L = 1$, no capacitance present.
2. $e(t) = e_0$, if $R = R$, $L = L$, no capacitance present.
3. $e(t) = 10$, if $R = 4$, $C = 10^{-5}$, no inductance present.
4. $e(t) = e_0$, if $R = R$, $C = C$, no inductance present.
5. $e(t) = 500$, if $R = 400$, $L = 1$, $C = \tfrac{1}{3} \times 10^{-4}$.

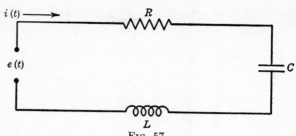

FIG. 57.

6. $e(t) = 100$, if $R = 100$, $L = 1$, $C = 8 \times 10^{-5}$.
7. $e(t) = \sin 20t$, if $L = 2$, $C = 2 \times 10^{-4}$, no resistance present.
8. $e(t) = \sin 10t$, if $R = 400$, $L = 10$, $C = \frac{1}{3} \times 10^{-3}$.
9. $e(t) = \sin 2t$, if $R = 100$, $L = 5$, $C = 4 \times 10^{-4}$.

Use the initial value theorem of Prob. 54 of Exercise XXVIII

10. And Eq. (123) to show that $i(0) = 0$ in Eq. (124).
11. And Eq. (133) to show that $i(0) = 2$ in Eq. (134).

12. The motion of the mass in Fig. 58 is governed by Eq. (135) of Sec. 11.   Let

$$F = f(t), F(p) = \text{Lap } f(t)$$

and

$$S(p) = \text{Lap } s(t).$$

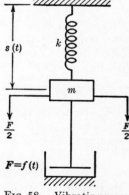

FIG. 58.   Vibrating mass.

Let the mass be initially at rest, and let $s(0) = 0$.   Show that if $A(p) = mp^2 + \beta p + k$, then $Z(p)S(p) = F(p)$.

Use Prob. 12 to find $Z(p)$ when the mass weighs $2g$ lb. so that $m = 2$, $\beta = 8$, and $k = 26$.   For this case determine $s(t)$ when the suddenly applied force $F = f(t)$ is

13. $f(t) = 4$.   **14.** $f(t) = 4 \sin 2t$.

15. The oscillatory motion of the disk in Fig. 59 is governed by Eq. (138) of Sec. 11. Let $M = f(t)$, $F(p) = \text{Lap } f(t)$ and

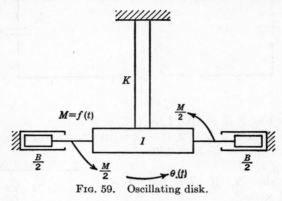

FIG. 59.   Oscillating disk.

$\Theta(p) = \text{Lap } \theta(t)$. Let the disk be initially at rest, and let $\theta(0) = 0$. Show that if

$$Z(p) = Ip^2 + Bp + K, \text{ then } Z(p)\Theta(p) = F(p).$$

Use Prob. 15 to find $Z(p)$ when $I = 1$ slug-ft.^{2}, $B = 4$, and $K = 5$. For this case determine $\theta(t)$ when there is suddenly applied

16. A torque $M = f(t) = 6$.

17. A unit impulsive torque. That is, $\int_0^t f(t)dt = 1$. Hence $\frac{1}{p} F(p) = \text{Lap } 1 = \frac{1}{p}$, and $F(p) = 1$.

In each case assume the indicated circuit initially dead, and find the transient current response in the first element to the given applied emf.

18. $e(t) = 10$ in the circuit of Fig. 60.
19. $e(t) = 10 \sin 2t$ in the circuit of Fig. 60.
20. $e(t) = 100$ in the circuit of Fig. 61.
21. $e(t) = 100 \sin 10t$ in the circuit of Fig. 61.

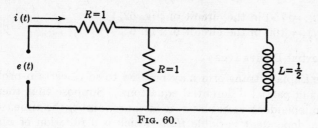

FIG. 60.

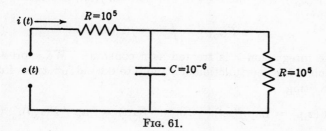

FIG. 61.

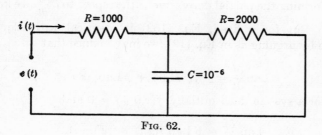

FIG. 62.

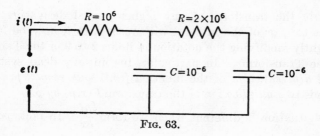

FIG. 63.

22. $e(t) = 750$ in the circuit of Fig. 62.
23. $e(t) = 100$ in the circuit of Fig. 63.

57. Partial Derivatives

The Laplace transform may be used to solve certain problems involving partial differential equations. Suppose that there are two independent variables x, a distance, and t, the time. Consider a dependent variable $f(x,t)$ which is a function of x and t. Then $F(x,p)$, the time *Laplace transform* of $f(x,t)$ is defined by the equation

$$F(x,p) = \int_0^\infty e^{-pt} f(x,t) dt. \tag{152}$$

In the integration x is treated as a constant. We express the relation of the new function of x and p to the old function of x and t by writing

$$F(x,p) = \text{Lap } f(x,t) \qquad \text{or} \qquad f(x,t) = \text{Lap}^{-1} F(x,p), \tag{153}$$

In forming the partial derivative with respect to t, $\dfrac{\partial f}{\partial t}$, we keep x fixed. But for x fixed, Eq. (152) is identical with Eq. (1). Hence by arguing as in Eq. (19), we may deduce that

$$\text{Lap } \frac{\partial f}{\partial t} = -f(x,0+) + p \text{ Lap } f(x,t). \tag{154}$$

And for a system dead initially, $f(x,0+) = 0$ and

$$\text{Lap } \frac{\partial f}{\partial t} = p \text{ Lap } f(x,t) = pF(x,p). \tag{155}$$

Similarly the transform of any higher partial derivative with respect to t, or of the integral with respect to t, may be found by slightly modifying the notation in items 2 to 9 of the Table of Laplace Transforms. In particular, for initially dead systems, *partial differentiation* of the function $f(x,t)$ *with respect to t* corresponds to *multiplication* of the transform $F(x,p)$ *by p*.

The situation is different when we form $\dfrac{\partial f}{\partial x}$. In fact, *partial differentiation* of the function $f(x,t)$ *with respect to x*, keeping t fixed, corresponds to *partial differentiation* of the transform $F(x,p)$ *with respect to x*, keeping p fixed. To see this, we calculate $\frac{\partial F}{\partial x}$ from Eq. (152). Assuming that $f(x,t)$ and $\frac{\partial f}{\partial x}$ are regular and do not increase too rapidly for large values of t, we may carry out the differentiation on the right inside the integral sign and thus obtain

$$\frac{\partial F}{\partial x} = \int_0^\infty e^{-pt}\frac{\partial f}{\partial x}\,dt. \tag{156}$$

Since this differs from Eq. (152) only in having $\frac{\partial F}{\partial x} = F_x(x,p)$ in place of $F(x,p)$ and $\frac{\partial f}{\partial x} = f_x(x,t)$ in place of $f(x,t)$, it shows that

$$\text{Lap } f_x(x,t) = F_x(x,p) \qquad \text{or} \qquad \text{Lap }\frac{\partial f}{\partial x} = \frac{\partial F}{\partial x}. \tag{157}$$

This shows that differentiation with respect to x on the function corresponds to a similar operation on the transform.

As illustrations of the principles just derived, assuming a system initially dead, we have for the second derivatives

$$\text{Lap }\frac{\partial^2 f}{\partial x^2} = \frac{\partial^2 F}{\partial x^2}, \qquad \text{Lap }\frac{\partial^2 f}{\partial x\,\partial t} = p\frac{\partial F}{\partial x}, \qquad \text{Lap }\frac{\partial^2 f}{\partial t^2} = p^2 F. \tag{158}$$

We turn now to specific examples. Our first problem is to find the solution of the partial differential equation

$$\frac{\partial f}{\partial t} = 8xt + 2\sin x \tag{159}$$

which satisfies the initial condition

$$f(x,0) = x^2. \tag{160}$$

By substituting from Eq. (160) into the analogue of item 2 or Eq. (154) we may determine the transform of $\frac{\partial f}{\partial t}$. And we may find the transform of the right member of Eq. (159) by treating x as a constant and using items 1, 16, and 14. Thus the transform of Eq. (159) is

$$-x^2 + pF = \frac{8x}{p^2} + \frac{2\sin x}{p} \quad \text{or}$$

$$F = 8x\frac{1}{p^3} + 2\sin x\frac{1}{p^2} + x^2\frac{1}{p}. \tag{161}$$

We next find $f(x,t) = \text{Lap}^{-1} F(x,p) = \text{Lap}^{-1} F$ by using items 1, 17, 16, and 14. This gives the solution of our problem

$$f(x,t) = 4xt^2 + 2t\sin x + x^2.$$

As a second problem let us find the solution of the equation

$$\frac{\partial^2 f}{\partial x\,\partial t} = 8xt \tag{162}$$

which satisfies the initial and boundary conditions

$$f(x,0) = x^2, \qquad f(0,t) = 3t. \tag{163}$$

To find the transform of $\dfrac{\partial^2 f}{\partial x\,\partial t}$ we first substitute $f(x,0+) = x^2$ in Eq. (154) and then replace the f in Eq. (157) by $\dfrac{\partial f}{\partial t}$. And as in Eq. (161), $\text{Lap } 8xt = 8x/p^2$. Thus the transform of Eq. (162) is

$$-2x + p\frac{\partial F}{\partial x} = \frac{8x}{p^2}, \qquad \text{or} \qquad \frac{\partial F}{\partial x} = \frac{8x}{p^3} + \frac{2x}{p}. \tag{164}$$

Since this involves no differentiation with respect to p, it is essentially an ordinary differential equation in F and x. Hence we may proceed as in Sec. 27. Integrating with respect to x keeping p constant, we obtain

$$F(x,p) = \frac{4x^2}{p^3} + \frac{x^2}{p} + G(p). \tag{165}$$

Since $F(x,p) = \text{Lap } f(x,t)$, $F(0,p) = \text{Lap } f(0,t) = \text{Lap } 3t$ by Eq.

(163).   Hence from items 1 and 16, $F(0,p) = 3/p^2$.   But from Eq. (165) we find $F(0,p) = G(p)$, so that

$$G(p) = \frac{3}{p^2} \quad \text{and} \quad F = 4x^2 \frac{1}{p^3} + x^2 \frac{1}{p} + 3 \frac{1}{p^2}. \quad (166)$$

We next use items 1, 17, 14, and 16 to find $\text{Lap}^{-1} F$.   The result is

$$F(x,t) = 2x^2t^2 + x^2 + 3t. \quad (167)$$

This is the solution of Prob. 2, or Eqs. (162) and (163).

The partial differential equation of the first order

$$2 \frac{\partial u}{\partial t} + \frac{\partial u}{\partial x} = 0 \quad (168)$$

has a unique solution assuming any prescribed set of values on the broken line consisting of the positive half of the t axis and the positive half of the x axis.   Suppose we demand that

$$u(x,0) = 0 \quad \text{for} \quad x > 0 \quad \text{and} \quad u(0,t) = 3t^2 \quad \text{for } t > 0. \quad (169)$$

As our third problem, let us find the solution of Eq. (168) which satisfies the boundary conditions of Eq. (169).   Since $u(x,0+) = 0$, we may use the analogue of item 7 or Eq. (155) to determine the transform of $\dfrac{\partial u}{\partial t}$.   And Eq. (157) gives the transform of $\dfrac{\partial u}{\partial x}$.   In each case we replace f, F by u, U.   Thus the transform of Eq. (168) is

$$2pU + \frac{\partial U}{\partial x} = 0 \quad \text{or} \quad \frac{\partial U}{\partial x} = -2pU. \quad (170)$$

To solve this we proceed as in Prob. 21 of Exercise XIII.   Treating it as essentially an ordinary linear differential equation with constant coefficients we find the solution

$$U(x,p) = A(p)e^{-2px}. \quad (171)$$

Since $U(x,p) = \text{Lap } u(x,t)$, $U(0,p) = \text{Lap } u(0,t) = \text{Lap } 3t^2$ by Eq. (169).   Hence from items 1 and 17, $U(0,p) = 6/p^3$.   But from Eq. (171) we find $U(0,p) = A(p)$, so that

$$A(p) = \frac{6}{p^3} \quad \text{and} \quad U = 6e^{-(2x)p}\frac{1}{p^3}. \tag{172}$$

We next use items 1, 12, and 17 to find $\text{Lap}^{-1} U$. The result is

$$
\begin{aligned}
u(x,t) &= 0 \quad \text{for } t < 2x \\
u(x,t) &= 3(t - 2x)^2 \quad \text{for } t > 2x.
\end{aligned} \tag{173}
$$

This is the solution of our problem.

Let us define $g(z) = 0$ for $z < 0$ and $g(z) = 3z^2$ for $z > 0$. Then $u(x,t) = g(t - 2x)$, since if $z = t - 2x$, $t < 2x$ when $z < 0$ and $t > 2x$ when $z > 0$. But $(t - 2x) = -2(x - t/2)$. Hence from the discussion of $f(x - vt)$ in Sec. 31 in connection with Eq. (81) it follows that the $u(x,t)$ of Eq. (173) represents a wave traveling to the right with velocity $\frac{1}{2}$.

As our fourth problem, let us find the solution of the equation

$$2\frac{\partial u}{\partial t} + \frac{\partial u}{\partial x} = -4u \tag{174}$$

which on the half axes satisfies the boundary conditions

$$u(x,0) = 0 \quad \text{for } x > 0 \quad \text{and} \quad u(0,t) = 3t^2 \quad \text{for } t > 0. \tag{175}$$

If $U = \text{Lap } u$, by item 1, $\text{Lap } (-4u) = -4U$. And the transform of the left member of Eq. (174) is found as in Eq. (170). Thus we find

$$2pU + \frac{\partial U}{\partial x} = -4U, \quad \text{or} \quad \frac{\partial U}{\partial x} = -(4 + 2p)U. \tag{176}$$

Solving this as we did Eq. (170), we find

$$U(x,p) = A(p)e^{-(4+2p)x}. \tag{177}$$

From Eqs. (177) and (175) we find that

$$A(p) = U(0,p) = \text{Lap } u(0,t) = \text{Lap } 3t^2 = 6/p^3.$$

By substituting this in Eq. (177), we obtain

$$U = \frac{6}{p^3} e^{-4x-2px} = 6e^{-4x}e^{-(2x)p}\frac{1}{p^3}. \tag{178}$$

To find Lap^{-1} U, we treat x as constant and use items 1, 12 and 17. This gives as the solution of Prob. 4, or Eqs. (174) and (175),

$$u(x,t) = 0 \qquad \text{for } t < 2x$$
$$u(x,t) = 3e^{-4x}(t - 2x)^2 \qquad \text{for } t > 2x. \tag{179}$$

Let us define $g(z) = 0$ for $z < 0$ and $g(z) = 3e^{2z}z^2$ for $z > 0$.

Then $u(x,t) = e^{-2t}g(t - 2x)$. Since $t - 2x = -2\left(x - \dfrac{t}{2}\right)$, by the property of $f(x - vt)$ referred to above $g(t - 2x)$ represents a wave traveling to the right with velocity $\frac{1}{2}$. And the solution $u(x,t)$ is this wave modulated with the damping factor e^{-2t}.

58. The Lossless Transmission Line

The equations governing the flow of electricity in a long lossless transmission line are

$$-\frac{\partial e}{\partial x} = L\frac{\partial i}{\partial t}, \qquad -\frac{\partial i}{\partial x} = C\frac{\partial e}{\partial t}. \tag{180}$$

There is a third relation derivable from these

$$\frac{\partial^2 e}{\partial x^2} = LC\frac{\partial^2 e}{\partial t^2} \quad \text{or} \quad \frac{\partial^2 e}{\partial t^2} = v^2\frac{\partial^2 e}{\partial x^2}, \quad \text{if } v = \frac{1}{\sqrt{LC}}. \tag{181}$$

Compare Eq. (97) of Sec. 33 and Eqs. (102) and (103) of Sec. 44. We recall that x represents distance along the line in miles and t represents the time in seconds. The potential $e(x,t)$ volts and the current $i(x,t)$ amperes are each function of position and time or of x and t like the function $f(x,t)$ of Eq. (152) and thus have time Laplace transforms $E(x,t)$ and $I(x,t)$ defined by relations similar to Eq. (152). Here the series inductance of L henrys per mile and the shunt capacitance of C farads per mile are thought of as uniformly distributed. They are thus unlike the corresponding letters in Eqs. (131) and (143) which represented lumped parameters and had the units of henrys and farads.

We shall confine our applications to systems initially dead, so that in transforming time derivatives we may use the analogues of items 7 and 8, or Eqs. (155) and (158). For space derivatives we use Eqs. (157) and (158). Thus on taking transforms of Eq. (180) we find

$$-\frac{\partial E}{\partial x} = LpI, \quad -\frac{\partial I}{\partial x} = CpE. \tag{182}$$

And the transform of Eq. (181) is

$$\frac{\partial^2 E}{\partial x^2} = LCp^2E \quad \text{or} \quad \frac{\partial^2 E}{\partial x^2} = \frac{p^2}{v^2}E. \tag{183}$$

Note that the first form might have been obtained from Eq. (182) by differentiating the first relation partially with respect to x and substituting for $\dfrac{\partial I}{\partial x}$ from the second relation.

To solve Eq. (183) we proceed as in Prob. 25 of Exercise XIII. Treating it as essentially an ordinarily differential equation with constant coefficients, we find the solution

$$E(x,p) = A(p)\epsilon^{-px/v} + B(p)\epsilon^{px/v}. \tag{184}$$

By differentiating this relation with respect to x, we find

$$\frac{\partial E}{\partial x} = -\frac{p}{v}A(p)\epsilon^{-px/v} + \frac{p}{v}B(p)\epsilon^{px/v}. \tag{185}$$

We may combine this with the first relation of Eq. (182) to deduce

$$I = -\frac{1}{Lp}\frac{\partial E}{\partial x} = \frac{1}{Lv}[A(p)\epsilon^{-px/v} - B(p)\epsilon^{px/v}]. \tag{186}$$

In Prob. 7 of Exercise XVIII we defined the *characteristic impedance* of a transmission line with constants R, L, G, C as $Z_K = \sqrt{\dfrac{R + j\omega L}{G + j\omega C}}.$ For the lossless line considered here, $R = 0$, $G = 0$ so that the characteristic impedance reduces to

$$Z_K = \sqrt{\frac{L}{C}}.$$

But by Eq. (181), $v = 1/\sqrt{LC}$. Hence $Lv = \sqrt{L/C} = Z_K$ and

Eq. (186) may be written

$$I(x,p) = \frac{A(p)\epsilon^{-px/v} - B(p)\epsilon^{px/v}}{Z_K} \qquad (187)$$

If $e(x,t)$ and $i(x,t)$ satisfy Eq. (180) and the system is initially dead, their Laplace transforms are given by Eqs. (184) and (187).

59. The Infinite Line

Suppose that we apply the results of Sec. 58 to a line which is of infinite length.   We seek solutions $e(x,t)$ and $i(x,t)$ which for any fixed t remain finite as $x \to +\infty$.   Hence the transforms $E(x,p)$ and $I(x,p)$ for any fixed p will remain finite as $x \to +\infty$.   But for any fixed p, we have

$$\lim_{x \to +\infty} \epsilon^{-px/v} = 0, \quad \lim_{x \to +\infty} \epsilon^{px/v} = +\infty$$

This shows that we must take $B(p) = 0$ in Eq. (184) to make $E(x,p)$ finite as $x \to +\infty$.   With $B(p) = 0$, Eqs. (184) and (187) become

$$E(x,p) = A(p)\epsilon^{-px/v}, \qquad (188)$$

and

$$I(x,p) = \frac{A(p)}{Z_K} \epsilon^{-px/v} = \frac{E(x,p)}{Z_K}. \qquad (189)$$

From item 1 the inverse of the last relation is

$$i(x,t) = \frac{e(x,t)}{Z_K}. \qquad (190)$$

Thus for an infinite line the knowledge of $e(x,t)$ is practically a complete solution since to determine $i(x,t)$ from it we merely have to divide by the characteristic impedance $Z_K = \sqrt{L/C}$.

In particular, let us consider the infinite line of Fig. 64.   Since $L = 0.8$ and $C = 2 \times 10^{-7}$, we find for the propagation velocity v and the characteristic impedance Z_K the following values:

$$v = \frac{1}{\sqrt{LC}} = 2,500 \quad \text{and} \quad Z_K = \sqrt{\frac{L}{C}} = 2,000. \quad (191)$$

The lumped parameters of the first element, $L_1 = 2,000$ henrys and $R_1 = 4,000$ ohms in series, are equivalent to an impedance

$$Z_1(p) = 2,000p + 4,000 \tag{192}$$

by Eq. (143). We wish to find the transient potential of the line $e(x,t)$ in response to the suddenly impressed emf $e_i(t) = 240$. To do this, we consider the voltage drop across the first element MN

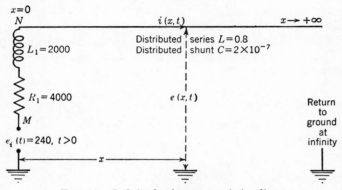

FIG. 64.   Infinite lossless transmission line.

in two ways.   We first observe that this drop $e_1(t)$ is the difference between the potential at M, $e_i(t)$ and the potential at N, $e(0,t)$. Hence

$$e_1(t) = e_i(t) - e(0,t) = 240 - e(0,t). \tag{193}$$

By items 1 and 14, this leads to the transformed equation

$$E_1(p) = \frac{240}{p} - E(0,p). \tag{194}$$

The current passing through the first element is $i(0,t)$.   Its transform $I(0,p)$ is related to $E_1(p)$ and $Z_1(p)$ by the Laplace transform analogue of Ohm's law, Eq. (127).   From this and Eq. (192) we find

$$E_1(p) = Z_1(p)I(0,p) = (2,000p + 4,000)I(0,p). \tag{195}$$

We next put $Z_K = 2,000$ from Eq. (191) into Eq. (189) to obtain

$$I(x,p) = \frac{E(x,p)}{2,000} \quad \text{and} \quad I(0,p) = \frac{E(0,p)}{2,000}. \quad (196)$$

Substitution in Eq. (195) and comparison with Eq. (194) shows that

$$(2,000p + 4,000)\frac{E(0,p)}{2,000} = \frac{240}{p} - E(0,p). \quad (197)$$

It follows that

$$(p + 3)E(0,p) = \frac{240}{p}, \quad E(0,p) = \frac{240}{p(p+3)}$$

$$= 80\left(\frac{1}{p} - \frac{1}{p+3}\right). \quad (198)$$

But with $x = 0$, Eq. (188) gives $E(0,p) = A(p)$. Consequently

$$E(x,p) = E(0,p)\epsilon^{-px/v} = 80\epsilon^{-(x/v)p}\left(\frac{1}{p} - \frac{1}{p+3}\right). \quad (199)$$

To find Lap^{-1} $E(x,p)$, we treat x as a constant and use items 1, 12, 14, and 15. This gives as the solution for $e(x,t)$

$$e(x,t) = 0 \quad \text{for } t < \frac{x}{v}, \quad \text{where } v = 2,500,$$

$$e(x,t) = 80[1 - \epsilon^{-3(t-x/v)}] \quad \text{for } t > \frac{x}{v}. \quad (200)$$

Let us define $g(z) = 0$ for $z < 0$ and $g(z) = 80(1 - \epsilon^{-3z})$ for $z > 0$. Then $e(x,t) = g(t - x/v)$, since if $z = t - (x/v)$, $t < x/v$ when $z < 0$ and $t > x/v$ when $z > 0$. But

$$t - \left(\frac{x}{v}\right) = -\frac{1}{v}(x - vt).$$

Hence from the discussion of $f(x - vt)$ in connection with Eq. (81) of Sec. 31 it follows that the $e(x,t)$ of Eq. (200) represents a wave traveling to the right with velocity $v = 2,500$. In particular, consider a time t_1. For any x_2 between 0 and vt_1, $0 < x_2 < vt_1$, so that $t_1 > x_2/v$. Hence $e(x_2,t_1)$ is determined from the second relation of Eq. (200) and is positive. But for any x_3 beyond vt_1, $x_3 > vt_1$, so that $t_1 < x_3/v$. Hence $e(x_3,t_1)$ is determined from the first relation of Eq. (200) and is zero. Thus at t_1 sec. after closing the switch at $t = 0$, the effect has made itself felt for vt_1 miles down the line. Since vt_1 is the distance that would be traveled by a point starting at the origin and moving to the right with velocity v, we may say that the effect of closing the switch

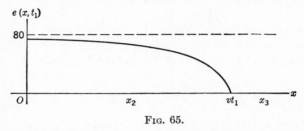

Fig. 65.

covers distance at velocity $v = 2,500$ miles per second [see Fig. 65 for a graph of $e(x,t_1)$].

More generally, let us consider an infinite line with constants v and Z_K. Suppose that the home end, $x = 0$, is connected to the ground through an element, or combination of elements, having a total series impedance $Z_1(p)$, in series with an impressed voltage $e_i(t)$. Then corresponding to Eqs. (193) and (194) we now have

$$e_1(t) = e_i(t) - e(0,t) \tag{201}$$

and

$$E_1(p) = E_i(p) - E(0,p). \tag{202}$$

From Eq. (189) we obtain

$$I(x,p) = \frac{E(x,p)}{Z_K} \quad \text{and} \quad I(0,p) = \frac{E(0,p)}{Z_K}. \tag{203}$$

We substitute this into the equation similar to Eq. (195)

$$E_1(p) = Z_1(p)I(0,p) = Z_1(p)\frac{E(0,p)}{Z_K}. \tag{204}$$

A comparison with Eq. (202) shows that

$$Z_1(p) \frac{E(0,p)}{Z_K} = E_i(p) - E(0,p). \tag{205}$$

By solving this for $E(0,p)$, we find

$$E(0,p) = \frac{Z_K E_i(p)}{Z_1(p) + Z_K}. \tag{206}$$

For given values of Z_K, $Z_1(p)$, and $e_i(t)$ determining

$$E_i(p) = \text{Lap } e_i(t),$$

$E(0,p)$ becomes a known function of p whose inverse transform may be found by the method of Sec. 54. This gives

$$e(0,t) = \text{Lap}^{-1} E(0,p).$$

Let us define $g(z) = 0$ for $z < 0$ and $g(z) = e(0,z)$ for $z > 0$. Then, as in Eq. (199), from Eq. (188) we find

$$E(x,p) = E(0,p)\epsilon^{-px/v} = \epsilon^{-(x/v)p} \text{ Lap } g(t). \tag{207}$$

We may now obtain $\text{Lap}^{-1} E(x,p)$ from item 12 as

$$e(x,t) = g\left(t - \frac{x}{v}\right). \tag{208}$$

Since $t - (x/v) = -(1/v)(x - vt)$, this represents a wave traveling to the right with velocity v. At t_1 sec. the effect has made itself felt for vt_1 miles down the line, since if $x_3 > vt_1$, $vt_1 - x_3 < 0$ and $[t_1 - (x_3/v)] < 0$, so that $e(x_3,t_1) = 0$.

We may substitute from Eq. (206) into Eq. (203) to deduce that

$$I(0,p) = \frac{E_i(p)}{Z_1(p) + Z_K}. \tag{209}$$

The similarity of this relation to Eq. (144) shows that $i(0,t)$, the current through the impedance $Z_1(p)$ in series with the infinite line due to the impressed voltage $e_i(t)$ is the same as the current through the impedance $Z_1(p)$ in series with a lumped resistance $R = Z_K$ due to an impressed voltage $e_i(t)$.

60. The Finite Line

We shall now apply the results of Sec. 58 to a finite line of length S miles.   We recall that

$$v = \frac{1}{\sqrt{LC}}, \quad \text{and} \quad Z_K = \sqrt{\frac{L}{C}}. \tag{210}$$

And in terms of these constants we found in Eqs. (184) and (187) that

$$E(x,p) = A(p)\epsilon^{-px/v} + B(p)\epsilon^{px/v}, \tag{211}$$

$$I(x,p) = \frac{A(p)\epsilon^{-px/v} - B(p)\epsilon^{px/v}}{Z_K}. \tag{212}$$

Let us consider the finite line of Fig. 66.   Here there is no

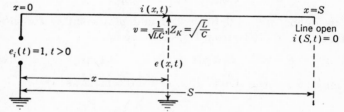

FIG. 66.   Lossless transmission line of length S.

impedance in series with the line, and the impressed voltage at the home end $e_i(t) = 1$.   Hence

$$e(0,t) = e_i(t) = 1 \quad \text{and} \quad E(0,p) = \frac{1}{p}. \tag{213}$$

As the line is open at the far end, $x = S$, no current flows there. Hence

$$i(S,t) = 0 \quad \text{and} \quad I(S,p) = 0. \tag{214}$$

We may determine $A(p)$ and $B(p)$ from the last two conditions. To do this, first put $x = 0$ in Eq. (211) and use Eq. (213).   The result is

$$\frac{1}{p} = A(p) + B(p). \tag{215}$$

Then put $x = S$ in Eq. (212), and use Eq. (214).   The result is

$$0 = \frac{1}{Z_K} [A(p)\epsilon^{-pS/v} - B(p)\epsilon^{pS/v}]. \tag{216}$$

We solve Eqs. (215) and (216) as simultaneous in $A(p),B(p)$. From Eq. (216),

$$A(p)\epsilon^{-pS/v} = B(p)\epsilon^{pS/v} \quad \text{and} \quad B(p) = A(p)\epsilon^{-2pS/v}. \tag{217}$$

Substitution of this in Eq. (215) leads to

$$\frac{1}{p} = A(p)[1 + \epsilon^{-2pS/v}] \quad \text{and} \quad A(p) = \frac{1}{p(1 + \epsilon^{-2pS/v})}. \tag{218}$$

We may now substitute this expression in Eq. (217) to obtain

$$B(p) = \frac{\epsilon^{-2pS/v}}{p(1 + \epsilon^{-2pS/v})}. \tag{219}$$

Let us now use the values of $A(p)$ and $B(p)$ just found in Eqs. (218) and (219) in Eqs. (211) and (212).   The results may be written

$$E(x,p) = \frac{1}{p} \frac{1}{1 + \epsilon^{-2pS/v}} [\epsilon^{-px/v} + \epsilon^{(x-2S)p/v}], \tag{220}$$

$$I(x,p) = \frac{1}{Z_K} \frac{1}{p} \frac{1}{1 + \epsilon^{-2pS/v}} [\epsilon^{-px/v} - \epsilon^{(x-2S)p/v}]. \tag{221}$$

The inverse transforms of these may be found by using a suitable series expansion.   We begin with the Maclaurin's series

$$\frac{1}{1 + y} = 1 - y + y^2 - \cdots + (-1)^n y^n + \cdots. \tag{222}$$

This is valid for $|y| < 1$, and is essentially the result used to find the sum of an infinite geometric series in elementary algebra. Since

$$\frac{2pS}{v} > 0, \quad y = \epsilon^{-2pS/v} \text{ makes } 0 < y < 1 \text{ and } |y| < 1. \tag{223}$$

Hence we may use this as the y of Eq. (222) and derive

$$\frac{1}{1 + \epsilon^{-2ps/v}} = 1 - \epsilon^{-2ps/v} + \epsilon^{-4ps/v} - \epsilon^{-6ps/v} + \cdots . \quad (224)$$

Substitution of this in Eq. (220) leads to

$$E(x,p) = \frac{1}{p}(1 - \epsilon^{-2ps/v} + \cdots)[\epsilon^{-px/v} + \epsilon^{(x-2S)p/v}]$$

$$= \epsilon^{-(x/v)p}\frac{1}{p} + \epsilon^{-[(2S-x)/v]p}\frac{1}{p} - \epsilon^{-[(2S+x)/v]p}\frac{1}{p}$$

$$- \epsilon^{-[(4S-x)/v]p}\frac{1}{p} + \epsilon^{-[(4S+x)/v]p}\frac{1}{p}\cdots . \quad (225)$$

Let us introduce the symbol $1(z)$ to represent the *unit-step function* of z defined by

$$\begin{align}
1(z) &= 0 \quad\quad \text{for } z < 0 \\
1(z) &= 1 \quad\quad \text{for } z > 0.
\end{align} \quad (226)$$

Then from items 12 and 14 it follows that

$$\text{Lap}^{-1}\,\epsilon^{-bp}\frac{1}{p} = 1(t - b). \quad (227)$$

The function $1(t - b)$ is a unit-step function of $(t - b)$, or a *delayed unit-step function* of t, with delay or lag b. That is, it is zero until $t = b$, and from then on it equals 1.

By item 1, $\text{Lap}^{-1}\,E(x,p)$ may be found by suitably combining the inverse transforms of the individual terms of the series in Eq. (225). And these may be found by using Eq. (227) with $b = x/v$, $(2S - x)/v$, etc. Thus we find

$$e(x,t) = 1\left(t - \frac{x}{v}\right) + 1\left(t - \frac{2S - x}{v}\right) - 1\left(t - \frac{2S + x}{v}\right)$$

$$- 1\left(t - \frac{4S - x}{v}\right) + 1\left(t - \frac{4S + x}{v}\right) + \cdots . \quad (228)$$

The lags in these terms depend on x, but for interior points of the line $0 < x < S$ so that

$$0 < \frac{x}{v} < \frac{S}{v}, \quad \frac{S}{v} < \frac{2S - x}{v} < \frac{2S}{v},$$

$$\frac{2S}{v} < \frac{2S + x}{v} < \frac{3S}{v}, \cdots \quad (229)$$

It follows that for any time t_1 such that $0 < t_1 < S/v$, only the first unit function in Eq. (228) can be different from zero. The graph of $e(x,t_1)$ is shown in Fig. 67. The arrow indicates that as t_1

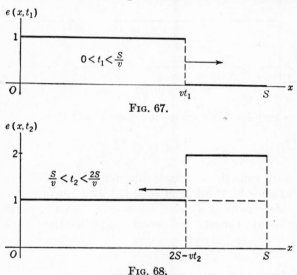

Fig. 67.

Fig. 68.

increases the wave moves toward the right. When t increases through S/v, we reach times t_2 such that $S/v < t_2 < 2S/v$. For any such time t_2 the first unit function in Eq. (228) is always 1, the second unit function may be different from zero, but all the unit functions which follow are zero. Hence the graph of $e(x,t_2)$ is as shown in Fig. 68. The arrow here indicates that as t_2 increases the second unit wave moves toward the left. When t increases through $2S/v$, we reach times t_3 such that $2S/v < t_3 < 3S/v$. For any such time t_3, the first unit function in Eq. (228) as well as the second, is always 1.   The third unit function may be different from zero, but all the unit functions which follow are zero. Because of the minus sign, when the third function is 1 it cancels the second, and the graph of $e(x,t_3)$ is as shown in Fig. 69.   When

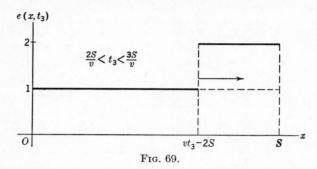

Fig. 69.

t increases through $3S/v$ we reach times t_4 such that

$$\frac{3S}{v} < t_4 < \frac{4S}{v}.$$

For any such time the first unit function in Eq. (228), as well as the second and the third, is always 1.   The fourth may be zero, and all which follow are zero.   Because of the two minus signs, the third always cancels the second, and when the fourth is 1, it

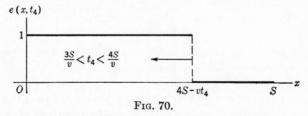

Fig. 70.

cancels the first.   Thus the graph of $e(x,t_4)$ is as shown in Fig. 70. After this the cycle repeats, the graph for t_5 being similar to that for t_1, the graph for t_6 being similar to that for t_2, etc., where $(n - 1)S/v < t_n < nS/v$.   The four steps of the cycle are (1) a voltage wave which travels up the line with velocity v, Fig. 67; (2) a reflected wave from the open end of the line without change of sign, Fig. 68; (3) this reflected wave after reaching the closed end is reflected with a change of sign, Fig. 69; (4) after reaching the open end, it is again reflected retaining its minus sign, Fig. 70.

To find the current, we substitute the series from Eq. (224) in Eq. (221). The result is

$$I(x,p) = \frac{1}{Z_K} \frac{1}{p} (1 - \epsilon^{-2pS/v} + \cdots)[\epsilon^{-px/v} - \epsilon^{(x-2S)p/v}]$$

$$= \frac{1}{Z_K} \left\{ \epsilon^{-(x/v)p} \frac{1}{p} - \epsilon^{-[(2S-x)/v]p} \frac{1}{p} - \epsilon^{-[(2S+x)/v]p} \frac{1}{p} \right.$$

$$\left. + \epsilon^{-[(4S-x)/v]p} \frac{1}{p} + \epsilon^{-[(4S+x)/v]p} \frac{1}{p} - \cdots \right\}. \quad (230)$$

Applying Eq. (227) with $b = x/v$, $(2S - x)/v$, etc., and item 1 we find

$$i(x,t) = \frac{1}{Z_K} \left[1\left(t - \frac{x}{v}\right) - 1\left(t - \frac{2S - x}{v}\right) - 1\left(t - \frac{2S + x}{v}\right) \right.$$

$$\left. + 1\left(t - \frac{4S - x}{v}\right) + 1\left(t - \frac{4S + x}{v}\right) - \cdots \right]. \quad (231)$$

This may be interpreted for times t_1, t_2, etc., by using considerations similar to those applied in the discussion of Eq. (228). We again find that the behavior for t_5 is like that for t_1. For the current, the four steps of the cycle are (1) a current wave of height

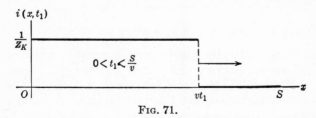

FIG. 71.

$1/Z_K$ which travels up the line with velocity v, Fig. 71; (2) this wave is reflected from the open end of the line with a change of sign, Fig. 72; (3) this reflected wave, after reaching the closed end and completely canceling the first wave when $t = 2S/v$, is

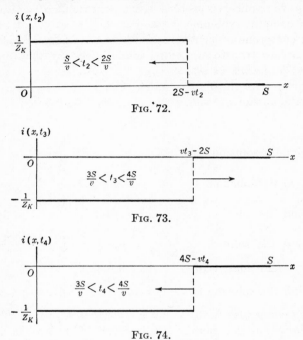

FIG. 72.

FIG. 73.

FIG. 74.

reflected without losing its minus sign, Fig. 73; (4) after reaching the open end, it is again reflected with a change of sign, Fig. 74.

61. References

A somewhat fuller, but elementary, account of Laplace transforms and a more extensive table than we have given here will be found in Churchill's *Modern Operational Mathematics in Engineering.* This includes some theory and a number of applications to problems in heat conduction and in mechanical vibrations.

A summary of the transform method is given in Chap. 3, and approximate methods of finding direct and inverse transforms are described in Chap. 11 of Brown and Campbell's *Principles of Servomechanisms.* Throughout this book Laplace transform methods are applied to problems arising in the analysis and synthesis of complex systems.

For a comprehensive treatment of the theory and application of the Laplace transform, the reader is referred to Gardner and Barnes's *Transients in Linear Systems.* Enough theory to serve as background for the discussion here given will be found in Chap. XIV of the author's *Treatise on Advanced Calculus.*

EXERCISE XXXI

1. Find the solution of $\dfrac{\partial f}{\partial t} = 3x + 6t$ which has $f(x,0) = 2\cos x$.

2. Find the solution of $\dfrac{\partial f}{\partial t} = 4\cos 2t$ which has $f(x,0) = \sin x$.

3. Find the solution of $\dfrac{\partial u}{\partial t} = e^{x+t}$ which has $f(x,0) = 3e^x$.

4. Find the solution of $\dfrac{\partial^2 f}{\partial x\,\partial t} = 4x - 4t$ which satisfies the boundary conditions $f(x,0) = 3\sin x$ and $f(0,t) = \sin 2t$.

5. Find the solution of $\dfrac{\partial^2 u}{\partial x\,\partial t} = \sin x \sin t$ which satisfies the boundary conditions $f(x,0) = 2\cos x$ and $f(0,t) = 2\cos t$.

6. Show that in general the transforms of the second derivatives are given by $\text{Lap } \dfrac{\partial^2 f}{\partial x^2} = \dfrac{\partial^2 F}{\partial x^2}$; $\text{Lap } \dfrac{\partial^2 f}{\partial x\,\partial t} = -f_x(x,0+) + p\,\dfrac{\partial F}{\partial x}$,

where $f_x(x,t) = \dfrac{\partial f}{\partial x}$; and

$$\text{Lap } \frac{\partial^2 f}{\partial t^2} = -f_t(x,0+) - pf(x,0+) + p^2 F(x,p),$$

where $f_t(x,t) = \dfrac{\partial f}{\partial t}$.

7. When a system whose equations contain all three partial derivatives is initially dead, $f(x,0+) = 0$, $f_x(x,0+) = 0$, and $f_t(x,0+) = 0$. Verify that in this case the relations of Prob. 6 reduce to those of Eq. (158).

8. Use the transform method as in Sec. 53 to show that the solution of $\dfrac{dy}{dt} = at$ which has $y(0+) = b$ is $y = \frac{1}{2} at^2 + b$. Now replace y, t, a, b by F, x, $\left(\dfrac{8}{p^3} + \dfrac{2}{p}\right)$, $G(p)$, and thus check Eq. (165).

9. Use the transform method as in Sec. 53 to show that the solution of $\dfrac{dy}{dt} = ay$ which has $y(0+) = b$ is $y = be^{at}$. Now replace y, t, a, b by U, x, $-2p$, $A(p)$, and thus check Eq. (171).

10. Use the transform method as in Sec. 53 to show that the solution of $\dfrac{d^2y}{dt^2} = a^2y$, when $a \neq 0$, which has $y(0+) = b$ and $y'(0) = c$ is $y = b \cosh at + \dfrac{c}{a} \sinh at = Ae^{-at} + Be^{at}$ if $b = A + B$ and $c = a(B - A)$. Now replace y, t, e, a, A, B by E, x, ϵ, $\dfrac{p}{v}$, $A(p)$, $B(p)$, and thus check Eq. (184).

11. Find the solution of $\dfrac{\partial u}{\partial t} + \dfrac{\partial u}{\partial x} = 0$ which satisfies the boundary conditions $u(x,0) = 0$ for $x > 0$ and $u(0,t) = \sin t$ for $t > 0$.

12. Find the solution of $\dfrac{\partial u}{\partial t} + 3\dfrac{\partial u}{\partial x} = 0$ which satisfies the boundary conditions $u(x,0) = 0$ for $x > 0$ and $u(0,t) = 5$ for $t > 0$.

13. Find the solution of $\dfrac{\partial u}{\partial t} + \dfrac{\partial u}{\partial t} = 0$ which satisfies the boundary conditions $u(x,0) = e^x$ for $x > 0$ and $u(0,t) = e^{-t}$ for $t > 0$.

14. Find the solution of $\dfrac{\partial u}{\partial t} - \dfrac{\partial u}{\partial x} = 0$ which satisfies the boundary conditions $u(x,0) = 0$ for $x < 0$ and $u(0,t) = \sin t$ for $t > 0$.

15. Show the solution of $\dfrac{\partial u}{\partial t} + v\dfrac{\partial u}{\partial x} = 0$, $v > 0$, which satisfies

the boundary conditions $u(x,0) = 0$ for $x > 0$ and $u(0,t) = g(t)$
for $t > 0$ is $u(x,t) = 0$ for $t < \dfrac{x}{v}$ and $u(x,t) = g\left(t - \dfrac{x}{v}\right)$ for $t > \dfrac{x}{v}$.

16. Check Prob. 14 by putting $x = -x_1$ in Prob. 11.

17. Find the solution of $\dfrac{\partial u}{\partial t} + \dfrac{\partial u}{\partial x} = 0$ which satisfies the
boundary conditions $u(x,0) = 0$ for $x < 0$ and $u(0,t) = \sin t$ for
$t < 0$. HINT: Put $t = -t_1$ and use Prob. 14.

18. Find the solution of $\dfrac{\partial u}{\partial t} + v\,\dfrac{\partial u}{\partial x} = -au$ which satisfies the
boundary conditions $u(x,0) = 0$ for $x < 0$ and $u(0,t) = g(t)$ for
$t > 0$.

The infinite transmission line of Fig. 75 has $L = 0.5$ henry per

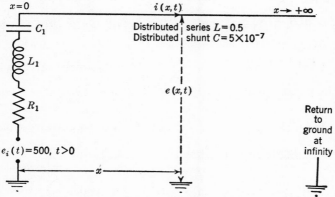

FIG. 75.   Infinite lossless transmission line.

mile and $C = 0.5$ microfarad per mile or 5×10^{-7} farad per mile.
Hence $v = 1/\sqrt{LC} = 2{,}000$ and $Z_K = \sqrt{L/C} = 1{,}000$. At
time $t = 0$ the line was dead, and the emf $e_i(t) = 500$ volts was
suddenly impressed. Find the resulting potential $e(x,t)$ and current $i(x,t)$ if for the lumped parameters of the first element

19. $L_1 = 250$, $R_1 = 500$, no capacitance present.
20. $L_1 = 1{,}500$, $R_1 = 2{,}500$, no capacitance present.

21. $R_1 = 4{,}000$, $C_1 = 5 \times 10^{-5}$, no inductance present.
22. $L_1 = 5{,}000$, $R_1 = 9{,}000$, $C_1 = 10^{-4}$.

23. Find $e(x,t)$ and $e(0,t)$ for an infinite line with $v = 20$, $Z_K = 3$, in response to a suddenly impressed emf $e_i(t) = 540 \sin t$, if the initial element has $R_1 = 10$ in series with $L_1 = 1$.

Find $e(x,t)$ for an infinite line with constants v, Z_K in response to a suddenly impressed emf $e_i(t) = 1$ if the initial element in series with the line

24. Contains no impedance.   **25.** Is a resistance $R_1 = aZ_K$.
26. Is an inductance $L_1 = Z_K/a$.
27. Is a capacitance $C_1 = 1/aZ_K$.

An infinite line has constants v, Z_K. The suddenly impressed emf is $e_i(t)$. We define $g(z) = 0$ for $z < 0$ and $g(z) = e_i(z)$ for $z > 0$. Show that if the initial element in series with the line

28. Contains no impedance, $e(x,t) = g\left(t - \dfrac{x}{v}\right)$.

29. Is a resistance R_1, $e(x,t) = \dfrac{Z_K}{R_1 + Z_K}\, g\left(t - \dfrac{x}{v}\right)$.

30. The finite line of Fig. 76 is of length S and has constants

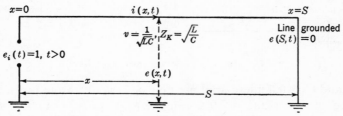

Fig. 76.   Lossless transmission line of length S.

v, Z_K. There is no impedance in series with the line, and the suddenly impressed voltage at the home end is $e_i(t) = 1$, so that Eqs. (213) and (215) still hold and $1/p = A(p) + B(p)$. But at the far end the line is grounded, so that $e(S,t) = 0$. By putting

$x = S$ in Eq. (211) deduce that $0 = A(p)\epsilon^{-pS/v} + B(p)\epsilon^{pS/v}$. Solve the two equations as simultaneous in $A(p)$, $B(p)$. Use these values in Eqs. (211) and (212) and thus show that

$$\text{Lap } e(x,t) = E(x,p) = \frac{1}{p} \frac{1}{1 - \epsilon^{-2pS/v}} [\epsilon^{-px/v} - \epsilon^{(x-2S)p/v}],$$

$$\text{Lap } i(x,t) = I(x,p) = \frac{1}{Z_K} \frac{1}{p} \frac{1}{1 - \epsilon^{-2pS/v}} [\epsilon^{-px/v} + \epsilon^{(x-2S)p/v}].$$

31. Use the Maclaurin's series or infinite geometric series relation $\dfrac{1}{1 - y} = 1 + y + y^2 + y^3 + \cdots$, $|y| < 1$, with $y = \epsilon^{-2pS/v}$, to derive the expansion

$$\frac{1}{1 - \epsilon^{-2pS/v}} = 1 + \epsilon^{-2pS/v} + \epsilon^{-4pS/v} + \epsilon^{-6pS/v} + \cdots.$$

32. Use the results of Probs. 30 and 31 to find the resulting potential $e(x,t)$.

33. Use the results of Probs. 30 and 31 to find the resulting current $i(x,t)$.

34. The finite line of Fig. 77 is of length S and has constants

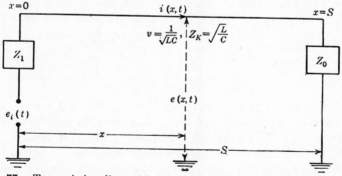

Fig. 77. Transmission line with initial impedance Z_1 and with output impedance Z_0.

v, Z_K. The suddenly impressed emf is $e_i(t)$. This acts at the home end through an initial impedance Z_1 in series with the line. At the far end the line is connected to the ground by a load or output impedance Z_0. By applying reasoning like that used to derive Eq. (202) and the first part of Eq. (204) to the home end $x = 0$, deduce that $E_i(p) = E(0,p) + Z_1(p)I(0,p)$. And by applying similar reasoning to the far end $x = S$, deduce that $E(S,p) = Z_0(p)I(S,p)$.

35. Put $x = 0$ and $x = S$ in Eqs. (211) and (212). Substitute these results in the relations found in Prob. 34 and thus show that

$$Z_K E_i(p) = [Z_K + Z_1(p)]A(p) + [Z_K - Z_1(p)]B(p),$$
$$B(p) = A(p)\frac{Z_0(p) - Z_K}{Z_0(p) + Z_K}\epsilon^{-2pS/v}.$$

36. Show that if we introduce the abbreviations

$$M_{1K}(p) = \frac{Z_1(p) - Z_K}{Z_1(p) + Z_K} \quad \text{and} \quad M_{0K}(p) = \frac{Z_0(p) - Z_K}{Z_0(p) + Z_K}$$

the two equations of Prob. 35 may be written

$$\frac{Z_K E_i(p)}{Z_1(p) + Z_K} = A(p) - M_{1K}(p)B(p),$$

$$B(p) = A(p)M_{0K}(p)\epsilon^{-2pS/v}.$$

Solve these last two equations as simultaneous in $A(p)$, $B(p)$. Use the values found in Eqs. (211) and (212) and thus show that

$$E(x,p) = \frac{Z_K E_i(p)}{Z_1(p) + Z_K}\frac{\epsilon^{-px/v} + M_{0K}(p)\epsilon^{(x-2S)p/v}}{1 - M_{1K}(p)M_{0K}(p)\epsilon^{-2pS/v}},$$
$$I(x,p) = \frac{E_i(p)}{Z_1(p) + Z_K}\frac{\epsilon^{-px/v} - M_{0K}(p)\epsilon^{(x-2S)p/v}}{1 - M_{1K}(p)M_{0K}(p)\epsilon^{-2pS/v}}.$$

37. Observing that when $S \to +\infty$, $\epsilon^{-2pS/v} \to 0$, verify that in this case the relations of Prob. 36 reduce to those found for the infinite line by combining Eqs. (206), (207), and (203).

38. If Z_0 is a resistance numerically equal to Z_K, the output impedance is said to be matched to the characteristic impedance. Show that in this case $Z_0(p) = Z_K$, the output mismatch function $M_{0K}(p) = 0$, and the equations of Prob. 36 take the same form as those for the infinite line mentioned in Prob. 37.

39. If Z_1 is a resistance numerically equal to Z_K, the initial impedance is matched to the characteristic impedance. Show that in this case $Z_1(p) = Z_K$, the initial mismatch function

$M_{1K}(p) = 0$, and the equations of Prob. 36 reduce to

$$E(x,p) = \frac{1}{2}\left[E_i(p)\epsilon^{-px/v} + M_{0K}(p)\epsilon^{(x-2S)p/v}\right],$$

$$I(x,p) = \frac{1}{2Z_K}\left[E_i(p)\epsilon^{-px/v} - M_{0K}(p)\epsilon^{(x-2S)p/v}\right].$$

A finite line has constants v, Z_K and is of length S as in Fig. 77. The initial impedance Z_1 is matched to Z_K, $Z_1(p) = Z_K$, and the results of Prob. 39 hold. Find $e(x,t)$ in response to a suddenly impressed emf $e_i(t) = 1$ if at the far end

40. The line is open, $Z_0(p) = \infty$ so that $M_{0K}(p) = 1$.

41. The line is grounded, $Z_0(p) = 0$ so that $M_{0K} = -1$.

42. The load is a resistance $R_0 = aZ_K$ so that $Z_0(p) = aZ_K$ and
$$M_{0K}(p) = \frac{a-1}{a+1}.$$

43. Find $i(x,t)$ for the line of Prob. 40.

44. Find $i(x,t)$ for the line of Prob. 41.

45. Find $i(x,t)$ for the line of Prob. 42.

46. A finite line has constants v, Z_K and is of length S as in Fig. 77. The initial impedance is a resistance matched to Z_K. $R_1 = Z_K$. Hence $Z_1(p) = Z_K$ and the results of Prob. 39 hold. The load at the far end is a resistance $R_0 = aZ_K$ so that

$$M_{0K}(p) = \frac{a-1}{a+1}.$$

The suddenly impressed emf is $e_i(t)$. We define $g(z) = 0$ for $z < 0$ and $g(z) = e_i(z)$ for $z > 0$. Show that

$$e(x,t) = \frac{1}{2}\left[g\left(t - \frac{x}{v}\right) + \frac{a-1}{a+1}g\left(t - \frac{2S-x}{v}\right)\right].$$

47. Use Prob. 46 to check Prob. 42.

48. Check Eqs. (220) and (221) by suitably specializing the relations of Prob. 36. Note that here $Z_0(p) = \infty$ so that $M_{0K}(p) = 1$, $Z_1(p) = 0$ so that $M_{1K}(p) = -1$, and $E_i(p) = 1/p$.

49. Check the relations of Prob. 30 by suitably specializing the relations of Prob. 36. Note that here $Z_0(p) = 0$ so that $M_{0K}(p) = -1$, $Z_1(p) = 0$ so that $M_{1K}(p) = -1$, and $E_i(p) = 1/p$.

BIBLIOGRAPHY

BROWN, G. S., and D. P. CAMPBELL: "Principles of Servomechanisms," John Wiley & Sons, Inc., New York, 1948.

CARSLAW, H. S.: "Theory of Fourier Series and Integrals," Macmillan & Co., Ltd., London, 1921.

————: "Mathematical Theory of the Conduction of Heat in Solids," Macmillan & Co., Ltd., London, 1921.

CHURCHILL, R. V.: "Fourier Series and Boundary Value Problems," McGraw-Hill Book Company, Inc., New York, 1941.

————: "Modern Operational Mathematics in Engineering," McGraw-Hill Book Company, Inc., New York, 1944.

————: "Introduction to Complex Variables and Applications," McGraw-Hill Book Company, Inc., New York, 1948.

COURANT, R., and D. HILBERT: "Methoden der mathematischen Physik," Verlag Julius Springer, Berlin, Vol. 1, 1931; Vol. 2, 1937.

DEN HARTOG, J. P.: "Mechanical Vibrations," 3d ed., McGraw-Hill Book Company, Inc., New York, 1947.

DWIGHT, H. B.: "Mathematical Tables of Elementary and Some Higher Mathematical Functions," McGraw-Hill Book Company, Inc., New York, 1941.

————: "Tables of Integrals and Other Mathematical Data," The Macmillan Company, New York, 1947.

FRANK, P., and R. VON MISES: "Differential- und Integralgleichungen der Mechanik und Physik," Rosenberg, New York, 1943.

FRANKLIN, P.: "Differential Equations for Electrical Engineers," John Wiley & Sons, Inc., New York, 1933.

————: "A Treatise on Advanced Calculus," John Wiley & Sons, Inc., New York, 1940.

————: "Methods of Advanced Calculus," McGraw-Hill Book Company, Inc., New York, 1944.

GARDNER, M. F., and J. L. BARNES: "Transients in Linear Systems," John Wiley & Sons, Inc., New York, 1942.

GUILLEMIN, E. A.: "Communication Networks," John Wiley & Sons, Inc., New York, Vol. 1, 1931; Vol. 2, 1935.

————: "The Mathematics of Circuit Analysis," John Wiley & Sons, Inc., New York, 1949.

JAHNKE, E., and F. EMDE: "Tables of Functions," B. G. Teubner, Leipzig, 1938.

LIPKA, J.: "Graphical and Mechanical Computation," John Wiley & Sons, Inc., New York, 1918.

MORSE, P. M.: "Vibration and Sound," 2d ed., McGraw-Hill Book Company, Inc., New York, 1948.

SCARBOROUGH, J. B.: "Numerical Mathematical Analysis," Johns Hopkins Press, Baltimore, 1930.

SLATER, J. C.: "Microwave Transmission," McGraw-Hill Book Company, Inc., New York, 1942.

STRATTON, J. A.: "Electromagnetic Theory," McGraw-Hill Book Company, Inc., New York, 1941.

TIMOSHENKO, S.: "Vibration Problems in Engineering," D. Van Nostrand Company, Inc., New York, 1928.

ANSWERS

Exercise I (Pages 5 to 6)

1. $2 + 29i$.   **2.** $5 + 5i$.   **3.** $-4i$.   **4.** 6.

5. $-13i$.   **6.** -13.   **7.** $52 - 78i$.   **8.** i.

9. $6 + 4i$.   **10.** $-4 - 6i$.   **11.** $5 - 12i$.   **12.** -676.

27. $x - (\sin 4x)/4$.

28. $(\sin 4x)/4 + 2 \sin 2x + 3x$.

29. $(\sin 4x)/4 - 2 \sin 2x + 3x$.

30. $\dfrac{e^{ax}(a \cos bx + b \sin bx)}{a^2 + b^2}$,

$\dfrac{e^{ax}(a \sin bx - b \cos bx)}{a^2 + b^2}$.

Exercise II (Pages 10 to 12)

1. $0.500 + 0.866i$.   **2.** -1.   **3.** -1.

4. 1.   **5.** 3.762.   **6.** $10.02i$.

7. 0.540.   **8.** $0.909i$.   **9.** $10.85 - 16.89i$.

10. $0.072 + 0.114i$.   **11.** $-22.9 - 49.6i$.   **12.** $-920 - 596i$.

13. $1.30 - 0.63i$.   **14.** $2.03 + 3.05i$ **15.** $-4.17 - 9.16i$.

16. $-589 - 3982i$.   **32.** 1.3018.

Exercise III (Pages 18 to 19)

1. $7, 0$.   **2.** $3, \pi/2 = 1.571$.   **3.** $5, -\pi/2 = -1.571$

4. $6.403, 2.246$.   **5.** $9.220, -1.352$.   **6.** $8.062, 4.194$.

9. $3.1416i$.   **10.** $1.5708i$.   **11.** $1.733 - 1.571i$.

12. $1.609 + 3.785i$.   **13.** $1.609 + 0.927i$.   **14.** $3.606 - 0.983i$.

15. -4.   **16.** $-10 - 3i$.   **17.** $-4 - 8i$.

18. $-18i$.   **19.** i.   **20.** 5.

21. $-1 + 1.732i$.   **22.** $4.242i$.   **23.** $12i$.

24. $90.63 + 42.26i$.   **25.** $1.813 + 0.845i$.   **26.** $-4i$.

27. $5i, -5i$.   **28.** $\pm(2.828 + 2.828i)$.

29. $\pm(3.01 + 0.166i)$.   **30.** $\pm(2.47 - 0.400i)$.

31. $-4, 2 \pm 3.464i$.   **32.** $\pm2, \pm2i$.

33. $2i, \pm1.902 + 0.618i$,   **34.** $1, (0.5 + 0.866i)$,

$\pm1.176 - 1.618i$. $(0.5 - 0.866i)$.

Exercise IV (Pages 26 to 29)

32. $y = 6.16$ ft., $H = 4.08$ lb., $T = 4.20$ lb.

33. $H = 22.7$ tons, $T = 26.6$ tons, $s = 3180$ ft., weight $= 28$ tons.

Exercise V (Pages 42 to 47)

1. $i = -0.849e^{-0.15t} \sin 141.4t$. 3. $1.43 \sin (120\pi t - 88.4°)$.
4. $1.43 \cos (120\pi t - 88.4°)$. 5. $0.0163 \sin (360\pi t - 44.4°)$.
6. $0.00075 \sin (600\pi t - 107.5°)$.
7. $0.086 \sin (120\pi t + 84.1°) + 0.032 \sin (360\pi t - 44.4°)$.
8. $0.086 \sin (120\pi t + 84.1°) + 0.0015 \sin (600\pi t - 107.5°)$

In Probs. 9 to 12 let $X = L\omega - \dfrac{1}{\omega C}$, $|Z| = \sqrt{R^2 + X^2}$, $\theta_Z = \tan^{-1} \dfrac{X}{R}$.

9. $\dfrac{1}{|Z|} \sin (\omega t - \theta_Z)$.

10. $\dfrac{1}{|Z|} \cos (\omega t - \theta_Z)$.

11. $\dfrac{A}{|Z|} \cos (\omega t - \theta_Z) + \dfrac{B}{|Z|} \sin (\omega t - \theta_Z)$.

12. $\dfrac{1}{|Z|} \cos (\omega t + \alpha - \theta_Z)$.

14. $s = 4.85 \sin (4t - 86.0°)$
15. $\theta = 0.000213 \sin (300t - 179.4°)$.
16. $i_1 + i_2 + i_3 = 0$, $Z_1i_1 - Z_2i_2 = e_1 - e_2$, $Z_2i_2 - Z_3i_3 = e_2 - e_3$.
18. $i_1 + i_2 - i_5 = 0$, $i_5 + i_3 + i_4 = 0$, $-i_1 - i_2 + i_6 = 0$, $i_1Z_1 - i_2Z_2 = 0$,
    $i_2Z_2 + i_5Z_5 - i_3Z_3 + i_6Z_6 = e_6$, $i_3Z_3 - i_4Z_4 = 0$.
19. $i_6 = \dfrac{e_6}{Z}$, where $Z = \dfrac{Z_1Z_2}{Z_1 + Z_2} + \dfrac{Z_3Z_4}{Z_3 + Z_4} + Z_5 + Z_6$.
21. $i_1 = P/Q \sin (\omega t + p - q)$, where $Pe^{jp} = R_3e_1 + (L_3e_1 - Me_3)\omega j$,
    and $Qe^{jq} = M^2\omega^2 + R_1R_3 - L_1L_3\omega^2 + (L_1R_3 + L_3R_1)\omega j$.

Exercise VI (Pages 54 to 57)

1. -6. 2. 106. 3. $e^{-1} - e^{-3}$.
4. $\frac{5}{2}(3 \ln 3 - 2)$. 5. $(\frac{4}{3})^{1/2}$. 6. $[\frac{3}{4}(e^{24} - e^8)]^{1/2}$.
7. $(\frac{1}{6})^{1/2}$. 8. $(6{,}348)^{1/2}$. 9. $5, 5$.
10. $\frac{8}{3}$, $(6\frac{4}{5})^{1/2}$. 11. $4\frac{8}{5}$, 16.
12. $(\sin 2)/2$, $(2 + \sin 2 \cos 2)^{1/2}/2$.
13. 4, $(6\frac{4}{3})^{1/2}$.
14. 16, $(4{,}096/7)^{1/2}$.
15. $(1 - \cos 2)/2$, $(2 - \sin 2 \cos 2)^{1/2}/2$.
16. $(\sin^2 2)/4$, $(4 - \sin 4 \cos 4)^{1/2}/4$.
17. 0. 18. 4. 19. 2.
20. -5. 21. 2, $(1\frac{9}{3})^{1/2}$. 22. $2E/\pi$, $E/2^{1/2}$.
23. E/π, $E/2$.

Exercise VII (Pages 63 to 66)

2. $\frac{2}{5}$. 3. $\frac{1}{10}$. 4. $\frac{1}{2}$. 5. $\frac{2}{3}$.
6. 12. 7. 30. 13. $(25{,}450)^{1/2}$. 14. $(16{,}288)^{1/2}$.

15. $(29,952)½$.   **16.** $(3.84)½$.   **17.** $(32,500)½$.   **18.** $(204.5)½$.

19. $(82,450)½$.   **20.** $(3.29)½$.   **21.** $(325)½$.   **22.** $(325)½$.

23. $20,360$.   **24.** 282.   **25.** 494.   **26.** 323.

27. 325.

Exercise VIII (Pages 71 to 73)

1. $\Sigma(-1)^{n+1}2n^{-1}\sin nx$.

2. $\pi^2/3 + \Sigma(-1)^n 4n^{-2}\cos nx$.

3. $\Sigma(-1)^{n+1}2(\pi^2 n^{-1} - 6n^{-3})\sin nx$.

4. $\dfrac{\sinh \pi}{\pi}\left[1 + \sum (-1)^n 2\,\dfrac{\cos nx - n\sin nx}{1 + n^2}\right]$.

5. $1 - \dfrac{\cos x}{2} + \sum (-1)^n\,\dfrac{2\cos (n+1)x}{n^2 + 2n}$.

6. $-\dfrac{\sin x}{2} + \sum (-1)^{n+1}\dfrac{2n + 2}{n^2 + 2n}\sin (n+1)x$.

7. $\pi/2 - \Sigma 2m^{-1}\sin mx, m$ odd.

8. $-\dfrac{\pi}{4} + \sum \dfrac{2\cos (2n-1)x}{\pi(2n-1)^2} + \sum (-1)^{n+1}\dfrac{\sin nx}{n}$.

9. $\pi - \Sigma 2n^{-1}\sin nx$.

10. $\tfrac{4}{3}\pi^2 + \Sigma 4n^{-2}\cos nx - 4\pi n^{-1}\sin nx$.

11. $2\pi^3 + \Sigma 12\pi n^{-2}\cos nx + \Sigma(12n^{-3} - 8\pi^2 n^{-1})\sin nx$.

12. $\dfrac{e^{2\pi} - 1}{\pi}\left(\dfrac{1}{2} + \sum \dfrac{\cos nx - n\sin nx}{1 + n^2}\right)$.

13. $\pi \sin x - 1 - \dfrac{\cos x}{2} + \sum \dfrac{2\cos (n+1)x}{n^2 + 2n}$.

14. $\pi \cos x - \dfrac{\sin x}{2} - \sum \dfrac{2n + 2}{n^2 + 2n}\sin (n+1)x$.

15. $\pi/2 + \Sigma 2m^{-1}\sin mx, m$ odd.

16. $\dfrac{\pi}{4} - \dfrac{2\cos nx}{n^2} + \sum (-1)^{n+1}\dfrac{\sin nx}{n}$.

17. $5 + \sum \dfrac{20}{\pi}\sin \dfrac{m\pi x}{5}, m$ odd.

18. $\dfrac{5}{4} + \sum \left\{\dfrac{5[(-1)^n - 1]}{n^2\pi^2}\cos \dfrac{n\pi x}{5} + \dfrac{5(-1)^{n+1}}{n\pi}\sin \dfrac{n\pi x}{5}\right\}$.

19. $\dfrac{e^5 - 1}{10} + \sum \left\{\dfrac{5[(-1)^n e^5 - 1]}{5^2 + n^2\pi^2}\cos \dfrac{n\pi x}{5} + \dfrac{n\pi[(-1)^{n+1}e^5 + 1]}{5^2 + n^2\pi^2}\sin \dfrac{n\pi x}{5}\right\}$.

20. $\dfrac{1}{\pi} + \dfrac{1}{2}\sin \dfrac{\pi x}{5} - \dfrac{2}{\pi}\sum \dfrac{\cos \dfrac{2n\pi x}{5}}{4n^2 - 1}$.

21. $\dfrac{25}{6} + \sum \left\{\dfrac{50(-1)^n}{n^2\pi^2}\cos \dfrac{n\pi x}{5} + \left[\dfrac{25(-1)^{n+1}}{n\pi} + \dfrac{50[(-1)^n - 1]}{n^3\pi^3}\right]\sin \dfrac{n\pi x}{5}\right\}$.

Exercise IX (Pages 80 to 83)

1. $\dfrac{2}{\pi} - \sum \dfrac{4\cos 2nx}{\pi(4n^3 - 1)}.$

2. $\dfrac{2}{\pi} + \sum (-1)^{n+1} \dfrac{4\cos 2nx}{\pi(4n^3 - 1)}.$

3. $\frac{1}{2} - (\cos 2x)/2.$

4. $\frac{1}{2} + (\cos 2x)/2.$

5. $\dfrac{10}{3\pi} \sin x + \sum \dfrac{2}{\pi}\left[\dfrac{1}{4(n+1)^3 - 1} - \dfrac{1}{4n^3 - 1}\right] \sin (2n+1)x.$

6. $\dfrac{2}{3\pi} \sin x + \sum (-1)^n \dfrac{2}{\pi}\left[\dfrac{1}{4(n+1)^3 - 1} + \dfrac{1}{4n^3 - 1}\right] \sin (2n+1)x.$

7. $\frac{3}{4} \sin x - \frac{1}{4} \sin 3x.$

8. $\frac{1}{4} \sin x + \frac{1}{4} \sin 3x.$

9. $\dfrac{2}{3\pi} \cos x - \sum \dfrac{2}{\pi}\left[\dfrac{1}{4(n+1)^3 - 1} + \dfrac{1}{4n^3 - 1}\right] \cos (2n+1)x.$

10. $\dfrac{10}{3\pi} \cos x + \sum (-1)^n \dfrac{2}{\pi}\left[\dfrac{1}{4(n+1)^3 - 1} - \dfrac{1}{4n^3 - 1}\right] \cos (2n+1)x.$

11. $\frac{1}{4} \cos x - \frac{1}{4} \cos 3x.$

12. $\frac{3}{4} \cos x + \frac{1}{4} \cos 3x.$

13. $2 - \sum \dfrac{16}{m^2\pi^2} \cos \dfrac{m\pi x}{4}, \quad m$ odd.

14. $\sum \dfrac{16}{m^2\pi^2} \cos \dfrac{m\pi x}{4}, \quad m$ odd.

15. $2 + \sum \dfrac{8}{\pi} (-1)^n \dfrac{1}{2n - 1} \cos \dfrac{(2n-1)\pi x}{4}.$

16. $\dfrac{3}{2} + \sum \dfrac{8}{n^2\pi^2}\left(\cos \dfrac{n\pi}{2} - 1\right) \cos \dfrac{n\pi x}{4}.$

17. $\sum \dfrac{8}{\pi} (-1)^{n+1} n^{-1} \sin \dfrac{n\pi x}{4}.$

18. $\sum \dfrac{4}{n\pi} \sin \dfrac{n\pi x}{2}.$

19. $\sum \dfrac{8}{n\pi}\left(\cos \dfrac{n\pi}{2} - \cos n\pi\right) \sin \dfrac{n\pi x}{4}.$

20. $\sum \left[\dfrac{8}{n^2\pi^2} \sin \dfrac{n\pi}{2} - \dfrac{4}{n\pi} \cos n\pi\right] \sin \dfrac{n\pi x}{4}.$

Exercise X (Pages 87 to 89)

8. $B_1 = 0.373, B_2 = -0.173, B_3 = 0.100, B_4 = -0.057, B_5 = 0.027.$

9. $B_1 = 1.24, B_2 = 0, B_3 = 0.33, B_4 = 0, B_5 = 0.09.$

10. $B_1 = 0.496, B_2 = 0, B_3 = 0.066, B_4 = 0, B_5 = 0.036.$

11. $B_1 = 8, B_2 = 0, B_3 = -2, B_4 = 0, B_5 = 0.$

Exercise XII (Pages 103 to 106)

2. 6×10^7 cal./day, 14 kg./day.

3. 1.3×10^6 cal./day.

4. 15.3 kg./day.

5. 3 kwh./day.

10. 1.38×10^9 cal./day.

14. 23.7 cal./sec.

15. 392 cal./sec.

16. 393 cal./sec.

17. 4760 cal./sec.

18. 4760 cal./sec.

Exercise XIII (Pages 108 to 110)

1. $z = f(y)$.
3. $z = f(x)$.
2. $z = 2x^2y + f(y)$.
4. $z = 2y^2 + f(x)$.

5. $z = x^3 + 3xy^2 + f(y)$.
6. $z = x \sin \dfrac{y}{x} + f(x)$.

7. $z = f(x) + g(y)$.
8. $z = x^2y + 2xy^2 + f(x) + g(y)$.
9. $z = -\frac{1}{2}e^{2x-y} + f(x) + g(y)$.
10. $u = x^2 \ln t + f(x) + g(t)$.
11. $u = 2x^3t^2 + f(x) + tg(x)$.
12. $u = 4te^{2x} + f(t) + xg(t)$.
13. $u = -\frac{1}{4} \sin (2x - 3y) + f(y) + xg(y)$.
14. $u = 2xy^3 + f(x) + yg(x)$.
15. $u = 3p^2x^2 + f(x) + g(p)$.
16. $\ln z = x^2y + f(x)$.
17. $z^2 = x^2 - 2xy + g(y)$.
18. $e^{-z} = -xy + f(y)$.
19. $u = -2x/y - 2/y^2 + f(y)e^{xy}$.
20. $u = -2t + e^x f(t)$.
21. $u = f(p)e^{-2px}$.
22. $u = f(p)e^{-(4+2p)x}$.
23. $u = f(y)e^{2xy} + g(y)e^{-2xy}$.
24. $u = f(t) \sin 2tx - g(t) \cos 2tx$.
25. $u = f(p)e^{px/v} + g(p)e^{-px/v}$.
26. $u = f(p) \sin \dfrac{px}{v} + g(p) \cos \dfrac{px}{v}$.
27. $z = x^3y^2 + y^{-1}f(x) + g(y)$.

Exercise XIV (Pages 112 to 114)

1. $3\dfrac{\partial z}{\partial x} + 2\dfrac{\partial z}{\partial y} = 0$.
2. $\dfrac{\partial z}{\partial y} = 0$.

3. $\dfrac{\partial z}{\partial x} = 2y$.
4. $x\dfrac{\partial z}{\partial x} - y\dfrac{\partial z}{\partial y} = 0$.

5. $2\dfrac{\partial z}{\partial x} - \dfrac{\partial z}{\partial y} = 0$.
6. $x\dfrac{\partial z}{\partial x} + y\dfrac{\partial z}{\partial y} = z$.

7. $2\dfrac{\partial^2 z}{\partial x^2} - \dfrac{\partial^2 z}{\partial x \partial y} - 3\dfrac{\partial^2 z}{\partial y^2} = 0$.
8. $\dfrac{\partial^2 z}{\partial x \partial y} = \dfrac{1}{x}$.

9. $\dfrac{\partial^2 z}{\partial y^2} = 2$.
10. $\dfrac{\partial^2 z}{\partial x^2} + 2\dfrac{\partial^2 z}{\partial x \partial y} = 0$.

11. $\dfrac{\partial^2 z}{\partial x^2} - \dfrac{\partial^2 z}{\partial y^2} = 0$.
12. $z\dfrac{\partial^2 z}{\partial x \partial y} - \dfrac{\partial z}{\partial x}\dfrac{\partial z}{\partial y} = 0$.

Exercise XV (Pages 118 to 119)

1. $z = f(5x + y) + g(x + y)$.
2. $z = f(y) + g(2x + y)$.
3. $z = f(x - y) + g(3x - 2y)$.
4. $z = f(x) + g(x - 3y)$.
5. $z = f(3x + y) + xg(3x + y)$.
6. $z = f(2x + 3iy) + g(2x - 3iy)$.
7. $z = -2y^3/3 + f(x) + g(4x + y)$.
8. $z = x^4 + f(2x + y) + g(2x - y)$.

Exercise XVI (Pages 124 to 127)

2. $z = ce^{ax}e^{2ay}$.
3. $z = cx^ay^a$.
4. $z = cx^ay^{-a}$.
5. $z = ce^{ke^x}e^{ke^y}$.
6. $z = ce^{kx}e^{(2-k)y}$.
7. $z = ce^{kx^3}e^{-ky^3}$.

8. $z = (c_1 e^{2ax} + c_2 e^{-2ax})(c_3 e^{ay} + c_4 e^{-ay})$,

$z = (c_5 + c_6 x)(c_7 + c_8 y)$,

$z = (c_9 \sin 2bx + c_{10} \cos 2bx)(c_{11} \sin by + c_{12} \cos by)$.

9. $z = e^{2ax}(c_1 e^{ay} + c_2)$,

$z = c_3 y + c_4$.

10. $z = (c_1 e^{2ax} + c_2 e^{-2ax})(c_3 \sin ay + c_4 \cos ay)$,

$z = (c_5 + c_6 x)(c_7 + c_8 y)$,

$z = (c_9 \sin 2bx + c_{10} \cos 2bx)(c_{11} e^{by} + c_{12} e^{-by})$.

11. $U = (c_1 e^{3ax} + c_2 e^{-3ax})(c_3 e^{at} + c_4 e^{-at})$,

$U = (c_5 + c_6 x)(c_7 + c_8 t)$,

$U = (c_9 \sin 3bx + c_{10} \cos 3bx)(c_{11} \sin bt + c_{12} \cos bt)$.

12. $U = (c_1 e^{3ax} + c_2 e^{-3ax})(c_3 \sin at + c_4 \cos at)$,

$U = (c_5 + c_6 x)(c_7 + c_8 t)$,

$U = (c_9 \sin 3bx + c_{10} \cos 3bx)(c_{11} e^{bt} + c_{12} e^{-bt})$.

13. $U = e^{at}(c_1 e^{3ax} + c_2)$,

$U = c_3 x + c_4$.

Exercise XIX (Pages 143 to 146)

1. $\dfrac{\partial H_y}{\partial x} - \dfrac{\partial H_x}{\partial y} = \sigma E_z + K \dfrac{\partial E_z}{\partial t}$.

Exercise XX (Pages 152 to 155)

1. $\sum \dfrac{200}{m\pi} \sin \dfrac{m\pi x}{30} e^{-m\pi y/30}$, m odd. **2.** $\sum (-1)^{n+1} \dfrac{48}{n\pi} \sin \dfrac{n\pi x}{6} e^{-n\pi y/6}$.

3. $-\sum \dfrac{8}{n\pi} \sin \dfrac{n\pi x}{2} e^{-n\pi y/2}$. **4.** $100 \sin \dfrac{\pi x}{40} e^{-\pi y/40}$.

5. $4 \sin \dfrac{\pi x}{3} e^{-\pi y/3} - 6 \sin \dfrac{\pi x}{5} e^{-\pi y/5}$.

6. $\sum \dfrac{20}{n\pi} \left(1 - \cos \dfrac{n\pi}{2}\right) \sin \dfrac{n\pi x}{8} e^{-n\pi y/8}$.

7. $\sum \dfrac{4c}{m\pi} \sin \dfrac{m\pi x}{L} e^{-m\pi y/L}$, m odd.

8. $\sum \dfrac{2cL}{n\pi} (-1)^{n+1} \sin \dfrac{n\pi x}{L} e^{-n\pi y/L}$.

9. $-\sum \dfrac{2cL}{n\pi} \sin \dfrac{2n\pi x}{L} e^{-2n\pi y/L}$.

Exercise XXI (Pages 158 to 160)

1. $\dfrac{1}{2} + \sum \dfrac{2}{m\pi} \left(\dfrac{r}{9}\right)^m \sin m\theta$, m odd. **2.** $4r \sin \theta + 2r^2 \sin 2\theta$.

3. $2\pi - \Sigma 4n^{-1} r^n \sin n\theta$. **4.** $3r^3 \cos (3\theta - 25°)$.

6. $\sum \dfrac{400}{m\pi} \left(\dfrac{r}{a}\right)^{3m} \sin 3m\theta$, m odd.

7. $(4r - 4r^{-1}) \cos \theta + (4r + 4r^{-1}) \sin \theta$.

Exercise XXII (Pages 166 to 170)

1. $\sum (-1)^{n+1} \dfrac{200}{n\pi} \sin \dfrac{n\pi x}{50} e^{-bn^2 t}$, where $b = a^2 \pi^2 / 2{,}500$.

2. $100 - \sum \dfrac{200}{n\pi} \sin \dfrac{n\pi x}{50} e^{-bn^2 t}$, where $b = a^2 \pi^2 / 2{,}500$.

3. $x + \sum (-1)^{n+1} \dfrac{100}{n\pi} \sin \dfrac{n\pi x}{50} e^{-bn^2 t}$, where $b = a^2 \pi^2 / 2{,}500$.

4. $50 - x + \sum \dfrac{100}{n\pi} k_n \sin \dfrac{n\pi x}{50} e^{-bn^2 t}$, where $b = a^2 \pi^2 / 2{,}500$, $k_n = 1$ for n odd and $k_n = -3$ for n even.

5. $25 + x - \sum \dfrac{50}{n\pi} \sin \dfrac{n\pi x}{25} e^{-bn^2 t}$, where $b = a^2 \pi^2 / 625$.

6. $50 + 2x - \sum \dfrac{200}{m\pi} \sin \dfrac{m\pi x}{50} e^{-bm^2 t}$, m odd, where $b = a^2 \pi^2 / 2{,}500$.

7. $37.5°$.

8. $\sum \dfrac{100}{n\pi} \left(\cos \dfrac{n\pi}{2} - \cos n\pi\right) \sin \dfrac{n\pi x}{80} e^{-bn^2 t}$, where $b = a^2 \pi^2 / 6{,}400$.

9. $8.0°$.   10. $74.9°$.   11. $42.7°$.   12. $37.5°$.

13. $30.5°$.   14. $25°$.   15. 50.

17. $90 - \sum \dfrac{720}{m^2 \pi^2} \cos \dfrac{m\pi x}{60} e^{-bm^2 t}$, m odd, where $b = \pi^2 / 1{,}800$.

18. $x^2 - 120x + 2{,}400 - \sum \dfrac{14{,}400}{n^2 \pi^2} \cos \dfrac{n\pi x}{60} e^{-bn^2 t}$, where $b = \pi^2 / 1{,}800$.

20. $\sum \dfrac{800}{m^2 \pi^2} (-1)^{(m-1)/2} \sin \dfrac{m\pi x}{40} e^{-bm^2 t}$, m odd, where $b = a^2 \pi^2 / 1{,}600$.

21. See answer to Prob. 20.

24. $\sum (-1)^{n+1} \dfrac{20}{n\pi} \sin \dfrac{n\pi x}{10} e^{-c_n t}$, where $c_n = \dfrac{n^2 \pi^2}{50} + 5$.   32. $80.8°$.

Exercise XXIII (Pages 175 to 176)

1. $e = E \sin \dfrac{x}{500} \epsilon^{-4t}$,

    $i = -\dfrac{E}{1{,}500} \cos \dfrac{x}{500} \epsilon^{-4t}$.

2. $e = E_1 \sin \dfrac{x}{1{,}000} \epsilon^{-t} + E_{10} \sin \dfrac{x}{100} \epsilon^{-100t}$,

    $i = -\dfrac{E_1}{3{,}000} \cos \dfrac{x}{1{,}000} \epsilon^{-t} - \dfrac{E_{10}}{300} \cos \dfrac{x}{100} \epsilon^{-100t}$.

3. $e = \sum \dfrac{4E}{m\pi} \sin \dfrac{mx}{1,000} \, \epsilon^{-m^2 t}$,

$\quad i = -\sum \dfrac{4E}{3,000\pi} \cos \dfrac{mx}{1,000} \, \epsilon^{-m^2 t}$, m odd.

4. $e = \sum \dfrac{2E}{n\pi} (-1)^{n+1} \sin \dfrac{nx}{1,000} \, \epsilon^{-n^2 t}$,

$\quad i = \sum \dfrac{2E}{3,000\pi} (-1)^n \cos \dfrac{nx}{1,000} \, \epsilon^{-n^2 t}$.

5. $e = \sum \dfrac{2E}{n\pi} (-1)^{n+1} \sin \dfrac{n\pi x}{S} \, \epsilon^{-bn^2 t}$,

$\quad i = \sum \dfrac{2E}{RS} (-1)^n \cos \dfrac{n\pi x}{S} \, \epsilon^{-bn^2 t}$, where $b = \dfrac{\pi^2}{RCS^2}$.

6. $e = \sum \dfrac{4E}{m\pi} \sin \dfrac{m\pi x}{S} \, \epsilon^{-bm^2 t}$,

$\quad i = -\sum \dfrac{4E}{RS} \cos \dfrac{m\pi x}{S} \, \epsilon^{-bm^2 t}$, m odd, where $b = \dfrac{\pi^2}{RCS^2}$.

7. $e = \dfrac{Ex}{S} + \sum \dfrac{2E}{n\pi} (-1)^n \sin \dfrac{n\pi x}{S} \, \epsilon^{-bn^2 t}$,

$\quad i = -\dfrac{E}{RS} + \sum \dfrac{2E}{RS} (-1)^{n+1} \cos \dfrac{n\pi x}{S} \, \epsilon^{-bn^2 t}$, where $b = \dfrac{\pi^2}{RCS^2}$.

Exercise XXIV (Pages 180 to 183)

1. $2 \sin \dfrac{\pi x}{S} \cos \dfrac{\pi v t}{S}$.

2. $\dfrac{p}{4} \left(3 \sin \dfrac{\pi x}{S} \cos \dfrac{\pi v t}{S} - \sin \dfrac{3\pi x}{S} \cos \dfrac{3\pi v t}{S} \right)$.

3. $\sum \dfrac{8pS^2}{m^3 \pi^3} \sin \dfrac{m\pi x}{S} \cos \dfrac{m\pi v t}{S}$, $\quad m$ odd.

4. $p \sin \dfrac{k\pi x}{S} \cos \dfrac{k\pi v t}{S}$.

5. $\sum \dfrac{8p}{m^2 \pi^2} (-1)^{(m-1)/2} \sin \dfrac{m\pi x}{S} \cos \dfrac{m\pi v t}{S}$, $\quad m$ odd.

6. $\dfrac{5S}{3\pi v} \sin \dfrac{3\pi x}{S} \sin \dfrac{3\pi v t}{S}$.

7. $\dfrac{qS}{12\pi v} \left(9 \sin \dfrac{\pi x}{S} \sin \dfrac{\pi v t}{S} - \sin \dfrac{3\pi x}{S} \sin \dfrac{3\pi v t}{S} \right)$.

8. $\sum \dfrac{8qS^3}{m^4 \pi^4 v} \sin \dfrac{m\pi x}{S} \sin \dfrac{m\pi v t}{S}$, $\quad m$ odd.

9. $\dfrac{qS}{n\pi v} \sin \dfrac{k\pi x}{S} \sin \dfrac{k\pi v t}{S}$.

10. $\sum \dfrac{4qS}{n^2 \pi^2 v} \sin \dfrac{n\pi}{2} \sin \dfrac{w n\pi}{2S} \sin \dfrac{n\pi x}{S} \sin \dfrac{n\pi v t}{S}$.

11. $3 \sin \dfrac{2\pi x}{S} \cos \dfrac{2\pi v t}{S} + \dfrac{4S}{5\pi} \sin \dfrac{5\pi x}{S} \sin \dfrac{5\pi v t}{S}$.

Exercise XXV (Pages 188 to 190)

1. $e = E \sin \dfrac{\pi x}{S} \cos \dfrac{\pi v t}{S}$,

$i = I_0 - \dfrac{E}{vL} \cos \dfrac{\pi x}{S} \sin \dfrac{\pi v t}{S}$.

2. $e = E_2 \sin \dfrac{2\pi x}{S} \cos \dfrac{2\pi v t}{S} + E_5 \sin \dfrac{5\pi x}{S} \cos \dfrac{5\pi v t}{S}$,

$i = I_0 - \dfrac{E_2}{vL} \cos \dfrac{2\pi x}{S} \sin \dfrac{2\pi v t}{S} - \dfrac{E_5}{vL} \cos \dfrac{5\pi x}{S} \sin \dfrac{5\pi v t}{S}$.

3. $e = \sum \dfrac{4E}{m\pi} \sin \dfrac{m\pi x}{S} \cos \dfrac{m\pi v t}{S}$,

$i = I_0 - \dfrac{1}{vL} \sum \dfrac{4E}{m\pi} \cos \dfrac{m\pi x}{S} \sin \dfrac{m\pi v t}{S}$, $\quad m$ odd.

4. $e = \sum \dfrac{2E}{n\pi} (-1)^{n+1} \sin \dfrac{n\pi x}{S} \cos \dfrac{n\pi v t}{S}$,

$i = I_0 + \dfrac{1}{vL} \sum \dfrac{2E}{n\pi} (-1)^n \cos \dfrac{n\pi x}{S} \sin \dfrac{n\pi v t}{S}$.

5. $e = \dfrac{Ex}{S} + \sum \dfrac{2E}{n\pi} (-1)^n \sin \dfrac{n\pi x}{S} \cos \dfrac{n\pi v t}{S}$,

$i = - \dfrac{Et}{LS} + \dfrac{1}{vL} \sum \dfrac{2E}{n\pi} (-1)^{n+1} \cos \dfrac{n\pi x}{S} \sin \dfrac{n\pi v t}{S}$.

7. $e = \sum \dfrac{4E}{m^2\pi^2} (-1)^{(m-1)/2} \sin \dfrac{m\pi x}{S} \cos \dfrac{m\pi v t}{S}$, m odd.

8. $e = E - \sum \dfrac{4E}{m\pi} \sin \dfrac{m\pi x}{S} \cos \dfrac{m\pi v t}{S}$,

$i = \dfrac{1}{vL} \sum \dfrac{4E}{m\pi} \cos \dfrac{m\pi x}{S} \sin \dfrac{m\pi v t}{S}$, $\quad m$ odd.

13. $e = \dfrac{6{,}000 n\pi I_0 [1 - (-1)^n \epsilon^{0.002}]}{n^2\pi^2 + 4 \times 10^{-6}} \sin \dfrac{n\pi x}{50} \epsilon^{-30.3t} \left(\dfrac{30.3}{\beta_n} \sin \beta_n t + \cos \beta_n t \right)$.

14. $e = \dfrac{E \sinh 0.00004 x}{\sinh 0.002}$

$\qquad + \sum \dfrac{2En\pi(-1)^n}{n^2\pi^2 + 4 \times 10^{-6}} \sin \dfrac{n\pi x}{50} \epsilon^{-30.3t} \left(\dfrac{30.3}{\beta_n} \sin \beta_n t + \cos \beta_n t \right)$.

Exercise XXVIII (Pages 213 to 217)

1. $5/p$.

2. $5/p^2$.

3. $\dfrac{4p - 2}{p^2}$.

4. $\dfrac{5}{p + 1}$.

5. $\dfrac{2}{(p + 3)^2}$.

6. $\dfrac{2p}{(p + 3)^2}$.

7. $\dfrac{20}{p^2 - 25}$.

8. $\dfrac{4p}{p^2 - 25}$.

9. $\dfrac{16}{p(p^2 - 16)}$.

10. $\dfrac{15}{p^2 + 9}$.

11. $\dfrac{5p}{p^2 + 9}$.

12. $\dfrac{-25}{p(p^2 + 25)}$.

13. $\dfrac{6p - 48}{p^5}$.

14. $\dfrac{1}{(p + 2)^2 + 1}$.

15. $\dfrac{p + 3}{(p + 3)^2 + 4}$.

16. $\dfrac{6e^{-4p}}{p}$.

17. $\dfrac{2e^{-4p}}{p^2}$.

18. $\dfrac{8p + 2}{p^2} e^{-4p}$.

19. $\dfrac{e^{-2p}}{p + 1}$.

20. $\dfrac{e^{-2}e^{-2p}}{p + 1}$.

21. $\dfrac{-e^{-\pi p}}{p^2 + 1}$.

22. 3.

23. $7t$.

24. $t^2 + 6t$.

25. $4e^{-5t}$.

26. $2te^{-3t}$.

27. $2 - 2e^{-3t}$.

28. $2 \sin 2t$.

29. $4 \cos 2t$.

30. $(2 - 6t)e^{-3t}$.

31. $2 \sinh 2t$.

32. $4 \cosh 2t$.

33. $2 - 2 \cos t$.

34. 0 for $t < \pi$, $-\sin t$ for $t > \pi$.

35. $2e^{-2t} \sin 3t$.

36. $6e^{-2t} \cos 3t$.

Exercise XXIX (Pages 229 to 232)

1. $x = \cos 2t + 3 \sin 2t$.

2. $x = e^{-3t} \cos t + 4e^{-3t} \sin t$.

3. $q = q_0 \cos \dfrac{t}{\sqrt{LC}}, \; i = -\dfrac{q_0}{\sqrt{LC}} \sin \dfrac{t}{\sqrt{LC}}$.

5. $x = 5 \cosh 3t + \sinh 3t = 3e^{3t} + 2e^{-3t}$.

6. $x = Ae^{-at}$.

7. $x = A \cos bt + \dfrac{B}{b} \sin bt$.

8. $x = Ae^{-at} \cos bt + \dfrac{B + aA}{b} e^{-at} \sin bt$.

9. $x = A \cosh bt + \dfrac{B}{b} \sinh bt$.

10. $x = Ae^{-at} + (B + aA)te^{-at}$.

11. $\dfrac{9}{p - 3} - \dfrac{7}{p - 2}$.

12. $\dfrac{\frac{1}{2}}{p - 1} - \dfrac{\frac{5}{2}}{p - 3} + \dfrac{2}{p - 4}$.

13. $\dfrac{1}{2} \dfrac{a + b}{p - k} + \dfrac{1}{2} \dfrac{a - b}{p + k}$.

14. $-\dfrac{3}{2} \dfrac{1}{p} + \dfrac{4}{p + 1} - \dfrac{5}{2} \dfrac{1}{p + 2}$.

15. $\dfrac{4}{p^2} + \dfrac{3}{p} - \dfrac{2}{p - 1}$.

16. $\dfrac{ac + d}{a - b} \dfrac{1}{p - a} + \dfrac{bc + d}{b - a} \dfrac{1}{p - b}$.

17. $\dfrac{ac + d}{(p - a)^2} + \dfrac{c}{p - a}$.

18. $\dfrac{\frac{1}{2}}{p - 1} + \dfrac{\frac{1}{2} - p/2}{p^2 + 1}$.

19. $\dfrac{4}{p^2} + \dfrac{-4}{p^2 + 1}$.

20. $\dfrac{5}{(p - 1)^2} + \dfrac{13}{p - 1} + \dfrac{12p + 32}{p^2 + 4}$.

21. $x = \frac{1}{2} - \frac{1}{2} \cos 2t$.

22. $x = e^{-2t} + te^{-t} - e^{-t}$.

23. $x = \frac{1}{3} \cosh 2t - \frac{1}{3} \cosh t$.

24. $x = \frac{1}{2}t^2 e^{-2t}$.

25. $x = \frac{2}{3} \sin t - \frac{1}{3} \sin 2t$.

26. $x = \frac{1}{10}e^t - \frac{1}{6}e^{-t} + \frac{1}{15}e^{-4t}$.

27. $x = \frac{1}{2} \sin t - \frac{1}{2}t \cos t$.

28. $x = 3 - 3e^{-t}$.

29. $x = 3 + 3e^{-t}$.

Exercise XXX (Pages 240 to 244)

1. $i = \frac{3}{2}(1 - \epsilon^{-2t})$.   **2.** $i = e_0/R(1 - \epsilon^{-Rt/L})$.

3. $i = \frac{5}{2}\epsilon^{-25,000t}$.   **4.** $i = e_0/R\epsilon^{-t/RC}$.

5. $i = \frac{5}{2}(\epsilon^{-100t} - \epsilon^{-300t})$.   **6.** $i = \epsilon^{-50t}\sin 100t$.

7. $i = \frac{1}{210}(\cos 20t - \cos 50t)$.

8. $i = -\frac{1}{400}\epsilon^{-10t} + 3/2,000\epsilon^{-30t} + 10^{-3}\cos 10t + 4 \times 10^{-3}\sin 10t$.

9. $i = 1/619,040(496\cos 2t + 40\sin 2t - 496\epsilon^{-20t}\cos 10t - 500\epsilon^{-20t}\sin 10t)$.

13. $s = \frac{2}{13} - \frac{2}{13}e^{-2t}\cos 3t - \frac{4}{39}e^{-2t}\sin 3t$.

14. $s = \frac{4}{145}(\frac{9}{2}\sin 2t - 4\cos 2t - \frac{1}{8}e^{-2t}\sin 3t + 4e^{-2t}\cos 3t)$.

16. $\theta = \frac{6}{5} - \frac{6}{5}e^{-2t}\cos t - 1\frac{2}{5}e^{-2t}\sin t$.

17. $\theta = e^{-2t}\sin t$.   **18.** $i = 5(2 - \epsilon^{-t})$.

19. $i = 2\epsilon^{-t} - 2\cos 2t + 6\sin 2t$.   **20.** $i = 1/2,000(1 + \epsilon^{-20t})$.

21. $i = 1/5,000(\cos 10t + 3\sin 10t - \epsilon^{-20t})$.

22. $i = 3/4,004(1 + 1,000\epsilon^{-2.002t})$.

23. $i = 10^{-4}\epsilon^{-t}\cosh\dfrac{t}{\sqrt{2}}$.

Exercise XXXI (Pages 263 to 269)

1. $f = 3xt + 3t^2 + 2\cos x$.

2. $f = 2\sin 2t + \sin x$.

3. $u = e^{x+t} + 2e^x$.

4. $f = 2x^2t - 2xt^2 + \sin 2t + 3\sin x$.

5. $f = \cos x\cos t + \cos t + \cos x - 1$.

11. $u = 0$ for $t < x$, $u = \sin(t - x)$ for $t > x$.

12. $u = 0$ for $t < x/3$, $u = 5$ for $t > x/3$.

13. $u = e^{x-t}$.

14. $u = 0$ for $t < -x$, $u = \sin(t + x)$ for $t > -x$.

17. $u = 0$ for $t > x$, $u = \sin(t - x)$ for $t < x$.

18. $u = 0$ for $t < x/v$, $u = e^{-ax/v}g\left(t - \dfrac{x}{v}\right)$ for $t > x/v$.

19. $e = 0$ for $t < x/2,000$,

$e = \dfrac{1,000}{3}[1 - \epsilon^{-6(t-x/2,000)}]$ for $t > \dfrac{x}{2,000}$.

20. $e = 0$ for $t < x/2,000$,

$e = \dfrac{1,000}{7}[1 - \epsilon^{-(7/3)(t-x/2,000)}]$ for $t > \dfrac{x}{2,000}$.

21. $e = 0$ for $t < x/2,000$,

$e = 100\epsilon^{-4(t-x/2,000)}$ for $t > \dfrac{x}{2,000}$.

22. $e = 0$ for $t < x/2,000$,

$e = 100\epsilon^{-(t-x/2,000)}\sin\left(t - \dfrac{x}{2,000}\right)$ for $t > \dfrac{x}{2,000}$.

23. $e = 0$ for $t < x/20$,

$$e = \frac{162}{17}\left[\epsilon^{-(t-x/20)} - 13\sin\left(t - \frac{x}{20}\right) + \cos\left(t - \frac{x}{20}\right)\right] \text{ for } t > \frac{x}{20}.$$

24. $e = 0$ for $t < x/v$, $e = 1$ for $t > x/v$.

25. $e = 0$ for $t < x/v$, $e = \dfrac{1}{a+1}$ for $t > x/v$.

26. $e = 0$ for $t < x/v$,

$e = 1 - \epsilon^{-a(t-x/v)}$ for $t > x/v$.

27. $e = 0$ for $t < x/v$,

$e = \epsilon^{-a(t-x/v)}$ for $t > x/v$.

32. $e = 1\left(t - \dfrac{x}{v}\right) - 1\left(t - \dfrac{2S-x}{v}\right) + 1\left(t - \dfrac{2S+x}{v}\right)$

$\qquad - 1\left(t - \dfrac{4S-x}{v}\right) + 1\left(t - \dfrac{4S+x}{v}\right) - \cdots .$

A square wave of height unity moving to the right as t changes from 0 to S/v, $2S/v$ to $3S/v$, etc., and receding as t changes from S/v to $2S/v$, $3S/v$ to $4S/v$, etc.

33. $i = \dfrac{1}{Z_K}\left[1\left(t - \dfrac{x}{v}\right) + 1\left(t - \dfrac{2S-x}{v}\right) + 1\left(t - \dfrac{2S+x}{a}\right) + \cdots\right]$

A square wave moving to the right, augmented by one moving to the left, etc. Thus if t exceeds NS/v, i exceeds N/Z_K.

40. $e = \dfrac{1}{2}\left[1\left(t - \dfrac{x}{v}\right) + 1\left(t - \dfrac{2S-x}{v}\right)\right]$, so that $e = 1$ for $t > \dfrac{2S}{v}$.

41. $e = \dfrac{1}{2}\left[1\left(t - \dfrac{x}{v}\right) - 1\left(t - \dfrac{2S-x}{v}\right)\right]$, so that $e = 0$ for $t > \dfrac{2S}{v}$.

42. $e = \dfrac{1}{2}\left[1\left(t - \dfrac{x}{v}\right) + \dfrac{a-1}{a+1}1\left(t - \dfrac{2S-x}{v}\right)\right]$,

so that $e = \dfrac{a}{a+1}$ for $t > \dfrac{2S}{v}$.

43. $i = \dfrac{1}{2Z_K}\left[1\left(t - \dfrac{x}{v}\right) - 1\left(t - \dfrac{2S-x}{v}\right)\right]$, so that $i = 0$ for $t > \dfrac{2S}{v}$.

44. $i = \dfrac{1}{2Z_K}\left[1\left(t - \dfrac{x}{v}\right) + 1\left(t - \dfrac{2S-x}{v}\right)\right]$, so that $i = \dfrac{1}{Z_K}$ for $t > \dfrac{2S}{v}$.

45. $i = \dfrac{1}{2Z_K}\left[1\left(t - \dfrac{x}{v}\right) - \dfrac{a-1}{a+1}1\left(t - \dfrac{2S-x}{v}\right)\right]$,

so that $i = \dfrac{1}{(a+1)Z_K}$ for $t > \dfrac{2S}{v}$.

INDEX

Numbers in a parenthesis refer to problems, the first of which begins on the page whose number immediately precedes the parenthesis.   Other numbers refer to pages.

CATALOG OF DOVER BOOKS

MATHEMATICS, ELEMENTARY TO INTERMEDIATE

HOW TO CALCULATE QUICKLY, Henry Sticker. This handy volume offers a tried and true method for helping you in the basic mathematics of daily life—addition, subtraction, multiplication, division, fractions, etc. It is designed to awaken your "number sense" or the ability to see relationships between numbers as whole quantities. It is not a collection of tricks working only on special numbers, but a serious course of over 9,000 problems and their solutions, teaching special techniques not taught in schools: left-to-right multiplication, new fast ways of division, etc. 5 or 10 minutes daily use will double or triple your calculation speed. Excellent for the scientific worker who is at home in higher math, but is not satisfied with his speed and accuracy in lower mathematics. 256pp. 5 x 7¼.   T295 Paperbound **$1.00**

TEACH YOURSELF books. For adult self-study, for refresher and supplementary study.

The most effective series of home study mathematics books on the market! With absolutely no outside help, they will teach you as much as any similar college or high-school course, or will helpfully supplement any such course. Each step leads directly to the next, each question is anticipated. Numerous lucid examples and carefully-wrought practice problems illustrate meanings. Not skimpy outlines, not surveys, not usual classroom texts, these 204- to 380-page books are packed with the finest instruction you'll find anywhere for adult self-study.

TEACH YOURSELF ALGEBRA, P. Abbott. Formulas, coordinates, factors, graphs of quadratic functions, quadratic equations, logarithms, ratio, irrational numbers, arithmetical, geometrical series, much more. 1241 problems, solutions. Tables. 52 illus. 307pp. 6⅞ x 4¼.
Clothbound **$2.00**

TEACH YOURSELF GEOMETRY, P. Abbott. Solids, lines, points, surfaces, angle measurement, triangles, theorem of Pythagoras, polygons, loci, the circle, tangents, symmetry, solid geometry, prisms, pyramids, solids of revolution, etc. 343 problems, solutions. 268 illus. 334pp. 6⅞ x 4¼.
Clothbound **$2.00**

TEACH YOURSELF TRIGONOMETRY, P. Abbott. Geometrical foundations, indices, logarithms, trigonometrical ratios, relations between sides, angles of triangle, circular measure, trig. ratios of angles of any magnitude, much more. Requires elementary algebra, geometry. 465 problems, solutions. Tables. 102 illus. 204pp. 6⅞ x 4¼. Clothbound **$2.00**

TEACH YOURSELF THE CALCULUS, P. Abbott. Variations in functions, differentiation, solids of revolution, series, elementary differential equations, areas by integral calculus, much more. Requires algebra, trigonometry. 970 problems, solutions. Tables. 89 illus. 380pp. 6⅞ x 4¼.
Clothbound **$2.00**

TEACH YOURSELF THE SLIDE RULE, B. Snodgrass. Fractions, decimals, A-D scales, log-log scales, trigonometrical scales, indices, logarithms. Commercial, precision, electrical, dualistic, Brighton rules. 80 problems, solutions. 10 illus. 207pp. 6⅞ x 4¼. Clothbound **$2.00**

ARITHMETICAL EXCURSIONS: AN ENRICHMENT OF ELEMENTARY MATHEMATICS, H. Bowers and J. Bowers. For students who want unusual methods of arithmetic never taught in school; for adults who want to increase their number sense. Little known facts about the most simple numbers, arithmetical entertainments and puzzles, figurate numbers, number chains, mysteries and folklore of numbers, the "Hin-dog-abic" number system, etc. First publication. Index. 529 numbered problems and diversions, all with answers. Bibliography. 50 figures. xiv + 320pp. 5⅜ x 8.   T770 Paperbound **$1.65**

HOW DO YOU USE A SLIDE RULE? by A. A. Merrill. Not a manual for mathematicians and engineers, but a lucid step-by-step explanation that presents the fundamental rules clearly enough to be understood by anyone who could benefit by the use of a slide rule in his work or business. This work concentrates on the 2 most important operations: multiplication and division. 10 easy lessons, each with a clear drawing, will save you countless hours in your banking, business, statistical, and other work. First publication. Index. 2 Appendixes. 10 illustrations. 78 problems, all with answers. vi + 36pp. 6⅛ x 9¼.   T62 Paperbound **60¢**

THE THEORY AND OPERATION OF THE SLIDE RULE, J. P. Ellis. Not a skimpy "instruction manual", but an exhaustive treatment that will save you hours throughout your career. Supplies full understanding of every scale on the Log Log Duplex Decitrig type of slide rule. Shows the most time-saving methods, and provides practice useful in the widest variety of actual engineering situations. Each operation introduced in terms of underlying logarithmic theory. Summary of prerequisite math. First publication. Index. 198 figures. Over 450 problems with answers. Bibliography. 12 Appendices. ix + 289pp. 5⅜ x 8.
S727 Paperbound **$1.50**

COLLEGE ALGEBRA, H. B. Fine. Standard college text that gives a systematic and deductive structure to algebra; comprehensive, connected, with emphasis on theory. Discusses the commutative, associative, and distributive laws of number in unusual detail, and goes on with undetermined coefficients, quadratic equations, progressions, logarithms, permutations, probability, power series, and much more. Still most valuable elementary-intermediate text on the science and structure of algebra. Index. 1560 problems, all with answers. x + 631pp. 5⅜ x 8.　　　　　　　　　　　　　　　　　　　　　　　　　　　T211 Paperbound **$2.25**

COORDINATE GEOMETRY, L. P. Eisenhart. Thorough, unified introduction. Unusual for advancing in dimension within each topic (treats together circle, sphere; polar coordinates, 3-dimensional coordinate systems; conic sections, quadric surfaces), affording exceptional insight into subject. Extensive use made of determinants, though no previous knowledge of them is assumed. Algebraic equations of 1st degree, 2 and 3 unknowns, carried further than usual in algebra courses. Over 500 exercises. Introduction. Appendix. Index. Bibliography. 43 illustrations. 310pp. 5⅜ x 8.　　　　　　　　　　　　　　S600 Paperbound **$1.65**

A TREATISE ON PLANE AND ADVANCED TRIGONOMETRY, E. W. Hobson. Extraordinarily wide coverage, going beyond usual college level trig, one of the few works covering advanced trig in full detail. By a great expositor with unerring anticipation and lucid clarification of potentially difficult points. Includes circular functions; expansion of functions of multiple angle; trig tables; relations between sides and angles of triangle; complex numbers; etc. Many problems solved completely. "The best work on the subject." Nature. Formerly entitled "A Treatise on Plane Trigonometry." 689 examples. 6 figures. xvi + 383pp. 5⅜ x 8.　　　　　　　　　　　　　　　　　　　　　　　　　　　　S353 Paperbound **$1.95**

FAMOUS PROBLEMS OF ELEMENTARY GEOMETRY, Felix Klein. Expanded version of the 1894 Easter lectures at Göttingen. 3 problems of classical geometry, in an excellent mathematical treatment by a famous mathematician: squaring the circle, trisecting angle, doubling cube. Considered with full modern implications: transcendental numbers, pi, etc. Notes by R. Archibald. 16 figures. xi + 92pp. 5⅜ x 8.　　　　　　　　　　　T298 Paperbound **$1.00**

MONOGRAPHS ON TOPICS OF MODERN MATHEMATICS, edited by J. W. A. Young. Advanced mathematics for persons who haven't gone beyond or have forgotten high school algebra. 9 monographs on foundation of geometry, modern pure geometry, non-Euclidean geometry, fundamental propositions of algebra, algebraic equations, functions, calculus, theory of numbers, etc. Each monograph gives proofs of important results, and descriptions of leading methods, to provide wide coverage. New introduction by Prof. M. Kline, N. Y. University. 100 diagrams. xvi + 416pp. 6⅛ x 9¼.　　　　　　　　　　　S289 Paperbound **$2.00**

HIGHER MATHEMATICS FOR STUDENTS OF CHEMISTRY AND PHYSICS, J. W. Mellor. Not abstract, but practical, building its problems out of familiar laboratory material, this covers differential calculus, coordinate, analytical geometry, functions, integral calculus, infinite series, numerical equations, differential equations, Fourier's theorem, probability, theory of errors, calculus of variations, determinants. "If the reader is not familiar with this book, it will repay him to examine it," CHEM. & ENGINEERING NEWS. 800 problems. 189 figures. Bibliography. xxi + 641pp. 5⅜ x 8.　　　　　　　　　　　　　　S193 Paperbound **$2.25**

TRIGONOMETRY REFRESHER FOR TECHNICAL MEN, A. Albert Klaf. 913 detailed questions and answers cover the most important aspects of plane and spherical trigonometry. They will help you to brush up or to clear up difficulties in special areas. The first portion of this book covers plane trigonometry, including angles, quadrants, trigonometrical functions, graphical representation, interpolation, equations, logarithms, solution of triangle, use of the slide rule and similar topics. 188 pages then discuss application of plane trigonometry to special problems in navigation, surveying, elasticity, architecture, and various fields of engineering. Small angles, periodic functions, vectors, polar coordinates, de Moivre's theorem are fully examined. The third section of the book then discusses spherical trigonometry and the solution of spherical triangles, with their applications to terrestrial and astronomical problems. Methods of saving time with numerical calculations, simplification of principal functions of angle, much practical information make this a most useful book. 913 questions answered. 1738 problems, answers to odd numbers. 494 figures. 24 pages of useful formulae, functions. Index. x + 629pp. 5⅜ x 8.　　　　　　　　　　　T371 Paperbound **$2.00**

TEXTBOOK OF ALGEBRA, G. Chrystal. One of the great mathematical textbooks, still about the best source for complete treatments of the topics of elementary algebra; a chief reference work for teachers and students of algebra in advanced high school and university courses, or for the mathematician working on problems of elementary algebra or looking for a background to more advanced topics. Ranges from basic laws and processes to extensive examination of such topics as limits, infinite series, general properties of integral numbers, and probability theory. Emphasis is on algebraic form, the foundation of analytical geometry and the key to modern developments in algebra. Prior course in algebra is desirable, but not absolutely necessary. Includes theory of quotients, distribution of products, arithmetical theory of surds, theory of interest, permutations and combinations, general expansion theorems, recurring fractions, and much, much more. Two volume set. Index in each volume. Over 1500 exercises, approximately half with answers. Total of xlviii + 1187pp. 5⅜ x 8.

S750 Vol I Paperbound **$2.35**
S751 Vol II Paperbound **$2.35**
The set **$4.70**

MATHEMATICS—INTERMEDIATE TO ADVANCED

General

INTRODUCTION TO APPLIED MATHEMATICS, Francis D. Murnaghan. A practical and thoroughly sound introduction to a number of advanced branches of higher mathematics. Among the selected topics covered in detail are: vector and matrix analysis, partial and differential equations, integral equations, calculus of variations, Laplace transform theory, the vector triple product, linear vector functions, quadratic and bilinear forms, Fourier series, spherical harmonics, Bessel functions, the Heaviside expansion formula, and many others. Extremely useful book for graduate students in physics, engineering, chemistry, and mathematics. Index. 111 study exercises with answers. 41 illustrations. ix + 389pp. 5⅜ x 8½.
S1042 Paperbound **$2.00**

OPERATIONAL METHODS IN APPLIED MATHEMATICS, H. S. Carslaw and J. C. Jaeger. Explanation of the application of the Laplace Transformation to differential equations, a simple and effective substitute for more difficult and obscure operational methods. Of great practical value to engineers and to all workers in applied mathematics. Chapters on: Ordinary Linear Differential Equations with Constant Coefficients;; Electric Circuit Theory; Dynamical Applications; The Inversion Theorem for the Laplace Transformation; Conduction of Heat; Vibrations of Continuous Mechanical Systems; Hydrodynamics; Impulsive Functions; Chains of Differential Equations; and other related matters. 3 appendices. 153 problems, many with answers. 22 figures. xvi + 359pp. 5⅜ x 8½.
S1011 Paperbound **$2.25**

APPLIED MATHEMATICS FOR RADIO AND COMMUNICATIONS ENGINEERS, C. E. Smith. No extraneous material here!—only the theories, equations, and operations essential and immediately useful for radio work. Can be used as refresher, as handbook of applications and tables, or as full home-study course. Ranges from simplest arithmetic through calculus, series, and wave forms, hyperbolic trigonometry, simultaneous equations in mesh circuits, etc. Supplies applications right along with each math topic discussed. 22 useful tables of functions, formulas, logs, etc. Index. 166 exercises, 140 examples, all with answers. 95 diagrams. Bibliography. x + 336pp. 5⅜ x 8.
S141 Paperbound **$1.75**

Algebra, group theory, determinants, sets, matrix theory

ALGEBRAS AND THEIR ARITHMETICS, L. E. Dickson. Provides the foundation and background necessary to any advanced undergraduate or graduate student studying abstract algebra. Begins with elementary introduction to linear transformations, matrices, field of complex numbers; proceeds to order, basal units, modulus, quaternions, etc.; develops calculus of linears sets, describes various examples of algebras including invariant, difference, nilpotent, semi-simple. "Makes the reader marvel at his genius for clear and profound analysis," Amer. Mathematical Monthly. Index. xii + 241pp. 5⅜ x 8.
S616 Paperbound **$1.50**

THE THEORY OF EQUATIONS WITH AN INTRODUCTION TO THE THEORY OF BINARY ALGEBRAIC FORMS, W. S. Burnside and A. W. Panton. Extremely thorough and concrete discussion of the theory of equations, with extensive detailed treatment of many topics curtailed in later texts. Covers theory of algebraic equations, properties of polynomials, symmetric functions, derived functions, Horner's process, complex numbers and the complex variable, determinants and methods of elimination, invariant theory (nearly 100 pages), transformations, introduction to Galois theory, Abelian equations, and much more. Invaluable supplementary work for modern students and teachers. 759 examples and exercises. Index in each volume. Two volume set. Total of xxiv + 604pp. 5⅜ x 8.
S714 Vol I Paperbound **$1.85**
S715 Vol II Paperbound **$1.85**
The set **$3.70**

COMPUTATIONAL METHODS OF LINEAR ALGEBRA, V. N. Faddeeva, translated by **C. D. Benster.** First English translation of a unique and valuable work, the only work in English presenting a systematic exposition of the most important methods of linear algebra—classical and contemporary. Shows in detail how to derive numerical solutions of problems in mathematical physics which are frequently connected with those of linear algebra. Theory as well as individual practice. Part I surveys the mathematical background that is indispensable to what follows. Parts II and III, the conclusion, set forth the most important methods of solution, for both exact and iterative groups. One of the most outstanding and valuable features of this work is the 23 tables, double and triple checked for accuracy. These tables will not be found elsewhere. Author's preface. Translator's note. New bibliography and index. x + 252pp. 5⅜ x 8.
S424 Paperbound **$1.95**

ALGEBRAIC EQUATIONS, E. Dehn. Careful and complete presentation of Galois' theory of algebraic equations; theories of Lagrange and Galois developed in logical rather than historical form, with a more thorough exposition than in most modern books. Many concrete applications and fully-worked-out examples. Discusses basic theory (very clear exposition of the symmetric group); isomorphic, transitive, and Abelian groups; applications of Lagrange's and Galois' theories; and much more. Newly revised by the author. Index. List of Theorems. xi + 208pp. 5⅜ x 8.
S697 Paperbound **$1.45**

ALGEBRAIC THEORIES, L. E. Dickson. Best thorough introduction to classical topics in higher algebra develops theories centering around matrices, invariants, groups. Higher algebra, Galois theory, finite linear groups, Klein's icosahedron, algebraic invariants, linear transformations, elementary divisors, invariant factors; quadratic, bi-linear, Hermitian forms, singly and in pairs. Proofs rigorous, detailed; topics developed lucidly, in close connection with their most frequent mathematical applications. Formerly "Modern Algebraic Theories." 155 problems. Bibliography. 2 indexes. 285pp. 5⅜ x 8. S547 Paperbound **$1.50**

LECTURES ON THE ICOSAHEDRON AND THE SOLUTION OF EQUATIONS OF THE FIFTH DEGREE, Felix Klein. The solution of quintics in terms of rotation of a regular icosahedron around its axes of symmetry. A classic & indispensable source for those interested in higher algebra, geometry, crystallography. Considerable explanatory material included. 230 footnotes, mostly bibliographic. 2nd edition, xvi + 289pp. 5⅜ x 8. S314 Paperbound **$1.85**

LINEAR GROUPS, WITH AN EXPOSITION OF THE GALOIS FIELD THEORY, L. E. Dickson. The classic exposition of the theory of groups, well within the range of the graduate student. Part I contains the most extensive and thorough presentation of the theory of Galois Fields available, with a wealth of examples and theorems. Part II is a full discussion of linear groups of finite order. Much material in this work is based on Dickson's own contributions. Also includes expositions of Jordan, Lie, Abel, Betti-Mathieu, Hermite, etc. "A milestone in the development of modern algebra," W. Magnus, in his historical introduction to this edition. Index. xv + 312pp. 5⅜ x 8. S482 Paperbound **$1.95**

INTRODUCTION TO THE THEORY OF GROUPS OF FINITE ORDER, R. Carmichael. Examines fundamental theorems and their application. Beginning with sets, systems, permutations, etc., it progresses in easy stages through important types of groups: Abelian, prime power, permutation, etc. Except 1 chapter where matrices are desirable, no higher math needed. 783 exercises, problems. Index. xvi + 447pp. 5⅜ x 8. S300 Paperbound **$2.25**

THEORY OF GROUPS OF FINITE ORDER, W. Burnside. First published some 40 years ago, this is still one of the clearest introductory texts. Partial contents: permutations, groups independent of representation, composition series of a group, isomorphism of a group with itself, Abelian groups, prime power groups, permutation groups, invariants of groups of linear substitution, graphical representation, etc. 45pp. of notes. Indexes. xxiv + 512pp. 5⅜ x 8. S38 Paperbound **$2.45**

CONTINUOUS GROUPS OF TRANSFORMATIONS, L. P. Eisenhart. Intensive study of the theory and geometrical applications of continuous groups of transformations; a standard work on the subject, called forth by the revolution in physics in the 1920's. Covers tensor analysis, Riemannian geometry, canonical parameters, transitivity, imprimitivity, differential invariants, the algebra of constants of structure, differential geometry, contact transformations, etc. "Likely to remain one of the standard works on the subject for many years . . . principal theorems are proved clearly and concisely, and the arrangement of the whole is coherent," MATHEMATICAL GAZETTE. Index. 72-item bibliography. 185 exercises. ix + 301pp. 5⅜ x 8. S781 Paperbound **$1.85**

THE THEORY OF GROUPS AND QUANTUM MECHANICS, H. Weyl. Discussions of Schroedinger's wave equation, de Broglie's waves of a particle, Jordan-Hoelder theorem, Lie's continuous groups of transformations, Pauli exclusion principle, quantization of Maxwell-Dirac field equations, etc. Unitary geometry, quantum theory, groups, application of groups to quantum mechanics, symmetry permutation group, algebra of symmetric transformation, etc. 2nd revised edition. Bibliography. Index. xxii + 422pp. 5⅜ x 8. S269 Paperbound **$2.25**

APPLIED GROUP-THEORETIC AND MATRIX METHODS, Bryan Higman. The first systematic treatment of group and matrix theory for the physical scientist. Contains a comprehensive, easily-followed exposition of the basic ideas of group theory (realized through matrices) and its applications in the various areas of physics and chemstry: tensor analysis, relativity, quantum theory, molecular structure and spectra, and Eddington's quantum relativity. Includes rigorous proofs available only in works of a far more advanced character. 34 figures, numerous tables. Bibliography. Index. xiii + 454pp. 5⅜ x 8⅜. S1147 Paperbound **$2.50**

THE THEORY OF GROUP REPRESENTATIONS, Francis D. Murnaghan. A comprehensive introduction to the theory of group representations. Particular attention is devoted to those groups—mainly the symmetric and rotation groups—which have proved to be of fundamental significance for quantum mechanics (esp. nuclear physics). Also a valuable contribution to the literature on matrices, since the usual representations of groups are groups of matrices. Covers the theory of group integration (as developed by Schur and Weyl), the theory of 2-valued or spin representations, the representations of the symmetric group, the crystallographic groups, the Lorentz group, reducibility (Schur's lemma, Burnside's Theorem, etc.), the alternating group, linear groups, the orthogonal group, etc. Index. List of references. xi + 369pp. 5⅜ x 8½. S1112 Paperbound **$2.35**

THEORY OF SETS, E. Kamke. Clearest, amplest introduction in English, well suited for independent study. Subdivision of main theory, such as theory of sets of points, are discussed, but emphasis is on general theory. Partial contents: rudiments of set theory, arbitrary sets and their cardinal numbers, ordered sets and their order types, well-ordered sets and their cardinal numbers. Bibliography. Key to symbols. Index. vii + 144pp. 5⅜ x 8. S141 Paperbound **$1.35**

THEORY AND APPLICATIONS OF FINITE GROUPS, G. A. Miller, H. F. Blichfeldt, L. E. Dickson. Unusually accurate and authoritative work, each section prepared by a leading specialist: Miller on substitution and abstract groups, Blichfeldt on finite groups of linear homogeneous transformations, Dickson on applications of finite groups. Unlike more modern works, this gives the concrete basis from which abstract group theory arose. Includes Abelian groups, prime-power groups, isomorphisms, matrix forms of linear transformations, Sylow groups, Galois' theory of algebraic equations, duplication of a cube, trisection of an angle, etc. 2 Indexes. 267 problems. xvii + 390pp. 5⅜ x 8. S216 Paperbound **$2.00**

THE THEORY OF DETERMINANTS, MATRICES, AND INVARIANTS, H. W. Turnbull. Important study includes all salient features and major theories. 7 chapters on determinants and matrices cover fundamental properties, Laplace identities, multiplication, linear equations, rank and differentiation, etc. Sections on invariants gives general properties, symbolic and direct methods of reduction, binary and polar forms, general linear transformation, first fundamental theorem, multilinear forms. Following chapters study development and proof of Hilbert's Basis Theorem, Gordan-Hilbert Finiteness Theorem, Clebsch's Theorem, and include discussions of apolarity, canonical forms, geometrical interpretations of algebraic forms, complete system of the general quadric, etc. New preface and appendix. Bibliography. xviii + 374pp. 5⅜ x 8. S699 Paperbound **$2.25**

AN INTRODUCTION TO THE THEORY OF CANONICAL MATRICES, H. W. Turnbull and A. C. Aitken. All principal aspects of the theory of canonical matrices, from definitions and fundamental properties of matrices to the practical applications of their reduction to canonical form. Beginning with matrix multiplications, reciprocals, and partitioned matrices, the authors go on to elementary transformations and bilinear and quadratic forms. Also covers such topics as a rational canonical form for the collineatory group, congruent and conjunctive transformation for quadratic and hermitian forms, unitary and orthogonal transformations, canonical reduction of pencils of matrices, etc. Index. Appendix. Historical notes at chapter ends. Bibliographies. 275 problems. xiv + 200pp. 5⅜ x 8. S177 Paperbound **$1.55**

A TREATISE ON THE THEORY OF DETERMINANTS, T. Muir. Unequalled as an exhaustive compilation of nearly all the known facts about determinants up to the early 1930's. Covers notation and general properties, row and column transformation, symmetry, compound determinants, adjugates, rectangular arrays and matrices, linear dependence, gradients, Jacobians, Hessians, Wronskians, and much more. Invaluable for libraries of industrial and research organizations as well as for student, teacher, and mathematician; very useful in the field of computing machines. Revised and enlarged by W. H. Metzler. Index. 485 problems and scores of numerical examples. iv + 766pp. 5⅜ x 8. S670 Paperbound **$3.00**

THEORY OF DETERMINANTS IN THE HISTORICAL ORDER OF DEVELOPMENT, Sir Thomas Muir. Unabridged reprinting of this complete study of 1,859 papers on determinant theory written between 1693 and 1900. Most important and original sections reproduced, valuable commentary on each. No other work is necessary for determinant research: all types are covered—each subdivision of the theory treated separately; all papers dealing with each type are covered; you are told exactly what each paper is about and how important its contribution is. Each result, theory, extension, or modification is assigned its own identifying numeral so that the full history may be more easily followed. Includes papers on determinants in general, determinants and linear equations, symmetric determinants, alternants, recurrents, determinants having invariant factors, and all other major types. "A model of what such histories ought to be," NATURE. "Mathematicians must ever be grateful to Sir Thomas for his monumental work," AMERICAN MATH MONTHLY. Four volumes bound as two. Indices. Bibliographies. Total of lxxxiv + 1977pp. 5⅜ x 8. S672-3 The set, Clothbound **$12.50**

Calculus and function theory, Fourier theory, infinite series, calculus of variations, real and complex functions

FIVE VOLUME "THEORY OF FUNCTIONS' SET BY KONRAD KNOPP

This five-volume set, prepared by Konrad Knopp, provides a complete and readily followed account of theory of functions. Proofs are given concisely, yet without sacrifice of completeness or rigor. These volumes are used as texts by such universities as M.I.T., University of Chicago, N. Y. City College, and many others. "Excellent introduction . . . remarkably readable, concise, clear, rigorous," JOURNAL OF THE AMERICAN STATISTICAL ASSOCIATION.

ELEMENTS OF THE THEORY OF FUNCTIONS, Konrad Knopp. This book provides the student with background for further volumes in this set, or texts on a similar level. Partial contents: foundations, system of complex numbers and the Gaussian plane of numbers, Riemann sphere of numbers, mapping by linear functions, normal forms, the logarithm, the cyclometric functions and binomial series. "Not only for the young student, but also for the student who knows all about what is in it," MATHEMATICAL JOURNAL. Bibliography. Index. 140pp. 5⅜ x 8. S154 Paperbound **$1.35**

THEORY OF FUNCTIONS, PART I, Konrad Knopp. With volume II, this book provides coverage of basic concepts and theorems. Partial contents: numbers and points, functions of a complex variable, integral of a continuous function, Cauchy's integral theorem, Cauchy's integral formulae, series with variable terms, expansion of analytic functions in power series, analytic continuation and complete definition of analytic functions, entire transcendental functions, Laurent expansion, types of singularities. Bibliography. Index. vii + 146pp. 5⅜ x 8. S156 Paperbound **$1.35**

ELEMENTS OF THE THEORY OF REAL FUNCTIONS, J. E. Littlewood. Based on lectures given at Trinity College, Cambridge, this book has proved to be extremely successful in introducing graduate students to the modern theory of functions. It offers a full and concise coverage of classes and cardinal numbers, well-ordered series, other types of series, and elements of the theory of sets of points. 3rd revised edition. vii + 71pp. 5⅜ x 8.

S171 Clothbound **$2.85**
S172 Paperbound **$1.25**

TRANSCENDENTAL AND ALGEBRAIC NUMBERS, A. O. Gelfond. First English translation of work by leading Soviet mathematician. Thue-Siegel theorem, its p-adic analogue, on approximation of algebraic numbers by numbers in fixed algebraic field; Hermite-Lindemann theorem on transcendency of Bessel functions, solutions of other differential equations; Gelfond-Schneider theorem on transcendency of alpha to power beta; Schneider's work on elliptic functions, with method developed by Gelfond. Translated by L. F. Boron. Index. Bibliography. 200pp. 5⅜ x 8.

S615 Paperbound **$1.75**

ELLIPTIC INTEGRALS, H. Hancock. Invaluable in work involving differential equations containing cubics or quartics under the root sign, where elementary calculus methods are inadequate. Practical solutions to problems that occur in mathematics, engineering, physics: differential equations requiring integration of Lamé's, Briot's, or Bouquet's equations; determination of arc of ellipse, hyperbola, lemniscate; solutions of problems in elastica; motion of a projectile under resistance varying as the cube of the velocity; pendulums; many others. Exposition is in accordance with Legendre-Jacobi theory and includes rigorous discussion of Legendre transformations. 20 figures. 5 place table. Index. 104pp. 5⅛ x 8.

S484 Paperbound **$1.25**

LECTURES ON THE THEORY OF ELLIPTIC FUNCTIONS, H. Hancock. Reissue of the only book in English with so extensive a coverage, especially of Abel, Jacobi, Legendre, Weierstrasse, Hermite, Liouville, and Riemann. Unusual fullness of treatment, plus applications as well as theory, in discussing elliptic function (the universe of elliptic integrals originating in works of Abel and Jacobi), their existence, and ultimate meaning. Use is made of Riemann to provide the most general theory. 40 page table of formulas. 76 figures. xxiii + 498pp.

S483 Paperbound **$2.55**

THE THEORY AND FUNCTIONS OF A REAL VARIABLE AND THE THEORY OF FOURIER'S SERIES, E. W. Hobson. One of the best introductions to set theory and various aspects of functions and Fourier's series. Requires only a good background in calculus. Provides an exhaustive coverage of: metric and descriptive properties of sets of points; transfinite numbers and order types; functions of a real variable; the Riemann and Lebesgue integrals; sequences and series of numbers; power-series; functions representable by series sequences of continuous functions; trigonometrical series; representation of functions by Fourier's series; complete exposition (200pp.) on set theory; and much more. "The best possible guide," Nature. Vol. I: 88 detailed examples, 10 figures. Index. xv + 736pp. Vol. II: 117 detailed examples, 13 figures. Index. x + 780pp. 6⅛ x 9¼.

Vol. I: S387 Paperbound **$3.00**
Vol. II: S388 Paperbound **$3.00**

ALMOST PERIODIC FUNCTIONS, A. S. Besicovitch. This unique and important summary by a well-known mathematician covers in detail the two stages of development in Bohr's theory of almost periodic functions: (1) as a generalization of pure periodicity, with results and proofs; (2) the work done by Stepanoff, Wiener, Weyl, and Bohr in generalizing the theory. Bibliography. xi + 180pp. 5⅜ x 8.

S18 Paperbound **$1.75**

THE ANALYTICAL THEORY OF HEAT, Joseph Fourier. This book, which revolutionized mathematical physics, is listed in the Great Books program, and many other listings of great books. It has been used with profit by generations of mathematicians and physicists who are interested in either heat or in the application of the Fourier integral. Covers cause and reflection of rays of heat, radiant heating, heating of closed spaces, use of trigonometric series in the theory of heat, Fourier integral, etc. Translated by Alexander Freeman. 20 figures. xxii + 466pp. 5⅜ x 8.

S93 Paperbound **$2.00**

AN INTRODUCTION TO FOURIER METHODS AND THE LAPLACE TRANSFORMATION, Philip Franklin. Concentrates upon essentials, enabling the reader with only a working knowledge of calculus to gain an understanding of Fourier methods in a broad sense, suitable for most applications. This work covers complex qualities with methods of computing elementary functions for complex values of the argument and finding approximations by the use of charts; Fourier series and integrals with half-range and complex Fourier series; harmonic analysis; Fourier and Laplace transformations, etc.; partial differential equations with applications to transmission of electricity; etc. The methods developed are related to physical problems of heat flow, vibrations, electrical transmission, electromagnetic radiation, etc. 828 problems with answers. Formerly entitled "Fourier Methods." Bibliography. Index. x + 289pp. 5⅜ x 8.

S452 Paperbound **$1.85**

THE FOURIER INTEGRAL AND CERTAIN OF ITS APPLICATIONS, Norbert Wiener. The only book-length study of the Fourier integral as link between pure and applied math. An expansion of lectures given at Cambridge. Partial contents: Plancherel's theorem, general Tauberian theorem, special Tauberian theorems, generalized harmonic analysis. Bibliography. viii + 201pp. 5⅜ x 8.

S272 Paperbound **$1.50**

FUNCTIONS OF A COMPLEX VARIABLE, James Pierpont. Long one of best in the field. A thorough treatment of fundamental elements, concepts, theorems. A complete study, rigorous, detailed, with carefully selected problems worked out to illustrate each topic. Partial contents: arithmetical operations, real term series, positive term series, exponential functions, integration, analytic functions, asymptotic expansions, functions of Weierstrass, Legendre, etc. Index. List of symbols. 122 illus. 597pp. 5⅜ x 8. **S560 Paperbound $2.45**

MODERN OPERATIONAL CALCULUS: WITH APPLICATIONS IN TECHNICAL MATHEMATICS, N. W. McLachlan. An introduction to modern operational calculus based upon the Laplace transform, applying it to the solution of ordinary and partial differential equations. For physicists, engineers, and applied mathematicians. Partial contents: Laplace transform, theorems or rules of the operational calculus, solution of ordinary and partial linear differential equations with constant coefficients, evaluation of integrals and establishment of mathematical relationships, derivation of Laplace transforms of various functions, etc. Six appendices deal with Heaviside's unit function, etc. Revised edition. Index. Bibliography. xiv + 218pp. 5⅜ x 8½. **S192 Paperbound $1.75**

ADVANCED CALCULUS, E. B. Wilson. An unabridged reprinting of the work which continues to be recognized as one of the most comprehensive and useful texts in the field. It contains an immense amount of well-presented, fundamental material, including chapters on vector functions, ordinary differential equations, special functions, calculus of variations, etc., which are excellent introductions to these areas. For students with only one year of calculus, more than 1300 exercises cover both pure math and applications to engineering and physical problems. For engineers, physicists, etc., this work, with its 54 page introductory review, is the ideal reference and refresher. Index. ix + 566pp. 5⅜ x 8. **S504 Paperbound $2.45**

ASYMPTOTIC EXPANSIONS, A. Erdélyi. The only modern work available in English, this is an unabridged reproduction of a monograph prepared for the Office of Naval Research. It discusses various procedures for asymptotic evaluation of integrals containing a large parameter and solutions of ordinary linear differential equations. Bibliography of 71 items. vi + 108pp. 5⅜ x 8. **S318 Paperbound $1.35**

INTRODUCTION TO ELLIPTIC FUNCTIONS: with applications, F. Bowman. Concise, practical introduction to elliptic integrals and functions. Beginning with the familiar trigonometric functions, it requires nothing more from the reader than a knowledge of basic principles of differentiation and integration. Discussion confined to the Jacobian functions. Enlarged bibliography. Index. 173 problems and examples. 56 figures, 4 tables. 115pp. 5⅜ x 8. **S922 Paperbound $1.25**

ON RIEMANN'S THEORY OF ALGEBRAIC FUNCTIONS AND THEIR INTEGRALS: A SUPPLEMENT TO THE USUAL TREATISES, Felix Klein. Klein demonstrates how the mathematical ideas in Riemann's work on Abelian integrals can be arrived at by thinking in terms of the flow of electric current on surfaces. Intuitive explanations, not detailed proofs given in an extremely clear exposition, concentrating on the kinds of functions which can be defined on Riemann surfaces. Also useful as an introduction to the origins of topological problems. Complete and unabridged. Approved translation by Frances Hardcastle. New introduction. 43 figures. Glossary. xii + 76pp. 5⅜ x 8½. **S1072 Paperbound $1.25**

COLLECTED WORKS OF BERNHARD RIEMANN. This important source book is the first to contain the complete text of both 1892 Werke and the 1902 supplement, unabridged. It contains 31 monographs, 3 complete lecture courses, 15 miscellaneous papers, which have been of enormous importance in relativity, topology, theory of complex variables, and other areas of mathematics. Edited by R. Dedekind, H. Weber, M. Noether, W. Wirtinger. German text. English introduction by Hans Lewy. 690pp. 5⅜ x 8. **S226 Paperbound $2.85**

THE TAYLOR SERIES, AN INTRODUCTION TO THE THEORY OF FUNCTIONS OF A COMPLEX VARIABLE, P. Dienes. This book investigates the entire realm of analytic functions. Only ordinary calculus is needed, except in the last two chapters. Starting with an introduction to real variables and complex algebra, the properties of infinite series, elementary functions, complex differentiation and integration are carefully derived. Also biuniform mapping, a thorough two part discussion of representation and singularities of analytic functions, overconvergence and gap theorems, divergent series, Taylor series on its circle of convergence, divergence and singularities, etc. Unabridged, corrected reissue of first edition. Preface and index. 186 examples, many fully worked out. 67 figures. xii + 555pp. 5⅜ x 8. **S391 Paperbound $2.75**

INTRODUCTION TO BESSEL FUNCTIONS, Frank Bowman. A rigorous self-contained exposition providing all necessary material during the development, which requires only some knowledge of calculus and acquaintance with differential equations. A balanced presentation including applications and practical use. Discusses Bessel Functions of Zero Order, of Any Real Order; Modified Bessel Functions of Zero Order; Definite Integrals; Asymptotic Expansions; Bessel's Solution to Kepler's Problem; Circular Membranes; much more. "Clear and straightforward . . . useful not only to students of physics and engineering, but to mathematical students in general," Nature. 226 problems. Short tables of Bessel functions. 27 figures. Index. x + 135pp. 5⅜ x 8. **S462 Paperbound $1.35**

THEORY OF FUNCTIONS, PART II, Konrad Knopp. Application and further development of general theory, special topics. Single valued functions, entire, Weierstrass, Meromorphic functions. Riemann surfaces. Algebraic functions. Analytical configuration, Riemann surface. Bibliography. Index. x + 150pp. 5⅜ x 8. S157 Paperbound **$1.35**

PROBLEM BOOK IN THE THEORY OF FUNCTIONS, VOLUME 1, Konrad Knopp. Problems in elementary theory, for use with Knopp's THEORY OF FUNCTIONS, or any other text, arranged according to increasing difficulty. Fundamental concepts, sequences of numbers and infinite series, complex variable, integral theorems, development in series, conformal mapping. 182 problems. Answers. viii + 126pp. 5⅜ x 8. S158 Paperbound **$1.35**

PROBLEM BOOK IN THE THEORY OF FUNCTIONS, VOLUME 2, Konrad Knopp. Advanced theory of functions, to be used either with Knopp's THEORY OF FUNCTIONS, or any other comparable text. Singularities, entire & meromorphic functions, periodic, analytic, continuation, multiple-valued functions, Riemann surfaces, conformal mapping. Includes a section of additional elementary problems. "The difficult task of selecting from the immense material of the modern theory of functions the problems just within the reach of the beginner is here masterfully accomplished," AM. MATH. SOC. Answers. 138pp. 5⅜ x 8. S159 Paperbound **$1.35**

A COURSE IN MATHEMATICAL ANALYSIS, Edouard Goursat. Trans. by E. R. Hedrick, O. Dunkel. Classic study of fundamental material thoroughly treated. Exceptionally lucid exposition of wide range of subject matter for student in 1 year of calculus. Vol. 1: Derivatives and Differentials, Definite Integrals, Expansion in Series, Applications to Geometry. Problems. Index. 52 illus. 556pp. Vol. 2, Part I: Functions of a Complex Variable, Conformal Representations, Doubly Periodic Functions, Natural Boundaries, etc. Problems. Index. 38 illus. 269pp. Vol. 2, Part 2: Differential Equations, Cauchy-Lipschitz Method, Non-linear Differential Equations, Simultaneous Equations, etc. Problems. Index. 308pp. 5⅜ x 8.

Vol. 1 S554 Paperbound **$2.50**
Vol. 2 part 1 S555 Paperbound **$1.85**
Vol. 2 part 2 S556 Paperbound **$1.85**
3 vol. set **$6.20**

MODERN THEORIES OF INTEGRATION, H. Kestelman. Connected and concrete coverage, with fully-worked-out proofs for every step. Ranges from elementary definitions through theory of aggregates, sets of points, Riemann and Lebesgue integration, and much more. This new revised and enlarged edition contains a new chapter on Riemann-Stieltjes integration, as well as a supplementary section of 186 exercises. Ideal for the mathematician, student, teacher, or self-studier. Index of Definitions and Symbols. General Index. Bibliography. x + 310pp. 5⅝ x 8⅜. S572 Paperbound **$2.25**

THEORY OF MAXIMA AND MINIMA, H. Hancock. Fullest treatment ever written; only work in English with extended discussion of maxima and minima for functions of 1, 2, or n variables, problems with subsidiary constraints, and relevant quadratic forms. Detailed proof of each important theorem. Covers the Scheeffer and von Dantscher theories, homogeneous quadratic forms, reversion of series, fallacious establishment of maxima and minima, etc. Unsurpassed treatise for advanced students of calculus, mathematicians, economists, statisticians. Index. 24 diagrams. 39 problems, many examples. 193pp. 5⅜ x 8. S665 Paperbound **$1.50**

AN ELEMENTARY TREATISE ON ELLIPTIC FUNCTIONS, A. Cayley. Still the fullest and clearest text on the theories of Jacobi and Legendre for the advanced student (and an excellent supplement for the beginner). A masterpiece of exposition by the great 19th century British mathematician (creator of the theory of matrices and abstract geometry), it covers the addition-theory, Landen's theorem, the 3 kinds of elliptic integrals, transformations, the q-functions, reduction of a differential expression, and much more. Index. xii + 386pp. 5⅜ x 8. S728 Paperbound **$2.00**

THE APPLICATIONS OF ELLIPTIC FUNCTIONS, A. G. Greenhill. Modern books forego detail for sake of brevity—this book offers complete exposition necessary for proper understanding, use of elliptic integrals. Formulas developed from definite physical, geometric problems; examples representative enough to offer basic information in widely useable form. Elliptic integrals, addition theorem, algebraical form of addition theorem, elliptic integrals of 2nd, 3rd kind, double periodicity, resolution into factors, series, transformation, etc. Introduction. Index. 25 illus. xi + 357pp. 5⅜ x 8. S603 Paperbound **$1.75**

THE THEORY OF FUNCTIONS OF REAL VARIABLES, James Pierpont. A 2-volume authoritative exposition, by one of the foremost mathematicians of his time. Each theorem stated with all variations, then followed by proof. No need to go through complicated reasoning to discover conditions added without specific mention. Includes a particularly complete, rigorous presentation of theory of measure; and Pierpont's own work on a theory of Lebesgue integrals, and treatment of area of a curved surface. Partial contents, Vol. 1: rational numbers, exponentials, logarithms, point aggregates, maxima, minima, proper integrals, improper integrals, multiple proper integrals, continuity, discontinuity, indeterminate forms. Vol. 2: point sets, proper integrals, series, power series, aggregates, ordinal numbers, discontinuous functions, sub-, infra-uniform convergence, much more. Index. 95 illustrations. 1229pp. 5⅜ x 8. S558-9, 2 volume set, paperbound **$4.90**

Differential equations, ordinary and partial; integral equations

INTRODUCTION TO THE DIFFERENTIAL EQUATIONS OF PHYSICS, L. Hopf. Especially valuable to the engineer with no math beyond elementary calculus. Emphasizing intuitive rather than formal aspects of concepts, the author covers an extensive territory. Partial contents: Law of causality, energy theorem, damped oscillations, coupling by friction, cylindrical and spherical coordinates, heat source, etc. Index. 48 figures. 160pp. 5⅜ x 8.
S120 Paperbound **$1.25**

INTRODUCTION TO THE THEORY OF LINEAR DIFFERENTIAL EQUATIONS, E. G. Poole. Authoritative discussions of important topics, with methods of solution more detailed than usual, for students with background of elementary course in differential equations. Studies existence theorems, linearly independent solutions; equations with constant coefficients; with uniform analytic coefficients; regular singularities; the hypergeometric equation; conformal representation; etc. Exercises. Index. 210pp. 5⅜ x 8.
S629 Paperbound **$1.65**

DIFFERENTIAL EQUATIONS FOR ENGINEERS, P. Franklin. Outgrowth of a course given 10 years at M. I. T. Makes most useful branch of pure math accessible for practical work. Theoretical basis of D.E.'s; solution of ordinary D.E.'s and partial derivatives arising from heat flow, steady-state temperature of a plate, wave equations; analytic functions; convergence of Fourier Series. 400 problems on electricity, vibratory systems, other topics. Formerly "Differential Equations for Electrical Engineers." Index 41 illus. 307pp. 5⅜ x 8.
S601 Paperbound **$1.65**

DIFFERENTIAL EQUATIONS, F. R. Moulton. A detailed, rigorous exposition of all the non-elementary processes of solving ordinary differential equations. Several chapters devoted to the treatment of practical problems, especially those of a physical nature, which are far more advanced than problems usually given as illustrations. Includes analytic differential equations; variations of a parameter; integrals of differential equations; analytic implicit functions; problems of elliptic motion; sine-amplitude functions; deviation of formal bodies; Cauchy-Lipschitz process; linear differential equations with periodic coefficients; differential equations in infinitely many variations; much more. Historical notes. 10 figures. 222 problems. Index. xv + 395pp. 5⅜ x 8.
S451 Paperbound **$2.00**

DIFFERENTIAL AND INTEGRAL EQUATIONS OF MECHANICS AND PHYSICS (DIE DIFFERENTIAL-UND INTEGRALGLEICHUNGEN DER MECHANIK UND PHYSIK), edited by P. Frank and R. von Mises. Most comprehensive and authoritative work on the mathematics of mathematical physics available today in the United States: the standard, definitive reference for teachers, physicists, engineers, and mathematicians—now published (in the original German) at a relatively inexpensive price for the first time! Every chapter in this 2,000-page set is by an expert in his field: Carathéodory, Courant, Frank, Mises, and a dozen others. Vol I, on mathematics, gives concise but complete coverages of advanced calculus, differential equations, integral equations, and potential, and partial differential equations. Index. xxiii + 916pp. Vol. II (physics): classical mechanics, optics, continuous mechanics, heat conduction and diffusion, the stationary and quasi-stationary electromagnetic field, electromagnetic oscillations, and wave mechanics. Index. xxiv + 1106pp. Two volume set. Each volume available separately. 5⅝ x 8⅜.
S787 Vol I Clothbound **$7.50**
S788 Vol II Clothbound **$7.50**
The set **$15.00**

LECTURES ON CAUCHY'S PROBLEM, J. Hadamard. Based on lectures given at Columbia, Rome, this discusses work of Riemann, Kirchhoff, Volterra, and the author's own research on the hyperbolic case in linear partial differential equations. It extends spherical and cylindrical waves to apply to all (normal) hyperbolic equations. Partial contents: Cauchy's problem, fundamental formula, equations with odd number, with even number of independent variables; method of descent. 32 figures. Index. iii + 316pp. 5⅜ x 8.
S105 Paperbound **$1.75**

THEORY OF DIFFERENTIAL EQUATIONS, A. R. Forsyth. Out of print for over a decade, the complete 6 volumes (now bound as 3) of this monumental work represent the most comprehensive treatment of differential equations ever written. Historical presentation includes in 2500 pages every substantial development. Vol. 1, 2: EXACT EQUATIONS, PFAFF'S PROBLEM; ORDINARY EQUATIONS, NOT LINEAR: methods of Grassmann, Clebsch, Lie, Darboux; Cauchy's theorem; branch points; etc. Vol. 3, 4: ORDINARY EQUATIONS, NOT LINEAR; ORDINARY LINEAR EQUATIONS: Zeta Fuchsian functions, general theorems on algebraic integrals, Brun's theorem, equations with uniform periodic coefficients, etc. Vol. 4, 5: PARTIAL DIFFERENTIAL EQUATIONS: 2 existence-theorems, equations of theoretical dynamics, Laplace transformations, general transformation of equations of the 2nd order, much more. Indexes. Total of 2766pp. 5⅜ x 8.
S576-7-8 Clothbound: the set **$15.00**

PARTIAL DIFFERENTIAL EQUATIONS OF MATHEMATICAL PHYSICS, A. G. Webster. A keystone work in the library of every mature physicist, engineer, researcher. Valuable sections on elasticity, compression theory, potential theory, theory of sound, heat conduction, wave propagation, vibration theory. Contents include: deduction of differential equations, vibrations, normal functions, Fourier's series, Cauchy's method, boundary problems, method of Riemann-Volterra. Spherical, cylindrical, ellipsoidal harmonics, applications, etc. 97 figures. vii + 440pp. 5⅜ x 8.
S263 Paperbound **$2.00**

ORDINARY DIFFERENTIAL EQUATIONS, E. L. Ince. A most compendious analysis in real and complex domains. Existence and nature of solutions, continuous transformation groups, solutions in an infinite form, definite integrals, algebraic theory, Sturmian theory, boundary problems, existence theorems, 1st order, higher order, etc. "Deserves the highest praise, a notable addition to mathematical literature," BULLETIN, AM. MATH. SOC. Historical appendix. Bibliography. 18 figures. viii + 558pp. 5⅜ x 8. S349 Paperbound **$2.75**

INTRODUCTION TO NONLINEAR DIFFERENTIAL AND INTEGRAL EQUATIONS, Harold T. Davis. A thorough introduction to this important area, of increasing interest to mathematicians and scientists. First published by the United States Atomic Energy Commission, it includes chapters on the differential equation of the first order, the Riccati equation (as a bridge between linear and nonlinear equations), existence theorems, second order equations, elliptic integrals, elliptic functions, and theta functions, second order differential equations of polynomial class, continuous analytic continuation, the phase plane and its phenomena, nonlinear mechanics, the calculus of variations, etc. Appendices on Painlevé transcendents and Van der Pol and Volterra equations. Bibliography of 350 items. 137 problems. Index. xv + 566pp. 5⅜ x 8½. S971 Paperbound **$2.00**

THEORY OF FUNCTIONALS AND OF INTEGRAL AND INTEGRO-DIFFERENTIAL EQUATIONS, Vito Volterra. Unabridged republication of the only English translation. An exposition of the general theory of the functions depending on a continuous set of values of another function, based on the author's fundamental notion of the transition from a finite number of variables to a continually infinite number. Though dealing primarily with integral equations, much material on calculus of variations is included. The work makes no assumption of previous knowledge on the part of the reader. It begins with fundamental material and proceeds to Generalization of Analytic Functions, Integro-Differential Equations, Functional Derivative Equations, Applications, Other Directions of Theory of Functionals, etc. New introduction by G. C. Evans. Bibliography and criticism of Volterra's work by E. Whittaker. Bibliography. Index of authors cited. Index of subjects. xxxx + 226pp. 5⅜ x 8. S502 Paperbound **$1.75**

LINEAR INTEGRAL EQUATIONS, W. V. Lovitt. Systematic survey of general theory, with some application to differential equations, calculus of variations, problems of math, physics. Partial contents: integral equation of 2nd kind by successive substitutions; Fredholm's equation as ratio of 2 integral series in lambda, applications of the Fredholm theory, Hilbert-Schmidt theory of symmetric kernels, application, etc. Neumann, Dirichlet, vibratory problems. Index. ix + 253pp. 5⅜ x 8. S176 Paperbound **$1.60**

Foundations of mathematics

THE CONTINUUM AND OTHER TYPES OF SERIAL ORDER, E. V. Huntington. This famous book gives a systematic elementary account of the modern theory of the continuum as a type of serial order. Based on the Cantor-Dedekind ordinal theory, which requires no technical knowledge of higher mathematics, it offers an easily followed analysis of ordered classes, discrete and dense series, continuous series, Cantor's transfinite numbers. 2nd edition. Index. viii + 82pp. 5⅜ x 8. S130 Paperbound **$1.00**

CONTRIBUTIONS TO THE FOUNDING OF THE THEORY OF TRANSFINITE NUMBERS, Georg Cantor. These papers founded a new branch of mathematics. The famous articles of 1895-7 are translated, with an 82-page introduction by P. E. B. Jourdain dealing with Cantor, the background of his discoveries, their results, future possibilities. Bibliography. Index. Notes. ix + 211 pp. 5⅜ x 8. S45 Paperbound **$1.35**

ELEMENTARY MATHEMATICS FROM AN ADVANCED STANDPOINT, Felix Klein.

This classic text is an outgrowth of Klein's famous integration and survey course at Göttingen. Using one field of mathematics to interpret, adjust, illuminate another, it covers basic topics in each area, illustrating its discussion with extensive analysis. It is especially valuable in considering areas of modern mathematics. "Makes the reader feel the inspiration of . . . a great mathematician, inspiring teacher . . . with deep insight into the foundations and interrelations," BULLETIN, AMERICAN MATHEMATICAL SOCIETY.

Vol. 1. ARITHMETIC, ALGEBRA, ANALYSIS. Introducing the concept of function immediately, it enlivens abstract discussion with graphical and geometrically perceptual methods. Partial contents: natural numbers, extension of the notion of number, special properties, complex numbers. Real equations with real unknowns, complex quantities. Logarithmic, exponential functions, goniometric functions, infinitesimal calculus. Transcendence of e and pi, theory of assemblages. Index. 125 figures. ix + 274pp . 5⅜ x 8. S150 Paperbound **$1.85**

Vol. 2. GEOMETRY. A comprehensive view which accompanies the space perception inherent in geometry with analytic formulas which facilitate precise formulation. Partial contents: Simplest geometric manifolds: line segment, Grassmann determinant principles, classification of configurations of space, derivative manifolds. Geometric transformations: affine transformations, projective, higher point transformations, theory of the imaginary. Systematic discussion of geometry and its foundations. Indexes. 141 illustrations. ix + 214pp. 5⅜ x 8. S151 Paperbound **$1.75**

ESSAYS ON THE THEORY OF NUMBERS: 1. CONTINUITY AND IRRATIONAL NUMBERS; 2. THE NATURE AND MEANING OF NUMBERS, Richard Dedekind. The two most important essays on the logical foundations of the number system by the famous German mathematician. The first provides a purely arithmetic and perfectly rigorous foundation for irrational numbers and thereby a rigorous meaning to continuity in analysis. The second essay is an attempt to give a logical basis for transfinite numbers and properties of the natural numbers. Discusses the logical validity of mathematical induction. Authorized English translations by W. W. Deman of "Stetigkeit und irrationale Zahlen" and "Was sind und was sollen die Zahlen?" vii + 115pp. 5⅜ x 8. T1010 Paperbound **$1.00**

Geometry

THE FOUNDATIONS OF EUCLIDEAN GEOMETRY, H. G. Forder. The first rigorous account of Euclidean geometry, establishing propositions without recourse to empiricism, and without multiplying hypotheses. Corrects many traditional weaknesses of Euclidean proofs, and investigates the problems imposed on the axiom system by the discoveries of Bolyai and Lobachevsky. Some topics discussed are Classes and Relations; Axioms for Magnitudes; Congruence and Similarity; Algebra of Points; Hessenberg's Theorem; Continuity; Existence of Parallels; Reflections; Rotations; Isometries; etc. Invaluable for the light it throws on foundations of math. Lists: Axioms employed, Symbols, Constructions. 295pp. 5⅜ x 8. S481 Paperbound **$2.00**

ADVANCED EUCLIDEAN GEOMETRY, R. A. Johnson. For years the standard textbook on advanced Euclidean geometry, requires only high school geometry and trigonometry. Explores in unusual detail and gives proofs of hundreds of relatively recent theorems and corollaries, many formerly available only in widely scattered journals. Covers tangent circles, the theorem of Miquel, symmedian point, pedal triangles and circles, the Brocard configuration, and much more. Formerly "Modern Geometry." Index. 107 diagrams. xiii + 319pp. 5⅜ x 8. S669 Paperbound **$1.65**

HIGHER GEOMETRY: AN INTRODUCTION TO ADVANCED METHODS IN ANALYTIC GEOMETRY, F. S. Woods. Exceptionally thorough study of concepts and methods of advanced algebraic geometry (as distinguished from differential geometry). Exhaustive treatment of 1-, 2-, 3-, and 4-dimensional coordinate systems, leading to n-dimensional geometry in an abstract sense. Covers projectivity, tetracyclical coordinates, contact transformation, pentaspherical coordinates, much more. Based on M.I.T. lectures, requires sound preparation in analytic geometry and some knowledge of determinants. Index. Over 350 exercises. References. 60 figures. x + 423pp. 5⅜ x 8. S737 Paperbound **$2.00**

CONTEMPORARY GEOMETRY, André Delachet. Translated by Howard G. Bergmann. The recent developments in geometry covered in uncomplicated fashion. Clear discussions of modern thinking about the theory of groups, the concept of abstract geometry, projective geometry, algebraic geometry, vector spaces, new kinds of metric spaces, developments in differential geometry, etc. A large part of the book is devoted to problems, developments, and applications of topology. For advanced undergraduates and graduate students as well as mathematicians in other fields who want a brief introduction to current work in geometry. 39 figures. Index. xix + 94pp. 5⅜ x 8½. S988 Paperbound **$1.00**

ELEMENTS OF PROJECTIVE GEOMETRY, L. Cremona. Outstanding complete treatment of projective geometry by one of the foremost 19th century geometers. Detailed proofs of all fundamental principles, stress placed on the constructive aspects. Covers homology, law of duality, anharmonic ratios, theorems of Pascal and Brianchon, foci, polar reciprocal figures, etc. Only ordinary geometry necessary to understand this honored classic. Index. Over 150 fully worked out examples and problems. 252 diagrams. xx + 302pp. 5⅜ x 8. S668 Paperbound **$1.75**

AN INTRODUCTION TO PROJECTIVE GEOMETRY, R. M. Winger. One of the best introductory texts to an important area in modern mathematics. Contains full development of elementary concepts often omitted in other books. Employing the analytic method to capitalize on the student's collegiate training in algebra, analytic geometry and calculus, the author deals with such topics as Essential Constants, Duality, The Line at Infinity, Projective Properties and Double Ratio, Projective Coordinates, The Conic, Collineations and Involutions in One Dimension, Binary Forms, Algebraic Invariants, Analytic Treatment of the Conic, Collineations in the Plane, Cubic Involutions and the Rational Cubic Curve, and a clear discussion of Non-Euclidean Geometry. For senior-college students and graduates. "An excellent textbook . . . very clearly written . . . propositions stated concisely," A. Emch, Am. Math. Monthly. Corrected reprinting. 928 problems. Index. 116 figures. xii + 443pp. 5⅜ x 8. S949 Paperbound **$2.00**

ALGEBRAIC CURVES, Robert J. Walker, Professor of Mathematics, Cornell University. Fine introduction to algebraic geometry. Presents some of the recently developed algebraic methods of handling problems in algebraic geometry, shows how these methods are related to the older analytic and geometric problems, and applies them to those same geometric problems. Limited to the theory of curves, concentrating on birational transformations. Contents: Algebraic Preliminaries, Projective Spaces, Plane Algebraic Curves, Formal Power Series, Transformations of a Curve, Linear Series. 25 illustrations. Numerous exercises at ends of sections. Index. x + 201pp. 5⅜ x 8½. S336 Paperbound **$1.60**

THE ADVANCED GEOMETRY OF PLANE CURVES AND THEIR APPLICATIONS, C. Zwikker. An un-usual study of many important curves, their geometrical properties and their applications, including discussions of many less well-known curves not often treated in textbooks on synthetic and analytic Euclidean geometry. Includes both algebraic and transcendental curves such as the conic sections, kinked curves, spirals, lemniscates, cycloids, etc. and curves generated as involutes, evolutes, anticaustics, pedals, envelopes and orthogonal trajectories. Dr. Zwikker represents the points of the curves by complex numbers instead of two real Cartesian coordinates, allowing direct and even elegant proofs. Formerly: "Advanced Plane Geometry." 273 figures. xii + 299pp. 5⅜ x 8½. S1078 Paperbound **$2.00**

A TREATISE ON THE DIFFERENTIAL GEOMETRY OF CURVES AND SURFACES, L. P. Eisenhart. Introductory treatise especially for the graduate student, for years a highly successful text-book. More detailed and concrete in approach than most more recent books. Covers space curves, osculating planes, moving axes, Gauss' method, the moving trihedral, geodesics, conformal representation, etc. Last section deals with deformation of surfaces, rectilinear congruences, cyclic systems, etc. Index. 683 problems. 30 diagrams. xii + 474pp. 5⅜ x 8. S667 Paperbound **$2.75**

A TREATISE ON ALGEBRAIC PLANE CURVES, J. L. Coolidge. Unabridged reprinting of one of few full coverages in English, offering detailed introduction to theory of algebraic plane curves and their relations to geometry and analysis. Treats topological properties, Riemann-Roch theorem, all aspects of wide variety of curves including real, covariant, polar, contain-ing series of a given sort, elliptic, polygonal, rational, the pencil, two parameter nets, etc. This volume will enable the reader to appreciate the symbolic notation of Aronhold and Clebsch. Bibliography. Index. 17 illustrations. xxiv + 513pp. 5⅜ x 8. S543 Paperbound **$2.75**

AN INTRODUCTION TO THE GEOMETRY OF N DIMENSIONS, D. M. Y. Sommerville. An introduc-tion presupposing no prior knowledge of the field, the only book in English devoted exclu-sively to higher dimensional geometry. Discusses fundamental ideas of incidence, parallelism, perpendicularity, angles between linear space; enumerative geometry; analytical geometry from projective and metric points of view; polytopes; elementary ideas in analysis situs; content of hyper-spacial figures. Bibliography. Index. 60 diagrams. 196pp. 5⅜ x 8. S494 Paperbound **$1.50**

GEOMETRY OF FOUR DIMENSIONS, H. P. Manning. Unique in English as a clear, concise intro-duction. Treatment is synthetic, and mostly Euclidean, although in hyperplanes and hyper-spheres at infinity, non-Euclidean geometry is used. Historical introduction. Foundations of 4-dimensional geometry. Perpendicularity, simple angles. Angles of planes, higher order. Symmetry, order, motion; hyperpyramids, hypercones, hyperspheres; figures with parallel elements; volume, hypervolume in space; regular polyhedroids. Glossary. 78 figures. ix + 348pp. 5⅜ x 8. S182 Paperbound **$2.00**

CONVEX FIGURES AND POLYHEDRA, L. A. Lyusternik. An excellent elementary discussion by a leading Russian mathematician. Beginning with the basic concepts of convex figures and bodies and their supporting lines and planes, the author covers such matters as centrally symmetric convex figures, theorems of Euler, Cauchy, Steinitz and Alexandrov on convex polyhedra, linear systems of convex bodies, planar sections of convex bodies, the Brunn-Minkowski inequality and its consequences, and many other related topics. No more than a high school background in mathematics needed for complete understanding. First English translation by T. J. Smith. 182 illustrations. Index. x + 176pp. 5⅜ x 8½. S1021 Paperbound **$1.50**

NON-EUCLIDEAN GEOMETRY, Roberto Bonola. The standard coverage of non-Euclidean geom-etry. It examines from both a historical and mathematical point of view the geometries which have arisen from a study of Euclid's 5th postulate upon parallel lines. Also included are complete texts, translated, of Bolyai's SCIENCE OF ABSOLUTE SPACE. Lobachevsky's THEORY OF PARALLELS. 180 diagrams. 431pp. 5⅜ x 8. S27 Paperbound **$2.00**

ELEMENTS OF NON-EUCLIDEAN GEOMETRY, D. M. Y. Sommerville. Unique in proceeding step-by-step, in the manner of traditional geometry. Enables the student with only a good knowledge of high school algebra and geometry to grasp elementary hyperbolic, elliptic, analytic non-Euclidean geometries; space curvature and its philosophical implications; theory of radical axes; homothetic centres and systems of circles; parataxy and parallelism; absolute measure; Gauss' proof of the defect area theorem; geodesic representation; much more, all with exceptional clarity. 126 problems at chapter endings provide progressive practice and familiarity. 133 figures. Index. xvi + 274pp. 5⅜ x 8. S460 Paperbound **$1.50**

INTRODUCTORY NON-EUCLIDEAN GEOMETRY, H. P. Manning. Sound elementary introduction to non-Euclidean geometry. The first two thirds (Pangeometry and the Hyperbolic Geometry) require a grasp of plane and solid geometry and trigonometry. The last sections (the Elliptic Geometry and Analytic Non-Euclidean Geometry) necessitate also basic college cal-culus for understanding the text. The book does not propose to investigate the foundations of geometry, but rather begins with the theorems common to Euclidean and non-Euclidean geometry and then takes up the specific differences between them. A simple and direct account of the bases of this important branch of mathematics for teachers and students. 94 figures. vii + 95pp. 5⅜ x 8. S310 Paperbound **$1.00**

ELEMENTARY CONCEPTS OF TOPOLOGY, P. Alexandroff. First English translation of the famous brief introduction to topology for the beginner or for the mathematician not undertaking extensive study. This unusually useful intuitive approach deals primarily with the concepts of complex, cycle, and homology, and is wholly consistent with current investigations. Ranges from basic concepts of set-theoretic topology to the concept of Betti groups. "Glowing example of harmony between intuition and thought," David Hilbert. Translated by A. E. Farley. Introduction by D. Hilbert. Index. 25 figures. 73pp. 5⅜ x 8.   S747 Paperbound **$1.00**

Number theory

INTRODUCTION TO THE THEORY OF NUMBERS, L. E. Dickson. Thorough, comprehensive approach with adequate coverage of classical literature, an introductory volume beginners can follow. Chapters on divisibility, congruences, quadratic residues & reciprocity, Diophantine equations, etc. Full treatment of binary quadratic forms without usual restriction to integral coefficients. Covers infinitude of primes, least residues, Fermat's theorem, Euler's phi function, Legendre's symbol, Gauss's lemma, automorphs, reduced forms, recent theorems of Thue & Siegel, many more. Much material not readily available elsewhere. 239 problems. Index. I figure. viii + 183pp. 5⅜ x 8.   S342 Paperbound **$1.65**

ELEMENTS OF NUMBER THEORY, I. M. Vinogradov. Detailed 1st course for persons without advanced mathematics; 95% of this book can be understood by readers who have gone no farther than high school algebra. Partial contents: divisibility theory, important number theoretical functions, congruences, primitive roots and indices, etc. Solutions to both problems and exercises. Tables of primes, indices, etc. Covers almost every essential formula in elementary number theory! Translated from Russian. 233 problems, 104 exercises. viii + 227pp. 5⅜ x 8.   S259 Paperbound **$1.60**

THEORY OF NUMBERS and DIOPHANTINE ANALYSIS, R. D. Carmichael. These two complete works in one volume form one of the most lucid introductions to number theory, requiring only a firm foundation in high school mathematics. "Theory of Numbers," partial contents: Eratosthenes' sieve, Euclid's fundamental theorem, G.C.F. and L.C.M. of two or more integers, linear congruences, etc "Diophantine Analysis": rational triangles, Pythagorean triangles, equations of third, fourth, higher degrees, method of functional equations, much more. "Theory of Numbers": 76 problems. Index. 94pp. "Diophantine Analysis": 222 problems. Index. 118pp. 5⅜ x 8.   S529 Paperbound **$1.35**

Numerical analysis, tables

MATHEMATICAL TABLES AND FORMULAS, Compiled by Robert D. Carmichael and Edwin R. Smith. Valuable collection for students, etc. Contains all tables necessary in college algebra and trigonometry, such as five-place common logarithms, logarithmic sines and tangents of small angles, logarithmic trigonometric functions, natural trigonometric functions, four-place antilogarithms, tables for changing from sexagesimal to circular and from circular to sexagesimal measure of angles, etc. Also many tables and formulas not ordinarily accessible, including powers, roots, and reciprocals, exponential and hyperbolic functions, ten-place logarithms of prime numbers, and formulas and theorems from analytical and elementary geometry and from calculus. Explanatory introduction. viii + 269pp. 5⅜ x 8½.
S111 Paperbound **$1.00**

MATHEMATICAL TABLES, H. B. Dwight. Unique for its coverage in one volume of almost every function of importance in applied mathematics, engineering, and the physical sciences. Three extremely fine tables of the three trig functions and their inverse functions to thousandths of radians; natural and common logarithms; squares; cubes; hyperbolic functions and the inverse hyperbolic functions; $(a^2 + b^2)$ exp. ½a; complete elliptic integrals of the 1st and 2nd kind; sine and cosine integrals; exponential integrals Ei(x) and Ei(— x); binomial coefficients; factorials to 250; surface zonal harmonics and first derivatives; Bernoulli and Euler numbers and their logs to base of 10; Gamma function; normal probability integral; over 60 pages of Bessel functions; the Riemann Zeta function. Each table with formulae generally used, sources of more extensive tables, interpolation data, etc. Over half have columns of differences, to facilitate interpolation. Introduction. Index. viii + 231pp. 5⅜ x 8.
S445 Paperbound **$1.75**

TABLES OF FUNCTIONS WITH FORMULAE AND CURVES, E. Jahnke & F. Emde. The world's most comprehensive 1-volume English-text collection of tables, formulae, curves of transcendent functions. 4th corrected edition, new 76-page section giving tables, formulae for elementary functions—not in other English editions. Partial contents: sine, cosine, logarithmic integral; factorial function; error integral; theta functions; elliptic integrals, functions; Legendre, Bessel, Riemann, Mathieu, hypergeometric functions, etc. Supplementary books. Bibliography. Indexed. "Out of the way functions for which we know no other source," SCIENTIFIC COMPUTING SERVICE, Ltd. 212 figures. 400pp. 5⅜ x 8.   S133 Paperbound **$2.00**

Catalogue of Dover Books

JACOBIAN ELLIPTIC FUNCTION TABLES, L. M. Milne-Thomson. An easy to follow, practical book which gives not only useful numerical tables, but also a complete elementary sketch of the application of elliptic functions. It covers Jacobian elliptic functions and a description of their principal properties; complete elliptic integrals; Fourier series and power series expansions; periods, zeros, poles, residues, formulas for special values of the argument; transformations, approximations, elliptic integrals, conformal mapping, factorization of cubic and quartic polynomials; application to the pendulum problem; etc. Tables and graphs form the body of the book: Graph, 5 figure table of the elliptic function sn (u m); cn (u m); dn (u m). 8 figure table of complete elliptic integrals K, K′, E, E′, and the nome q. 7 figure table of the Jacobian zeta-function Z(u). 3 figures. xi + 123pp. 5⅜ x 8.
S194 Paperbound **$1.35**

TABLES OF INDEFINITE INTEGRALS, G. Petit Bois. Comprehensive and accurate, this orderly grouping of over 2500 of the most useful indefinite integrals will save you hours of laborious mathematical groundwork. After a list of 49 common transformations of integral expressions, with a wide variety of examples, the book takes up algebraic functions, irrational monomials, products and quotients of binomials, transcendental functions, natural logs, etc. You will rarely or never encounter an integral of an algebraic or transcendental function not included here; any more comprehensive set of tables costs at least $12 or $15. Index. 2544 integrals. xii + 154pp. 6⅛ x 9¼.
S225 Paperbound **$2.00**

SUMMATION OF SERIES, Collected by L. B. W. Jolley. Over 1100 common series collected, summed, and grouped for easy reference—for mathematicians, physicists, computer technicians, engineers, and students. Arranged for convenience into categories, such as arithmetical and geometrical progressions, powers and products of natural numbers, figurate and polygonal numbers, inverse natural numbers, exponential and logarithmic series, binomial expansions, simple inverse products, factorials, and trigonometric and hyperbolic expansions. Also included are series representing various Bessel functions, elliptic integrals; discussions of special series involving Legendre polynomials, the zeta function, Bernoulli's function, and similar expressions. Revised, enlarged second edition. New preface. xii + 251pp. 5⅜ x 8½.
S23 Paperbound **$2.25**

A TABLE OF THE INCOMPLETE ELLIPTIC INTEGRAL OF THE THIRD KIND, R. G. Selfridge, J. E. Maxfield. The first complete 6-place tables of values of the incomplete integral of the third kind, prepared under the auspices of the Research Department of the U.S. Naval Ordnance Test Station. Calculated on an IBM type 704 calculator and thoroughly verified by echo-checking and a check integral at the completion of each value of **a.** Of inestimable value in problems where the surface area of geometrical bodies can only be expressed in terms of the incomplete integral of the third and lower kinds; problems in aero-, fluid-, and thermodynamics involving processes where nonsymmetrical repetitive volumes must be determined; various types of seismological problems; problems of magnetic potentials due to circular current; etc. Foreword. Acknowledgment. Introduction. Use of table. xiv + 805pp. 5⅝ x 8⅜.
S501 Clothbound **$7.50**

PRACTICAL ANALYSIS, GRAPHICAL AND NUMERICAL METHODS, F. A. Willers. Translated by R. T. Beyer. Immensely practical handbook for engineers, showing how to interpolate, use various methods of numerical differentiation and integration, determine the roots of a single algebraic equation, system of linear equations, use empirical formulas, integrate differential equations, etc. Hundreds of shortcuts for arriving at numerical solutions. Special section on American calculating machines, by T. W. Simpson. 132 illustrations. 422pp. 5⅜ x 8.
S273 Paperbound **$2.00**

NUMERICAL INTEGRATION OF DIFFERENTIAL EQUATIONS, A. A. Bennett, W. E. Milne, H. Bateman. Republication of original monograph prepared for National Research Council. New methods of integration of differential equations developed by 3 leading mathematicians: THE INTERPOLATIONAL POLYNOMIAL and SUCCESSIVE APPROXIMATIONS by A. A. Bennett; STEP-BY-STEP METHODS OF INTEGRATION by W. W. Milne; METHODS FOR PARTIAL DIFFERENTIAL EQUATIONS by H. Bateman. Methods for partial differential equations, transition from difference equations to differential equations, solution of differential equations to non-integral values of a parameter will interest mathematicians and physicists. 288 footnotes, mostly bibliographic; 235-item classified bibliography. 108pp. 5⅜ x 8.
S305 Paperbound **$1.35**

INTRODUCTION TO RELAXATION METHODS, F. S. Shaw. Fluid mechanics, design of electrical networks, forces in structural frameworks, stress distribution, buckling, etc. Solve linear simultaneous equations, linear ordinary differential equations, partial differential equations, Eigen-value problems by relaxation methods. Detailed examples throughout. Special tables for dealing with awkwardly-shaped boundaries. Indexes. 253 diagrams. 72 tables. 400pp. 5⅜ x 8.
S244 Paperbound **$2.45**

NUMERICAL SOLUTIONS OF DIFFERENTIAL EQUATIONS, H. Levy & E. A. Baggott. Comprehensive collection of methods for solving ordinary differential equations of first and higher order. All must pass 2 requirements: easy to grasp and practical, more rapid than school methods. Partial contents: graphical integration of differential equations, graphical methods for detailed solution. Numerical solution. Simultaneous equations and equations of 2nd and higher orders. "Should be in the hands of all in research in applied mathematics, teaching,"

Probability theory and information theory

AN ELEMENTARY INTRODUCTION TO THE THEORY OF PROBABILITY, B. V. Gnedenko and A. Ya. Khinchin. Translated by Leo F. Boron. A clear, compact introduction designed to equip the reader with a fundamental grasp of the theory of probability. It is thorough and authoritative within its purposely restricted range, yet the layman with a background in elementary mathematics will be able to follow it without difficulty. Covers such topics as the processes involved in the calculation of probabilities, conditional probabilities and the multiplication rule, Bayes's formula, Bernoulli's scheme and theorem, random variables and distribution laws, and dispersion and mean deviations. New translation of fifth (revised) Russian edition (1960)—the only translation checked and corrected by Gnedenko. New preface for Dover edition by B. V. Gnedenko. Index. Bibliography. Appendix: Table of values of function $\phi(a)$. xii + 130pp. 5⅜ x 8½. **T155 Paperbound $1.45**

AN INTRODUCTION TO MATHEMATICAL PROBABILITY, Julian Lowell Coolidge. A thorough introduction which presents the mathematical foundation of the theory of probability. A substantial body of material, yet can be understood with a knowledge of only elementary calculus. Contains: The Scope and Meaning of Mathematical Probability; Elementary Principles of Probability; Bernoulli's Theorem; Mean Value and Dispersion; Geometrical Probability; Probability of Causes; Errors of Observation; Errors in Many Variables; Indirect Observations; The Statistical Theory of Gases; and The Principles of Life Insurance. Six pages of logarithm tables. 4 diagrams. Subject and author indices. xii + 214pp. 5⅜ x 8½.
S258 Paperbound $1.35

A GUIDE TO OPERATIONS RESEARCH, W. E. Duckworth. A brief nontechnical exposition of techniques and theories of operational research. A good introduction for the layman; also can provide the initiate with new understandings. No mathematical training needed, yet not an oversimplification. Covers game theory, mathematical analysis, information theory, linear programming, cybernetics, decision theory, etc. Also includes a discussion of the actual organization of an operational research program and an account of the uses of such programs in the oil, chemical, paper, and metallurgical industries, etc. Bibliographies at chapter ends. Appendices. 36 figures. 145pp. 5¼ x 8½. **T1129 Clothbound $3.50**

MATHEMATICAL FOUNDATIONS OF INFORMATION THEORY, A. I. Khinchin. For the first time mathematicians, statisticians, physicists, cyberneticists, and communications engineers are offered a complete and exact introduction to this relatively new field. Entropy as a measure of a finite scheme, applications to coding theory, study of sources, channels and codes, detailed proofs of both Shannon theorems for any ergodic source and any stationary channel with finite memory, and much more are covered. Bibliography. vii + 120pp. 5⅜ x 8.
S434 Paperbound $1.35

SELECTED PAPERS ON NOISE AND STOCHASTIC PROCESS, edited by Prof. Nelson Wax, U. of Illinois. 6 basic papers for newcomers in the field, for those whose work involves noise characteristics. Chandrasekhar, Uhlenbeck & Ornstein, Uhlenbeck & Ming, Rice, Doob. Included is Kac's Chauvenet-Prize winning Random Walk. Extensive bibliography lists 200 articles, up through 1953. 21 figures. 337pp. 6⅛ x 9¼. **S262 Paperbound $2.50**

THEORY OF PROBABILITY, William Burnside. Synthesis, expansion of individual papers presents numerous problems in classical probability, offering many original views succinctly, effectively. Game theory, cards, selections from groups; geometrical probability in such areas as suppositions as to probability of position of point on a line, points on surface of sphere, etc. Includes methods of approximation, theory of errors, direct calculation of probabilities, etc. Index. 136pp. 5⅜ x 8. **S567 Paperbound $1.00**

Statistics

ELEMENTARY STATISTICS, WITH APPLICATIONS IN MEDICINE AND THE BIOLOGICAL SCIENCES, F. E. Croxton. A sound introduction to statistics for anyone in the physical sciences, assuming no prior acquaintance and requiring only a modest knowledge of math. All basic formulas carefully explained and illustrated; all necessary reference tables included. From basic terms and concepts, the study proceeds to frequency distribution, linear, non-linear, and multiple correlation, skewness, kurtosis, etc. A large section deals with reliability and significance of statistical methods. Containing concrete examples from medicine and biology, this book will prove unusually helpful to workers in those fields who increasingly must evaluate, check, and interpret statistics. Formerly titled "Elementary Statistics with Applications in Medicine." 101 charts. 57 tables. 14 appendices. Index. iv + 376pp. 5⅜ x 8.
S506 Paperbound $2.00

ANALYSIS & DESIGN OF EXPERIMENTS, H. B. Mann. Offers a method for grasping the analysis of variance and variance design within a short time. Partial contents: Chi-square distribution and analysis of variance distribution, matrices, quadratic forms, likelihood ration tests and tests of linear hypotheses, power of analysis, Galois fields, non-orthogonal data, interblock estimates, etc. 15pp. of useful tables. x + 195pp. 5 x 7⅜. **S180 Paperbound $1.45**

METHODS OF STATISTICS, L. H. C. Tippett. A classic in its field, this unusually complete systematic introduction to statistical methods begins at beginner's level and progresses to advanced levels for experimenters and poll-takers in all fields of statistical research. Supplies fundamental knowledge of virtually all elementary methods in use today by sociologists, psychologists, biologists, engineers, mathematicians, etc. Explains logical and mathematical basis of each method described, with examples for each section. Covers frequency distributions and measures, inference from random samples, errors in large samples, simple analysis of variance, multiple and partial regression and correlation, etc. 4th revised (1952) edition. 16 charts. 5 significance tables. 152-item bibliography. 96 tables. 22 figures. 395pp. 6 x 9.
S228 Clothbound **$7.50**

STATISTICS MANUAL, E. L. Crow, F. A. Davis, M. W. Maxfield. Comprehensive collection of classical, modern statistics methods, prepared under auspices of U. S. Naval Ordnance Test Station, China Lake, Calif. Many examples from ordnance will be valuable to workers in all fields. Emphasis is on use, with information on fiducial limits, sign tests, Chi-square runs, sensitivity, quality control, much more. "Well written . . . excellent reference work," Operations Research. Corrected edition of NAVORD Report 3360 NOTS 948. Introduction. Appendix of 32 tables, charts. Index. Bibliography. 95 illustrations. 306pp. 5⅜ x 8.
S599 Paperbound **$1.65**

Symbolic logic

AN INTRODUCTION TO SYMBOLIC LOGIC, Susanne K. Langer. Probably the clearest book ever written on symbolic logic for the philosopher, general scientist and layman. It will be particularly appreciated by those who have been rebuffed by other introductory works because of insufficient mathematical training. No special knowledge of mathematics is required. Starting with the simplest symbols and conventions, you are led to a remarkable grasp of the Boole-Schroeder and Russell-Whitehead systems clearly and quickly. PARTIAL CONTENTS: Study of forms, Essentials of logical structure, Generalization, Classes, The deductive system of classes, The algebra of logic, Abstraction of interpretation, Calculus of propositions, Assumptions of PRINCIPIA MATHEMATICA, Logistics, Logic of the syllogism, Proofs of theorems. "One of the clearest and simplest introductions to a subject which is very much alive. The style is easy, symbolism is introduced gradually, and the intelligent non-mathematician should have no difficulty in following the argument," MATHEMATICS GAZETTE. Revised, expanded second edition. Truth-value tables. 368pp. 5⅜ x 8.
S164 Paperbound **$1.75**

A SURVEY OF SYMBOLIC LOGIC: THE CLASSIC ALGEBRA OF LOGIC, C. I. Lewis. Classic survey of the field, comprehensive and thorough. Indicates content of major systems, alternative methods of procedure, and relation of these to the Boole-Schroeder algebra and to one another. Contains historical summary, as well as full proofs and applications of the classic, or Boole-Schroeder, algebra of logic. Discusses diagrams for the logical relations of classes, the two-valued algebra, propositional functions of two or more variables, etc. Chapters 5 and 6 of the original edition, which contained material not directly pertinent, have been omitted in this edition at the author's request. Appendix. Bibliography. Index. viii + 352pp. 5⅝ x 8⅜.
S643 Paperbound **$2.00**

INTRODUCTION TO SYMBOLIC LOGIC AND ITS APPLICATIONS, R. Carnap. One of the clearest, most comprehensive, and rigorous introductions to modern symbolic logic by perhaps its greatest living master. Symbolic languages are analyzed and one constructed. Applications to math (symbolic representation of axiom systems for set theory, natural numbers, real numbers, topology, Dedekind and Cantor explanations of continuity), physics (the general analysis of concepts of determination, causality, space-time-topology, based on Einstein), biology (symbolic representation of an axiom system for basic concepts). "A masterpiece," Zentralblatt für Mathematik und ihre Grenzgebiete. Over 300 exercises. 5 figures. Bibliography. Index. xvi + 241pp. 5⅜ x 8.
S453 Paperbound **$1.85**
Clothbound **$4.00**

SYMBOLIC LOGIC, C. I. Lewis, C. H. Langford. Probably the most cited book in symbolic logic, this is one of the fullest treatments of paradoxes. A wide coverage of the entire field of symbolic logic, plus considerable material that has not appeared elsewhere. Basic to the entire volume is the distinction between the logic of extensions and of intensions. Considerable emphasis is placed on converse substitution, while the matrix system presents the supposition of a variety of non-Aristotelian logics. It has especially valuable sections on strict limitations, existence of terms, 2-valued algebra and its extension to propositional functions, truth value systems, the matrix method, implication and deductibility, general theory of propositions, propositions of ordinary discourse, and similar topics. "Authoritative, most valuable," TIMES, London. Bibliography. 506pp. 5⅜ x 8. S170 Paperbound **$2.00**

THE ELEMENTS OF MATHEMATICAL LOGIC, Paul Rosenbloom. First publication in any language. This book is intended for readers who are mature mathematically, but have no previous training in symbolic logic. It does not limit itself to a single system, but covers the field as a whole. It is a development of lectures given at Lund University, Sweden, in 1948. Partial contents: Logic of classes, fundamental theorems, Boolean algebra, logic of propositions, logic of propositional functions, expressive languages, combinatory logics, development of mathematics within an object language, paradoxes, theorems of Post and Goedel, Church's theorem, and similar topics. iv + 214pp. 5⅜ x 8. S227 Paperbound **$1.45**

MATHEMATICS, HISTORIES AND CLASSICS

HISTORY OF MATHEMATICS, D. E. Smith. Most comprehensive non-technical history of math in English. Discusses lives and works of over a thousand major and minor figures, with footnotes supplying technical information outside the book's scheme, and indicating disputed matters. Vol I: A chronological examination, from primitive concepts through Egypt, Babylonia, Greece, the Orient, Rome, the Middle Ages, the Renaissance, and up to 1900. Vol 2: The development of ideas in specific fields and problems, up through elementary calculus. Two volumes, total of 510 illustrations, 1355pp. 5⅜ x 8. Set boxed in attractive container. T429, 430 Paperbound, the set **$5.00**

A SHORT ACCOUNT OF THE HISTORY OF MATHEMATICS, W. W. R. Ball. Most readable non-technical history of mathematics treats lives, discoveries of every important figure from Egyptian, Phoenician mathematicians to late 19th century. Discusses schools of Ionia, Pythagoras, Athens, Cyzicus, Alexandria, Byzantium, systems of numeration; primitive arithmetic; Middle Ages, Renaissance, including Arabs, Bacon, Regiomontanus, Tartaglia, Cardan, Stevinus, Galileo, Kepler; modern mathematics of Descartes, Pascal, Wallis, Huygens, Newton, Leibnitz, d'Alembert, Euler, Lambert, Laplace, Legendre, Gauss, Hermite, Weierstrass, scores more. Index. 25 figures. 546pp. 5⅜ x 8. S630 Paperbound **$2.00**

A HISTORY OF GEOMETRICAL METHODS, J. L. Coolidge. Full, authoritative history of the techniques which men have employed in dealing with geometric questions . . . from ancient times to the modern development of projective geometry. Critical analyses of the original works. Contents: Synthetic Geometry—the early beginnings, Greek mathematics, non-Euclidean geometries, projective and descriptive geometry; Algebraic Geometry—extension of the system of linear coordinates, other systems of point coordinates, enumerative and birational geometry, etc.; and Differential Geometry—intrinsic geometry and moving axes, Gauss and the classical theory of surfaces, and projective and absolute differential geometry. The work of scores of geometers analyzed: Pythagoras, Archimedes, Newton, Descartes, Leibniz, Lobachevski, Riemann, Hilbert, Bernoulli, Schubert, Grassman, Klein, Cauchy, and many, many others. Extensive (24-page) bibliography. Index. 13 figures. xviii + 451pp. 5⅜ x 8½. S1006 Paperbound **$2.25**

THE MATHEMATICS OF GREAT AMATEURS, Julian Lowell Coolidge. Enlightening, often surprising, accounts of what can result from a non-professional preoccupation with mathematics. Chapters on Plato, Omar Khayyam and his work with cubic equations, Piero della Francesca, Albrecht Dürer, as the true discoverer of descriptive geometry, Leonardo da Vinci and his varied mathematical interests, John Napier, Baron of Merchiston, inventor of logarithms, Pascal, Diderot, l'Hospital, and seven others known primarily for contributions in other fields. Bibliography. 56 figures. viii + 211pp. 5⅜ x 8½. S1009 Paperbound **$1.50**

ART AND GEOMETRY, Wm. M. Ivins, Jr. A controversial study which propounds the view that the ideas of Greek philosophy and culture served not to stimulate, but to stifle the development of Western thought. Through an examination of Greek art and geometrical inquiries and Renaissance experiments, this book offers a concise history of the evolution of mathematical perspective and projective geometry. Discusses the work of Alberti, Dürer, Pelerin, Nicholas of Cusa, Kepler, Desargues, etc. in a wholly readable text of interest to the art historian, philosopher, mathematician, historian of science, and others. x + 113pp. 5⅜ x 8⅜. T941 Paperbound **$1.00**

A SOURCE BOOK IN MATHEMATICS, D. E. Smith. Great discoveries in math, from Renaissance to end of 19th century, in English translation. Read announcements by Dedekind, Gauss, Delamain, Pascal, Fermat, Newton, Abel, Lobachevsky, Bolyai, Riemann, De Moivre, Legendre, Laplace, others of discoveries about imaginary numbers, number congruence, slide rule, equations, symbolism, cubic algebraic equations, non-Euclidean forms of geometry, calculus, function theory, quaternions, etc. Succinct selections from 125 different treatises, articles, most unavailable elsewhere in English. Each article preceded by biographical, historical introduction. Vol. I: Fields of Number, Algebra. Index. 32 illus. 338pp. 5⅜ x 8. Vol. II: Fields of Geometry, Probability, Calculus, Functions, Quaternions. 83 illus. 432pp. 5⅜ x 8.
Vol. 1: S552 Paperbound **$1.85**
Vol. 2: S553 Paperbound **$1.85**
2 vol. set, boxed **$3.50**

A COLLECTION OF MODERN MATHEMATICAL CLASSICS, edited by R. Bellman. 13 classic papers, complete in their original languages, by Hermite, Hardy and Littlewood, Tchebychef, Fejér, Fredholm, Fuchs, Hurwitz, Weyl, van der Pol, Birkhoff, Kellogg, von Neumann, and Hilbert. Each of these papers, collected here for the first time, triggered a burst of mathematical activity, providing useful new generalizations or stimulating fresh investigations. Topics discussed include classical analysis, periodic and almost periodic functions, analysis and number theory, integral equations, theory of approximation, non-linear differential equations, and functional analysis. Brief introductions and bibliographies to each paper. xii + 292pp. 6 x 9. S730 Paperbound **$2.00**

THE WORKS OF ARCHIMEDES, edited by T. L. Heath. All the known works of the great Greek mathematician are contained in this one volume, including the recently discovered Method of Archimedes. Contains: On Sphere & Cylinder, Measurement of a Circle, Spirals, Conoids, Spheroids, etc. This is the definitive edition of the greatest mathematical intellect of the ancient world. 186-page study by Heath discusses Archimedes and the history of Greek mathematics. Bibliography. 563pp. 5⅜ x 8. S9 Paperbound **$2.25**

THE THIRTEEN BOOKS OF EUCLID'S ELEMENTS, edited by **Sir Thomas Heath.** Definitive edition of one of the very greatest classics of Western world. Complete English translation of Heiberg text, together with spurious Book XIV. Detailed 150-page introduction discussing aspects of Greek and Medieval mathematics. Euclid, texts, commentators, etc. Paralleling the text is an elaborate critical apparatus analyzing each definition, proposition, postulate, covering textual matters, mathematical analysis, commentators of all times, refutations, supports, extrapolations, etc. This is the full Euclid. Unabridged reproduction of Cambridge U. 2nd edition. 3 volumes. Total of 995 figures, 1426pp. 5⅜ x 8.
S88,89,90, 3 volume set, paperbound **$6.75**

A CONCISE HISTORY OF MATHEMATICS, D. Struik. Lucid study of development of mathematical ideas, techniques from Ancient Near East, Greece, Islamic science, Middle Ages, Renaissance, modern times. Important mathematicians are described in detail. Treatment is not anecdotal, but analytical development of ideas. "Rich in content, thoughtful in interpretation," U.S. QUARTERLY BOOKLIST. Non-technical; no mathematical training needed. Index. 60 illustrations, including Egyptian papyri, Greek mss., portraits of 31 eminent mathematicians. Bibliography. 2nd edition. xix + 299pp. 5⅜ x 8.
T255 Paperbound **$1.75**

A HISTORY OF THE CALCULUS, AND ITS CONCEPTUAL DEVELOPMENT, Carl B. Boyer. Provides laymen and mathematicians a detailed history of the development of the calculus, from early beginning in antiquity to final elaboration as mathematical abstractions. Gives a sense of mathematics not as a technique, but as a habit of mind, in the progression of ideas of Zeno, Plato, Pythagoras, Eudoxus, Arabic and Scholastic mathematicians, Newton, Leibnitz, Taylor, Descartes, Euler, Lagrange, Cantor, Weierstrass, and others. This first comprehensive critical history of the calculus was originally titled "The Concepts of the Calculus." Foreword by R. Courant. Preface. 22 figures. 25-page bibliography. Index. v + 364pp. 5⅜ x 8.
S509 Paperbound **$2.00**

A MANUAL OF GREEK MATHEMATICS, Sir Thomas L. Heath. A non-technical survey of Greek mathematics addressed to high school and college students and the layman who desires a sense of historical perspective in mathematics. Thorough exposition of early numerical notation and practical calculation, Pythagorean arithmetic and geometry, Thales and the earliest Greek geometrical measurements and theorems, the mathematical theories of Plato, Euclid's "Elements" and his other works (extensive discussion), Aristarchus, Archimedes, Eratosthenes and the measurement of the earth, trigonometry (Hipparchus, Menelaus, Ptolemy), Pappus and Heron of Alexandria, and detailed coverage of minor figures normally omitted from histories of this type. Presented in a refreshingly interesting and readable style. Appendix. 2 Indexes. xvi + 552pp. 5⅜ x 8.
S279 Paperbound **$2.25**

THE GEOMETRY OF RENÉ DESCARTES. With this book Descartes founded analytical geometry. Excellent Smith-Latham translation, plus original French text with Descartes' own diagrams. Contains Problems the Construction of Which Requires Only Straight Lines and Circles; On the Nature of Curved Lines; On the Construction of Solid or Supersolid Problems. Notes. Diagrams. 258pp. 5⅜ x 8.
S68 Paperbound **$1.60**

A PHILOSOPHICAL ESSAY ON PROBABILITIES, Marquis de Laplace. This famous essay explains without recourse to mathematics the principle of probability, and the application of probability to games of chance, natural philosophy, astronomy, many other fields. Translated from the 6th French edition by F. W. Truscott, F. L. Emory, with new introduction for this edition by E. T. Bell. 204pp. 5⅜ x 8.
S166 Paperbound **$1.35**

Prices subject to change without notice.

Dover publishes books on art, music, philosophy, literature, languages, history, social sciences, psychology, handcrafts, orientalia, puzzles and entertainments, chess, pets and gardens, books explaining science, intermediate and higher mathematics, mathematical physics, engineering, biological sciences, earth sciences, classics of science, etc. Write to:

Dept. catrr.
Dover Publications, Inc.
180 Varick Street, N.Y. 14, N.Y.

K